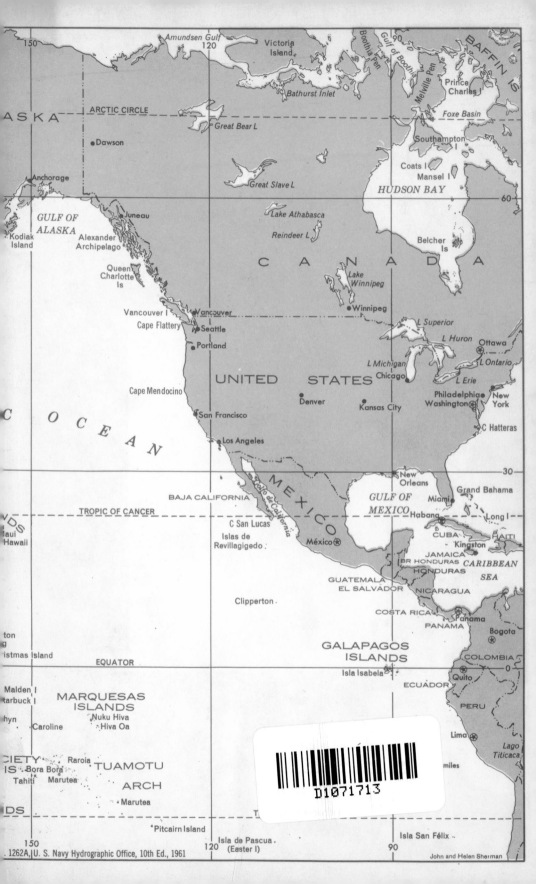

PROVING GROUND

*An Account of the Radiobiological Studies
in the Pacific, 1946-1961*

PROVING GROUND

An Account of the
Radiobiological Studies
in the Pacific,
1946-1961

by

NEAL O. HINES

University of Washington Press

Seattle   1962

To Martha

PREFACE

THE STORY that follows is the story of a single laboratory and of its studies of radioactivity in the Pacific.

The laboratory itself, originally the Applied Fisheries Laboratory and more recently the Laboratory of Radiation Biology of the University of Washington, was drawn into the Pacific because the nuclear tests at Bikini and Eniwetok created occasions and opportunities to explore the biological consequences of the release of radioactive materials in the ocean environment. Eventually, because it had persisted in accumulating experience over a long period of time, the Laboratory came to represent in the region of the tests—and at times almost to embody there—the widening concern with the complicated biological situations that resulted when nuclear devices were detonated at ocean sites. It is this story that the present account attempts to relate.

The story obviously is larger than the Laboratory's alone, not only because the theater of operations was so large but because the events that occurred at that first Pacific Proving Ground, whatever their inevitability or necessity, were momentous in their portent and reflections both of the scientific achievement and the deep anxieties of the middle years of the century. In such events the Laboratory of Radiation Biology played, actually, only a small and peripheral role. Yet the role was one which, because it was concerned with biology, was related to the residual environmental results and thus had a cumulative significance far larger than would have been suggested either by the size of the Laboratory's staff or by its loose connection to the test organizations. Because the Laboratory's Pacific work covered so many years—from 1946 through 1958, and on through that brief, hopeful period in which nuclear testing was first suspended by international agreement—the continuity of its effort was in itself important and probably unique.

There are risks, of course, in preparing an account of this kind. For one thing, the story is unfinished, denied in the beginning the satisfaction and security of an outcome and necessarily dealing, in its biological aspects, with studies in which certainties are few and conclusions endlessly elusive. For another, the man-made environment of the Pacific Proving Ground enters the story strongly, demanding a considerable share of attention because the conditions and necessities of the proving ground formed the background against which the field studies were conducted. The story is of biological studies carried forward during and between nuclear test operations, and in it are problems of balance and perspective. The pitfalls seem numberless, and it is quite possible that not all have been avoided. But let it be said here that *Proving Ground* is not concerned with the Pacific Proving Ground as an operational area, or with nuclear testing itself, but rather with a small laboratory's participation in the long and as yet unfinished search for a larger knowledge of the disposition and effect of radioactivity released in the natural environment. There is no attempt to point to a conclusion, to support a thesis, to assume a position. There is an attempt to put into a comprehensive record an account that may be in itself enlightening.

The idea of the preparation of a history and synthesis emerged tentatively and formlessly in 1958, when the moratorium on testing provided what seemed a time appropriate to recapitulation. Work actually was begun in the autumn of 1960, a year, as it turned out, before the moratorium was ended in the resumption of testing by the U.S.S.R. The objective of the effort, as it developed, was not specifically to summarize the details of the

Laboratory's findings (which had been recorded in segments over the years in various kinds of reports, papers, and program plans), but to trace the evolution of the Laboratory's field studies, indicating the slow accumulation of experience, and to sort out, if possible, the meanings of the Laboratory's fifteen years of involvement. This, in substance, is the objective of the account as it now appears.

The Laboratory's programs in the Pacific were sponsored and supported by the U.S. Atomic Energy Commission through its Division of Biology and Medicine. Support in the field was provided, as occasion demanded, by the U.S. Navy, by elements of the task force organizations, and by Holmes & Narver, Inc., the engineering firm in charge of design and construction at the test sites and of many of the communications and transportation facilities in the proving ground area. The reports of the Laboratory were submitted to the Division of Biology and Medicine, and most have been reproduced for distribution or published directly in the scientific literature. The materials for this account have been drawn from many sources, but principal reliance has been placed on the reports, documents, field notes, diaries, and correspondence available at the Laboratory on the University campus and on the personal recollections of members of the staff and others who have participated in one way or another in the studies in the field or in the discussions and decisions that made them possible.

My gratitude to the many persons who contributed encouragement or assistance in the preparation of this account is far deeper than can be adequately expressed in a brief acknowledgement. Foremost among those toward whom I feel such gratitude are Dr. Charles L. Dunham, Director of the Division of Biology and Medicine, whose interest in the project made possible the arrangements by which it was undertaken, and Dr. John N. Wolfe, chief of the Division's Environmental Sciences Branch, who shared Dr. Dunham's interest and who devoted more time than I had a right to ask to a review of the manuscript in the later stages of its preparation. They gave me not only complete freedom to search for appropriate historical materials but the encouragement of their own confidence that the effort needed to be made.

Acknowledgement is made particularly of the kindness of certain persons who gave me the benefit of their recollections of events or who took the time to read and make comments upon appropriate segments of the early drafts. These persons include Dr. Stafford L. Warren, dean of the School of Medicine of the University of California at Los Angeles, who was so largely responsible for the establishment of the Laboratory and whose use of its personnel during Operation Crossroads stimulated the later studies in the Pacific; Mr. Franklin P. Matthias, vice-president and manager of heavy construction of Kaiser Engineers, Oakland, California, who participated in the site selection and directed the development of the Hanford plant and who was closely associated with arrangements for the Laboratory's early studies on the Columbia River; Mr. Hanford Thayer, of the Seattle office of the U.S. Corps of Engineers, who was the Laboratory's World War II liaison officer and who permitted me to examine his diaries and papers relating to the early years; Dr. Richard F. Foster, one of the original members of the Laboratory staff, now manager of the environmental studies and evaluation program for the General Electric Company at Hanford, who read in rough draft and provided additional information for the account of the Laboratory's beginnings; Admiral James S. Russell, U.S.N., who was the Captain Russell serving as the deputy director of the Division of Military Application at the time of the Sandstone series of 1948 and who, as Vice-Chief of Naval Operations, reviewed for me in 1961 his recollections of the process by which Eniwetok was selected as the Pacific Proving Ground site; Mr. Robert J. Buettner, of the Special Projects Division of Holmes & Narver, Inc., who has been familiar with the Laboratory's work since Operation Crossroads and who assisted in the confirmation of certain information concerning proving ground development; Dr. Paul B. Pearson, of the Program in Science and Engineering of the Ford Foundation, who, as chief of the Biology Branch of the Division of Biology and Medicine, participated in the critical review of the Laboratory's Pacific programs and in certain decisions that led to their continuance and enlargement; and Dr. John H. Harley, of the Health and Safety Laboratory of the Commission's New York Operations Office, who was in charge of Operation Troll in 1955 and who supplied further information concerning activities of that period. Other persons within the Commission whose counsel or assistance was of great value include Dr. I. E. Wallen, in charge of oceanographic studies in the Environmental Science Branch; Dr. Richard G. Hewlett, AEC historian; Mr. Noble Simpson, of the Program Coordination Branch of the Division of Biology and Medicine; members of the Commission's public information staff, including particularly Mr. Frank Tobey; Mr. J. E. Travis, manager of the Hanford Operations Office; and Mr. Kenneth E. Englund, chief of the Radiation Sciences Branch of the Civilian Reactor Development and Research Division at Hanford.

Grateful acknowledgment also is made of the assistance given me by two distinguished Japanese scientists, Dr. Yoshio Hiyama, director of the Fisheries Institute of the Faculty of Agriculture, Tokyo University, and Dr. Toshiharu Kawabata, of the Department of Food Control of the National Institute of Health, Tokyo. Dr. Hiyama, whose memories of the events of 1954 and later are understandably vivid, talked to me when he visited Seattle in 1961 and amplified the information concerning Japan's emergency measures that I already had drawn from the remarkable series of Japanese reports. Dr. Kawabata, who had served briefly as a member of the Laboratory staff after his participation in the original *Shunkotsu Maru* survey, obtained at my request photographs of the 1954 monitoring activities in the Tokyo markets.

Finally there are the members of the Laboratory group on whose work in the field the present account is based: Professor Lauren R. Donaldson, Professor Allyn H. Seymour, Professor Arthur H. Welander, Professor Edward E. Held, Professor Ralph F. Palumbo, Professor Kelshaw Bonham, Mr. Paul Olson, and Professor Frank Lowman, who now has left the Laboratory to head the Radiobiology Program at the Puerto Rico Nuclear Center. They and their associates, including Professor Diptiman Chakravarti, head of the chemistry section, Mr. Derek Engstrom, head of the radiation counting section, and others who serve the Laboratory now or have been associated with it in the past, have given this work whatever it contains of permanent value. Among members of the staff to whom I am particularly indebted are Miss Marion Chase, editor and librarian, whose cheerful enthusiasm for the project and knowledge of the Laboratory's files and records always were equal to the demands I put upon them, and Miss Yuki Wada, who typed and retyped the manuscript with patience and care.

Permission to quote or use certain materials also is hereby

acknowledged. Special thanks are expressed to *Newsweek* magazine for permission to include certain relevant lines from an elec-
tion report of 1956; to Wm. H. Wise & Co., Inc., New York,
publishers of *Bombs at Bikini: The Official Report of Operation
Crossroads,* for permission to use quotations from that report by
W. A. Shurcliff, historian of Joint Task Force One; and to Holmes
& Narver, Inc., for supplying, under appropriate authority, certain
photographs to illustrate the text.

NEAL O. HINES

June 5, 1962

CONTENTS

One   1943-1945: The Laboratory   *3*

Two   1946: Crossroads   *20*

Three   1947: The Bikini Resurvey   *50*

Four   1948-1949: The Atolls   *78*

Five   1950-1951: Interim   *112*

Six   1952: Ivy   *133*

Seven   1954: Castle   *157*

Eight   1955-1956: Surveys of the Sea   *196*

Nine   1957-1959: Rongelap   *234*

Ten   1958: Hardtack   *270*

Eleven   1959-1961: The Known, the Unknown   *293*

Appendix I   *313*

Appendix II   *319*

Notes   *327*

Bibliography   *341*

Index   *353*

ILLUSTRATIONS

Photographs

Frontispiece: A thermonuclear cloud. An atoll reef

AFL group, 1944	13
AFL X-ray equipment, 1943	13
AFL holding ponds, 1945	13
Test Baker, 1946, surface view	39
Test Baker, 1946, aerial view	39
U.S.S. *Haven,* Bikini, 1946	42
Radiobiology Division group, Bikini, 1946	42
Autoradiograph of wrasse, 1946	42
U.S.S. *Chilton* en route to Bikini, 1947	55
Landing craft alongside the *Chilton,* 1947	55
Laboratory aboard the *Chilton,* 1947	55
Advance party on Bikini, 1947	58
Marine hydroids on boat frames, 1947	58
Juda, Bikini magistrate, 1947	58
Bikini Island lagoon beach, 1949	91
East reef, Bikini Atoll, 1949	91
LCI(L) 1054, Bikini, 1948	95
LSI(L) 1091, Bikini, 1949	95

LSI(L) 1091, 1949, showing pump   95
Lagoon beach of Likiep village   99
Marine dispatch tower, Bikini, 1949   99
Japanese monument, Bikini, 1949   99
Biddulph marking coconut samples, 1949   108
Bonham in laboratory, 1949   108
Coconut palm with spiraled fronds, 1949   108
Specimen of *Ipomoea tuba,* Engebi, 1949   108
Air view, Parry Island   116
Eniwetok Island runway and facilities, 1959   116
Chapel on Parry Island, 1957   119
Marine dispatch office, Parry Island, 1956   119
Liaison airstrip, Parry Island, 1957   119
Island complex on northeast reef, Eniwetok, 1959   142
Island complex on southwest rim, Eniwetok, 1959   142
EMBL on Parry Island, 1959   153
Test Mike crater, 1959   153
Autoradiograph of plankton sample, 1952   153
Campsite on Bikini Island   159
Station on Enyu Island, 1956   159
The *Fukuryu Maru* during quarantine   174
Radiation survey of tuna, Tokyo, 1954   174
Home of rat colonies, Engebi Island, 1955   208
Rat burrow, Engebi Island   208
Mullet specimens with algae growths, 1954   208
Abandoned Rongelap buildings, 1957   215
Beach at abandoned Rongelap village, 1956   215
Native well on Rongelap, 1956   215
Laboratory group boarding U.S.S. *Walton*   227
Welander conducting water sampling   227
Net used for plankton sampling   227
Group aboard U.S.S. *Walton,* 1956   228
Olson in laboratory aboard the *Walton,* 1956   228
Palumbo weighing algae samples in EMBL, 1957   228
Lowman and Held with probe, 1956   228
Rongelap Council returning to atoll, 1957   237
Rongelapese disembarking from LST 618, 1957   237
New Rongelap village, 1957   237

M. V. *Aloto* in Rongelap lagoon, 1959 256
The *Aloto* taking plankton samples 256
Coring device on the *Aloto,* Rongelap, 1959 256
Soil transect, Kabelle Island, 1959 256
Messerschmidia in wash area, Kabelle Island 266
Lysimeter plate showing root growth on Rongelap, 1959 266
Messerschmidia, Rongelap, showing meagre side growth, 1959 266

Maps

Northern Marshall Islands 23
Bikini Atoll 26
Bikini target area, 1946 37
Bikini sampling points, Resurvey of 1947 63
Eniwetok Atoll 82
Bikini sampling stations, 1949 104
Enweitok sampling stations, 1952 138
Rongelap and neighboring atolls 164
Fallout pattern of 1954 167
Track of the *Shunkotsu Maru,* 1954 190
Track of the *Roger B. Taney,* 1955 203
Track of the U.S.S. *Walton,* 1956 224
Track of the U.S.S. *Marsh,* 1956 231
Rongelap Atoll 249

Charts

Distribution of radioisotopes, Rongelap, 1959 262
Vertical distribution of ocean-borne radioactivity 284
Decline of radionuclide content in crab 299

PROVING GROUND

*An Account of the Radiobiological Studies
in the Pacific, 1946-1961*

Chapter One

1943-1945: THE LABORATORY

I

IN THE SPRING of 1943 the Manhattan District of the U.S. Army Corps of Engineers was preparing to take over from the Office of Scientific Research and Development, headed by Vannevar Bush, all research and development contracts relating to the effort to produce an atomic bomb.

The movement toward military direction of the secret program was the product of a series of scientific and administrative decisions at the highest levels. The Manhattan District had been established officially on August 13, 1942, although its organization had been in process for two months, and on September 17, 1942, Brigadier General Leslie R. Groves had been placed at its head. For security reasons, the District program was called the "DSM (Development of Substitute Materials) Project," and the new organization already had assumed procurement and engineering functions that had been handled briefly by an Office of Scientific Research and Development (OSRD) Planning Board. Early in 1943 there existed a joint OSRD-Manhattan management that would be ended on May 1 when full authority was transferred to the District and OSRD relinquished formal participation in the atomic project.[1]

The major decisions of the winter of 1942-43 had included those related to preparations for large-scale production of plutonium. Determinations of policy were made in conferences of persons designated by President Roosevelt to guide the atomic program and others serving in advisory capacities. These included Secretary of War Henry L. Stimson, Chief of Staff General George C. Marshall, Dr. Bush, James B. Conant, who had worked with Dr. Bush on the National Defense Research Committee; Major General Brehon Somervell, Commander of the Army Service Forces; Major General W. D. Styer, General Somervell's Chief of Staff, and Groves. The problem of plutonium production had to be approached even before an atomic pile had been successfully operated or a method of plutonium separation devised, but late in 1942 enough had been learned of plutonium chemistry to indicate the possibility of separation on a large scale. In anticipation of the requirements of the immediate future, it was necessary to create an organization of appropriate size, to press forward with matters of plant design, and to select a site for manufacturing activities. Groves faced each of these problems within the framework of the District's enlarging responsibility.

The Clinton Engineer Works in the Tennessee Valley had been acquired by the Army in the expectation that the subsequent scientific-technical-manufacturing activities would be centralized near a major power supply. Although a great many laboratories, operations offices, and production plants would be built in later years to accommodate nuclear activities, the embryonic programs of late 1942 were conducted at a relatively small number of laboratories or installations. The scientific forces included the University of Chicago group (operating as the "Metallurgical Laboratory") headed by Arthur H. Compton and attempting to perfect the first atomic pile. Certain additional university and other laboratories, notably those at Columbia and California, were contributing to theoretical and experimental investigations. The Manhattan District staffs were in Washington, D.C., and Tennessee, and in October, 1942, Groves had selected the E. I. du Pont de Nemours and Company to undertake under contract the design and construction of plutonium manufacturing facilities. The Los Alamos Laboratory would not be established until the spring of 1943. The Clinton Engineer Works thus represented at the end of 1942 the only potential production agency. Groves, however, in his review of production plans, became convinced that the Tennessee site was not sufficiently isolated if it were possible that a plant of the kind projected might, through the accidental escape of radioactive materials, prove a hazard to nearby communities. A new location, removed from population centers but similarly near a major power supply, was required.[2] Also required was an absolutely dependable supply of clean, and preferably cold, water. The search for a suitable alternative site within the continental limits of the United States led very soon to the expanse of rolling plains lying west of the Columbia River in the south central part of the State of Washington and near the Grand Coulee power lines.

The search for the new site was initiated while engineering staffs of du Pont and of the Manhattan District still were uncertain whether the reactors of the proposed plutonium plant would be cooled by helium or water. Somewhat earlier, apparently, the decision had leaned toward the helium-cooled unit, and a design of this type seems to have been accepted, perhaps conditionally, by du Pont.[3] Whatever the status of the question late in 1942, or whatever its relevance to the specific problems anticipated in plutonium manufacture, water would be essential to industrial processes and the criteria for the new plant site included a specification that there be at hand a flow of clean, cold water of at least 25,000 gallons per minute.[4] It also was stipulated that the site be distant from cities, highways, and main-line railroads, that it possess the physical characteristics normally expected in an industrial site, including foundation materials capable of carrying extraordinary loads, and that it have available an unfailing supply of power of about 200,000 kilowatts.

Groves' representative in the search for the site was Colonel Franklin T. Matthias, who later would become Officer in Charge of the Hanford project and would direct its construction and operational phases until the end of the war. On December 14, less than two weeks after the first self-sustaining chain reaction had been achieved at Chicago, the plutonium plant question was discussed at a meeting in the du Pont offices in Wilmington, Delaware, in which the participants included Compton and a number of his associates; C. H. Greenewalt, Roger Williams, and others of the du Pont staff; Colonel K. D. Nichols, District Engineer of the

Manhattan District; and Matthias, representing Groves. Before the year was out the Columbia River area had been visited by Matthias and two du Pont engineers, A. Hall and Gilbert Church (the latter subsequently Project Manager for du Pont at Hanford), who unanimously recommended the Hanford site.* Groves also personally inspected the area. Early in 1943 a 200-square-mile tract was acquired north of Pasco, Washington, by the Real Estate Division of the Office of the Chief of Engineers, and on it (the tract later was enlarged to 631 square miles) was placed the Hanford Engineer Works, designed, constructed, and operated until 1946 by the du Pont company. The reactors were water cooled.

II

The Columbia River, 1,207 miles long, is one of the largest streams of pure river water on the North American Continent, exceeded in volume and length only by the Mississippi, the Mackenzie, and the St. Lawrence. Originating in Columbia Lake in the Rocky Mountains of British Columbia, the river moves south into the State of Washington and through sparsely inhabited plains of sage until it becomes a westward-flowing boundary between the rich farm lands of Washington and Oregon, emptying finally into the Pacific in a broad estuarial region northwest of Portland, Oregon. On its wandering course from the Canadian border to the mouth of the Snake River, below Hanford and Richland, Washington, the Columbia drains approximately 95,000 square miles of an ancient lava plateau, semiarid and with an annual precipitation of not more than 14 inches, but in this area is Grand Coulee, a major source of hydroelectric power, and on the lower reaches of the river are based fisheries industries of great economic significance.

Ground was broken on April 6, 1943, for construction of the base camp at the tiny townsite at Hanford, Washington, which had been evacuated to make way for the establishment of the reservation.[5] Work would not begin on the first of the Hanford produc-

---

*Matthias, then an official of Kaiser Engineers, of Oakland, California, recalled in a letter to the author in 1961 that the report recommending the Hanford site also contained an analysis of another possible location, south and west of Grand Coulee, to which water might have been supplied by pumps installed in the Grand Coulee Dam in space originally provided to house pumps for irrigating the Columbia River valley. The study of this alternative area was cited to show the importance attached to the availability of water for plant operations.

tion piles until June 7, and operation of the first pile was more than a year in the future. In April, 1943, Groves and others were concerned, however, about the possible effect on the Columbia of the use of its waters for cooling. The problem of water supply in itself was complex. The water requirement would approach that of a city and would make necessary the design of pumping stations, filtration systems, and treatment plants. If the water were passed through the reactors rather than being recirculated, it also would be necessary to use a retention basin in which a portion of the induced radioactivity could be allowed to decay before the water was returned to the river. The volume of water would be so great that factors of temperature and toxicity might become critical. The questions of effect touched the relationship of the secret atomic program to a major natural resource, and they undoubtedly had a special meaning to Groves, who had spent his youth in the Northwest as the son of an Army chaplain stationed at Fort Lawton, Washington, and who had attended the University of Washington. Even if no problems were found to exist, it was essential to obtain data and experience sufficient to provide substantial reassurance.

Groves discussed the questions initially with Stafford L. Warren, of the faculty of the School of Medicine and Dentistry of the University of Rochester, then commissioned a colonel in the Army Medical Corps and serving as Chief of the Medical Section of the Manhattan District. Warren concurred wholly in the need for a program related to the Columbia. He himself had participated as early as 1922 in a series of observations of the effects of X-radiation on animals, which had included dogs, cats, rabbits, and, at the end, frogs.[6] Undoubtedly Warren could visualize the Columbia program as one projecting farther into the aquatic field the small amount of work that had been done in the intervening years. The specialized nature of the scientific problems, particularly as they related to water, indicated that the program should be set up outside of the Manhattan District by persons experienced in aquatic biology. Groves suggested inquiry at the University of Washington, where the School of Fisheries traditionally had placed emphasis on biological studies. Matthias, now in charge of Hanford plant development, was instructed to make arrangements for an initial contact through the Corps of Engineers.[7] In consultation with Colonel R. Park, Seattle District Engineer, a Seattle staff member, Hanford Thayer, was made available for later liaison activities.

On May 20, 1943, more than two weeks before work began on the first of the Hanford piles, the question of the possible contamination of the Columbia was discussed at a meeting at the University of Chicago attended by some twenty persons representing various elements of the atomic program. The group included Compton, Greenewalt, Warren, Robert S. Stone, director of the new Health Division of the Metallurgical Project at Chicago; Eugene Wigner, head of a group concerned with production pile design; C. D. Coryell, in charge of a group working on fission products; and Warren's executive officer in the Medical Section, Lt. Col. H. L. Friedell. Thayer attended the meeting, as did Major J. E. Travis, of Hanford, representing the Army.[8] Although records of the meeting are not available, later developments indicate agreement on the need for attention to the Columbia. The conditions or directions of the studies obviously were open, because there was at that stage neither a clear view of the problems nor a decision as to how or by whom the program should be undertaken.

The matter of the direction was pursued quietly in the summer of 1943 along the lines of Groves' suggestion to Warren. A number of biologists were available in the scientific manpower pool of the wartime period but few possessed extensive experience in aquatic biology. At the University of Washington the most eligible candidate appeared to be a forty-year-old assistant professor of fisheries, Lauren R. Donaldson, whose recent experience included five years as a consultant in fisheries to the Department of the Interior in connection with the Grand Coulee development and a year as a fish biologist for the Washington State Department of Fisheries. The examination of the records of Donaldson and others involved both Warren and Stone, but it was Warren who, when the selection of Donaldson had been agreed upon, made the initial approach early in August. Donaldson could be told nothing concerning the nature of the program, and he was, moreover, in Canada for meetings of the International Pacific Salmon Commission at New Westminster, B.C. Donaldson, nevertheless, was invited by telegram to return for a meeting in Washington,

D.C., while Matthias instructed Thayer to work out the details of security clearances and transportation.

The need to preserve secrecy was a condition enveloping the negotiations and the terms of the contract that would result. Donaldson was to be brought to Washington, D.C., for a conference with Warren and H. T. Wenzel, technical aid to the OSRD Executive Committee headed by Conant. On August 17, 1943, Warren called Wenzel at the Clinton Works to outline the approach to Donaldson, and on the following morning Wenzel called Thayer from Knoxville to ask him to arrange a meeting later in the month. Donaldson, Wenzel said, was not to know that the Corps of Engineers was involved or that Warren was anything more than an OSRD consultant.[9] The contract would be with the OSRD, not the Manhattan District. On August 19 Thayer sent telegrams to Warren and Donaldson concerning a meeting date, and on August 21 the proposal for radiation studies was broached to Donaldson in a conference in the OSRD headquarters at 1530 P Street.

The condition of secrecy, uncomfortable as it was, imposed on the planners of the Columbia program no restraints unusual in the scientific-industrial complex that would produce the atom bomb. In the atomic program thousands of persons and corporations undertook assignments of which the objectives were unknown. A peculiar quality of the Columbia development, however, was in the need to surround with secrecy an investigation in natural science by an investigator who, although a biologist, had no experience with the tools or apparatus he was expected to use. In the meeting in Washington, Donaldson was asked by Warren and Wenzel to undertake studies of the effects of radioactivity on aquatic organisms, specifically fish, to establish certain primary levels of understanding of problems that could not be stated or described but which involved high levels of radioactivity, were related to the Columbia River, and were of the utmost importance to the government. The program could not be identified with the Columbia, and all studies thus had to be conducted in a normal research setting on the University campus.

The contract as finally drawn was between the OSRD and the University (actually the contract form referred only to NDRC, the National Defense Research Committee), the tentative budget was placed at $65,000, and the terms made effective as of August 15, 1943.[10] By the time the contract was prepared, Warren and Donaldson had agreed on a research title that screened the actual objectives. The program, the contract said, related to an "Investigation of the use of X-rays in the treatment of fungoid infections in salmonoid fishes." Work under the contract was to extend to July 1, 1947.

III

The University agency created to begin the studies was called the Applied Fisheries Laboratory. Like the project title, the name was selected to disguise the nature of the Laboratory's work even though Donaldson himself still knew nothing of the Manhattan District or the connection of his program to the Army. It was not until late in 1944, in fact, that Donaldson was informed of the origins and significance of the work in which he was engaged. The University, on its part, also was ignorant of the kind of work proposed. Wenzel apparently made a contact with the University administration at the time of the first meeting with Donaldson, but thereafter, as hundreds of other organizations were doing, the University accepted the use of staff and facilities for an undisclosed purpose merely on the solemn assurance of persons in positions of responsibility that the use was essential to national security.

In view of the size of the problem, the smallness of the Laboratory scarcely could be comprehended. Donaldson's first move after the Washington conference was to invite Richard F. Foster, a Fisheries graduate then with the Washington State Pollution Commission, to come to the Applied Fisheries project as a research associate. Foster joined the Laboratory in September, 1943. Arthur D. Welander, a research associate in the School of Fisheries, also became a member of the staff before work was initiated, and the group of three was enlarged in February, 1943, by the addition of Kelshaw Bonham, who would specialize in autoradiograph technique. These four, in the earliest days, comprised the Laboratory group, but in a project of such ambiguity smallness was a virtue, and the four worked as a team that was literally enveloped by the interest of Warren and others in and out of the Manhattan Medical Section who came to the Laboratory representing, presumably, the OSRD.* Among the earliest of the Laboratory's informal consultants was Simeon T. Cantril, head of the Cancer Tumor Clinic of the Swedish Hospital, Seattle, who was for a time a Manhattan consultant and who later would serve the Atomic Energy Commission as a member of the Advisory Committee for Biology and Medicine.

The Laboratory's initial program was an investigation of the effects of X radiation on salmon. The program was one that would require years of observation of successive generations of fish and the maintenance of detailed records of possible radiation-induced genetic changes in animals that spend most of their lives at sea and are removed by hundreds of miles from Laboratory scrutiny or control. The salmon is a migrant fish which, born in fresh water, spends from two to four years in the ocean and then returns to the place of its birth to spawn and die. The eggs obtained from adult salmon in 1943 would produce fish that would not return until 1945, 1946, or 1947 to the point of their release, which was to be the Samish River, in Washington. Because the investigation was launched almost a year before the first reactor went into operation at Hanford, research could not at first be related physically to whatever problems would develop there, but those who took part in the program seem to have shared a sense of excitement attributable quite as much to the concept as to the secrecy surrounding it.

Other work was going forward elsewhere, of course, on questions of radiation effect, because it was essential to supplement as completely and as quickly as possible the thin layer of knowledge about the physiological consequences of exposure to radioactivity in the larger amounts and forms being made available. As head of the Health Division of the Chicago project, Stone had begun the development of an extensive program of animal experiments that ultimately would be carried on in laboratories at Chicago, at the Clinton Works, and at the University of California. These laboratories examined the effects on individual animals of external exposure to neutron, alpha, beta, and gamma radiation, of the ingestion of ura-

---

*Because of the inadequacy or unavailability of documents relating to the Laboratory's earliest days, the narrative rests heavily upon the memories of persons involved in the Laboratory's establishment or on information gleaned from correspondence of the time. Among the persons who have contributed recollections or materials are Warren, Foster, Donaldson, Welander, Thayer, and Matthias.

nium, plutonium, and other fission products, and of the inhalation of such products. The Applied Fisheries Laboratory also was working in such new fields, but it was approaching them from other directions. It worked with X radiation because it did not have access to the supplies of isotopes that would be produced by the new reactors. The Laboratory's focus, however, was on the effects of radioactivity introduced into a river and thus into a natural environment. It was interested in the effects of low-level irradiation and in the subtler changes, if any, caused by such irradiation in successive generations of living things. Above all, it worked with aquatic animals, with cold-blooded vertebrates, in an area that was all but untouched. The literature on the physiological effects of radioactivity was extremely limited in 1943, but the literature dealing with aquatic studies was even more so. When the Laboratory began its work, Duggar's two-volume *Biological Effects of Radiation* was its principal general reference.[11] Additional references probably totaled not more than one hundred. Corbella, in Italy, had worked with trout and perch, and Friederich Ellinger and C. Davison had reported experiments with goldfish. Little else had been done. The Applied Fisheries studies were conceived to produce information which had not been sought until the achievement of nuclear reaction gave urgency to the effort, and there was hope that they might solve problems which, as Warren recalled years later, were creating "worry at the laboratory level."[12] The studies were not in fact geared merely to the wartime need but to ideas of greater length and depth.

The new program, nonetheless, also bore a strange mixture of responsibilities, some stemming from practical considerations to which Groves had been sensitive. If the secret use of the waters of the Columbia should involve changes in temperature or the introduction of toxic or radioactive materials, the probable effects had to be known so that, at the proper time, data would be available to the commerical fisheries and other interests. The Columbia's salmon runs had been diminishing for years. There had been criticism of the lack at Grand Coulee of fish ladders and of other facilities for handling the salmon runs. Once a new use of the Columbia's waters became known, many ills might be ascribed, with reason or not, to the presence of the Hanford plant. Only a complete and scientifically impeccable record would be acceptable

Stafford Warren, Bishop, Donaldson, and Thayer at Applied Fisheries Laboratory, April, 1944 *(Laboratory of Radiation Biology)*

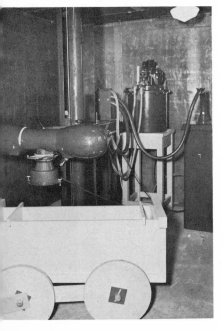

(Left) The X-radiation therapy equipment installed in the Applied Fisheries Laboratory, 1943 *(Laboratory of Radiation Biology)*

(Above) The Applied Fisheries Laboratory holding ponds at the University, January, 1945 *(Laboratory of Radiation Biology)*

if it became necessary at some future time to answer the questions of commercial fishermen, of ranchers along the Columbia's course, or of public bodies at any level concerned with the conservation and use of natural resources. Donaldson and his associates could not be made fully aware of these considerations, but such factors accounted for a share of the interest with which the Laboratory's work was followed in the Manhattan District and the OSRD.

The Applied Fisheries Laboratory was set up on the University campus in Fisheries Hall No. 2, one of several frame buildings surviving from the World War I period and then occupied by the School of Fisheries. The major item of equipment was a 200 P.Kv. Picker–Waite radiation therapy machine which would be used to expose eggs, larvae, and adult salmonoid fishes—Chinook and sockeye salmon and, later, rainbow trout—to controlled doses of X radiation. The conditions of the projected experiments had been worked out roughly by Donaldson in response to Warren's delineation in Washington of the needs and opportunities. The use of X radiation was necessary, and taken for granted, because controlled measurements of exposure were important, but also because radioactivity of no other type was available. Nowhere was there yet a source of supply of man-made radioisotopes that might have made possible the design of more sophisticated biological studies involving the use of internal emitters even if such studies had been somehow visualized. The atomic pile at the Clinton Works was not operating until November, 1943 (the first grams of plutonium were not delivered until March, 1944), and the first Hanford reactor was not in operation until September, 1944.[13] It was not until the first atomic explosion in 1945 that radioactive materials were produced by man in quantities sufficient to influence biological environments. In August, 1943, all these developments were in the future.

On September 20, 1943, Francis Bishop, a University of Rochester radiation technician, arrived at the Laboratory to supervise the installation of X-ray equipment. This arrangement had been made by Warren, who followed Bishop to Seattle on September 23.[14] Warren conferred for two days with Donaldson on the shape of the program and on administrative requirements. Confidential monthly reports were to be forwarded through Thayer to the OSRD. The first project was to be an observation of the effects of X radiation on the embryos and larvae of the Chinook salmon (*Oncorhynchus tschawytscha* Walbaum), and the equipment and salmon would be ready in October. Work was under way in October and proceeded into 1944. The experimental approach in the early period is reflected in the reports of the first months. In November, 1943, the Laboratory reported:

> During the month the chinook salmon secured and treated during October were spawned and the eggs held for future study. In this lot nine females had been exposed to radiations of 25, 50 and 100 r. The eggs produced by each female were divided into two portions, one portion fertilized with a control male and the second portion (with) the sperm from a male salmon that had received the same X-ray treatment as that given the female. Each male salmon was used to fertilize a portion of the eggs of a female salmon that had not been exposed to X-ray treatment. From these crosses, 34 egg lots were obtained. The number of eggs in the individual lots varied from 676 to 3,500. . . . A total of 55,084 eggs was used.
>
> During the month the chinook eggs developed to the "eyed stage." The mortalities experienced by the various lots to date do not indicate any injurious effects of the radiation at the levels used.[15]

The early experiments soon came to be regarded as crudely conceived. Long before the first experiment was producing results, the Laboratory started efforts to determine by histological analysis the effects on eyed embryos of the Chinook salmon of whole-body exposures ranging up to 10,000 roentgen units. These results were reported in part in a doctoral dissertation by Welander in 1945,[16] by which time the Laboratory had undertaken a series of studies of the effects of X radiation on Chinooks in the fingerling stage, on the adults, embryos and young of rainbow trout, and on snails, crustacea, and algae. The Laboratory's program achieved both experience and variety of interest as new lines of inquiry were opened. Warren, who visited the Laboratory in January and again in April, 1944, was intrigued by opportunities to investigate the blood-forming centers of the fish and the possible effects of irradiation on them. In a letter to Donaldson on May 4, 1944, he mentioned contract details and then said:

> The fact that the fish lacks a very definite bone marrow has been intriguing me ever since my visit. Perhaps some evidence for the site of manufacture of the blood may become apparent when the histological study of the eyed egg and the fingerling material is completed. In warm-blooded animals during the embryological stage of development, blood is formed

in masses of mesodermal tissue. These masses become connected with the primitive circulation and gradually disappear as discrete entities as soon as the heart chambers develop sufficiently to move the blood around. Blood formation can also be noted in late embryonic life in the liver and spleen, and occasionally in the kidneys. It is possible that when the adult salmon cease feeding and enter fresh water that new blood-cell formation ceases, and that the sites of formation disappear since all of the energy of the fish is from then on conserved for the purpose of locomotion and breeding. The rapidly growing fingerlings, therefore, should have evidence somewhere of blood formation. I would be interested to know whether this speculation turns out to be correct.

It will be important to know whether the irradiation will affect the development and function of these blood-forming centers if and when they are located.[17]

The work with the Chinook salmon embryos indicated that the syndrome resulting from irradiation of the cold-blooded vertebrates did not differ appreciably from that noted in mammals except that the latent period between exposure and death, about forty days, was longer than in warm-blooded animals. Chinook salmon in the eyed embryo stage given lethal doses of X radiation, 2,500 to 10,000 roentgen units, hatched and appeared normal for four weeks after exposure, when all began to develop degenerative symptoms that were similar in character, and all died from thirty to fifty-one days after irradiation.[18] It was believed that the lower temperatures of the water in which the salmon lives retarded to an extent the process of cell deterioration.

The experiment with rainbow trout *(Salmo gairdnerii* Richardson) was started late in 1944, when it became apparent that there were advantages in the rainbow trout's earlier maturity and in the fact that the animal could be held under observation in fresh-water ponds throughout a complete life cycle. The interest was in the effect of X radiation upon the spawning trout and upon the offspring, and the studies became the basis of a dissertation by Foster.[19] For the experiment the Laboratory used 148 fish which, chosen from the most recent generation of a trout bred selectively for many generations, were approximately twenty months old and approaching sexual maturity. The trout were divided into eight groups, a control group and seven others to which were administered whole body doses of X radiation ranging from 50 to 2,500 roentgens. When the fish became mature, about three months after irradiation, spawning produced a total of 115,454 eggs from sixty-seven females. The tabulation of results showed that the mean mortalities of the eggs obtained from parents subjected to 500 roentgens or more were significantly greater than that of the eggs from the control parents, that most of the eggs that died during the incubation period contained conspicuous and widely various deformities of the embryos, and that the heavier doses of radiation increased the abundance of malformed embryos although the types of malformations were those commonly found in the control group. The rate of growth of the young trout was found to be slowed and otherwise affected by the amount of irradiation received by the parents. Variations in mortality decreased with the age of the fish, but variations in size became greater. Fish whose parents had been exposed to 100 units were slightly impeded in growth, but those whose parents had received 500 or more units grew appreciably more slowly than normal.[20]

Findings such as these were remote from the problems of the Columbia, but they established working limits within which more refined approaches could be attempted. The extension of the studies to aquatic organisms other than fish was the product of the growing realization of the significance of environmental factors. This in turn reinforced, in the area of radiobiology, Donaldson's natural predilection for field work. At some point late in 1944 Donaldson began urging on Warren the importance of conducting observations in the Columbia itself. These discussions may have been a result of the beginning of reactor operation at Hanford in September, 1944. In any event, it was determined in 1945 to open a small on-site Aquatic Biological Laboratory to be operated at Hanford by the du Pont organization but with the consultative services of Donaldson and the Laboratory. Foster was transferred to du Pont to direct the river studies when the Hanford station was opened in June, 1945.

IV

In the two years that elapsed between its establishment in August, 1943, and the end of World War II in August, 1945, the Laboratory had begun a number of related projects. Nothing, however, was finished. The Samish River chinook salmon were only beginning to return. Data still were being processed on the trout studies and on those of the snails, the crustacea, and the other less complex aquatic forms, and publication of these results would not be made until 1947 and 1948. The detonation of atomic bombs over Hiroshima and Nagasaki revealed and illuminated suddenly the fearful product of the years of secret activity while obscuring, actually, the still-unformed meanings of the work on the Columbia.

The Laboratory had been viewed from its earliest days, by Warren, Stone, Cantril, and others, as one that had been given a matchless opportunity to develop methods and data that would be of fundamental importance in the time that was coming. While the war was in progress, the effort necessarily was linked to wartime calculations, yet even in a situation requiring maximum security measures the Laboratory program had been encouraged to find its own way along the paths that experience opened. The end of the war disclosed the existence of the atomic program and the end to which it had been directed, but so far as the Laboratory was concerned the time for recapitulation still was ahead. The Laboratory's original contract had been expected to continue until July, 1947, but the period had been attuned to the spawning cycle of the salmon rather than to an estimate of the probable duration of the war.

By 1945, nevertheless, certain accomplishments could be noted.

The Laboratory had started long-term observations of the biological effects of X radiation on salmon and had extended these to include a variety of aquatic animals and plants. No experiments similar either in concept or variety had been attempted before.

The Laboratory had been instrumental in establishing at Hanford the earliest aquatic biological laboratory conducting studies at an atomic site. Although the longer studies with X radiation still proceeded, the Hanford station had documented the case on the Columbia, where the toxicity of reactor effluents had been found, in fact, too low to have effect on salmon eggs and fry. The Columbia records would be presented in full at a meeting in the spring of 1946 of officials of the Washington State Department of Game and of the U.S. Fish and Wildlife Service.

The Laboratory had undertaken genetic studies on salmonoids. It had made analyses of the differences in sensitivity of various aquatic organisms to ionizing radiation, noting that the more complex the organism the greater its sensitivity. It had begun to develop its own rudimentary appreciation of the ecological breadth of the radiation problem. The use of X radiation had permitted experiment with controlled doses of ionizing radiation applied externally to aquatic animals and to other organisms in various stages of development, but these experiments, it was recognized, constituted only a framework.

It would have been difficult, perhaps impossible, in 1945 to state what had been accomplished in any substantive way. But this was because the experiments at the University and the observations on the Columbia had been set up on the longer time spans and for the measurement of biological result rather than of immediate physiological effect of ionizing radiation. The difference was not readily discernible to those searching for immediate answers. But somehow, in the secrecy and the excitement of the war years, and out of the curiosity and interest focused on the Laboratory by Warren, Cantril, and others, had been created a small and persistent inquiry that was pointed, unknown to the participants, toward problems that were larger than anyone yet realized. The problems were those of radioactivity in the natural aquatic environment, and the Laboratory's contribution, perhaps, was solely in its developing conviction that such matters had to be studied in the field. Neither the first atomic device detonated at Alamogordo nor the two atomic bombs exploded over Japan had created situations involving aquatic contamination. But such situations would be created in 1946 in the Operation Crossroads tests at Bikini. There, and thereafter, the questions would be full size.

With the end of the war, the connection of the Laboratory's program to the Manhattan District was acknowledged. Soon, in February, 1946, the earlier contract with the National Defense Research Committee was assumed by the Corps of Engineers, and the Applied Fisheries work proceeded for some months under this arrangement. The postwar changes were coming, however, and the Manhattan District would go out of existence, at the end of the year, and its contracts, facilities, and management responsibilities would be transferred to the new U.S. Atomic Energy Commission created by passage of the Atomic Energy Act of 1946.

Before this occurred, members of the Laboratory staff were involved in the first of the atomic tests in the Pacific.

Chapter Two

1946: CROSSROADS

I

THE PACIFIC TESTS of nuclear devices were conducted on coral atolls and in an environment that was altogether oceanic. It is conceivable that circumstances might have been otherwise, but the size and character of the devices and the time of their creation determined the course that events would take. Thus tiny flecks of land in the largest of oceans were drawn into the orbit of nuclear developments, and it was because of their place in the ocean that the atolls became, in ways not originally foreseen, laboratories for the study of radioactivity in the marine environment.

The first such tests were conducted during Operation Crossroads at Bikini Atoll in the Marshall Islands.

The planning and conduct of the atomic tests of 1946 was a joint military enterprise. The impulse flowed not alone from the military, for there was in 1945 and 1946 an irrepressible curiosity about the magnitude and meaning of the new atomic force that had struck Japan with such cataclysmic impact and had ended, with a still scarcely believable suddenness, a long and bloody war. But the military interest was large, because the atomic weapon was recognized as having revolutionized and outmoded earlier concepts of warfare, even those developed by the proliferating technology of World War II, and the tests were conducted as a military exercise relying heavily on scientific support. As planning for the tests got under way, there was carried into the thinking the concepts of the joint military operation, the amalgamation of air, sea, and land forces for a single task. Early in the planning period the commander of the joint forces decided that the tests should be conducted under the code name "Crossroads," as one appropriately symbolic, presumably, of the dilemma of a world now offered a choice between peace and atomic destruction, and the tests were to be witnessed by political leaders, foreign representatives, and by members of the press so that all peoples could understand what had been wrought. Three explosions originally were projected, two finally detonated, the first on July 1, 1946 (June 30 in the United States) at a height of 518 feet over a fleet of naval vessels anchored within Bikini Atoll, and the second on July 25 at a depth of ninety feet beneath the surface of Bikini Lagoon. The devices were of the same type as those used over Japan, having yields equivalent to 20,000 tons of TNT, and thus they were of the size that would be referred to subsequently as "nominal." The second explosion, the underwater detonation, would be accompanied by phenomena never observed before.

Plans for atomic tests under controlled conditions were being discussed by military and political leaders in the weeks following the end of the war. Attention was focused almost immediately on the question of the possible effects of bombs employed against naval vessels,* and the proposals presented during September and October, 1945, resulted in the appointment on November 10, 1945, of a group called the Joint Staff Planners, a permanent working subcommittee of the Joint Chiefs of Staff, which in turn designated a subcommittee headed by Major General Curtis E. LeMay to develop detailed plans.† The predominance of Navy interest in tests of the kinds contemplated suggested that the op-

---

*On August 25, 1945, Senator Brian McMahon, later chairman of the Senate Special Committee on Atomic Energy, suggested that the new bomb be tested on naval vessels. On September 14, an Army spokesman in Tokyo proposed that atomic bombs be used to destroy the Japanese fleet.

† Serving with LeMay were Brigadier General W. A. Borden, and Colonel C. H. Bonesteel, Army members, and Captain G. W. Anderson Jr., Captain V. L. Pottle, and Commodore W. S. Parsons, of the Navy.

erations be headed by a Navy representative, and this proved to be Vice-Admiral W. H. P. Blandy, an ordnance specialist recently appointed Deputy Chief of Naval Operations for Special Weapons. The LeMay subcommittee's proposals were accepted by the Joint Chiefs with minor modifications on December 28, 1945, and approved by President Truman on January 10, 1946. On the following day Blandy was named commander of Joint Task Force One.

The search for a site for the test operation had been started even before the task force was created. The specifications set out by the planners called for selection of a site within the control of the United States, uninhabited or subject to evacuation without imposing unnecessary hardship on large numbers of inhabitants, within 1,000 miles of the nearest B-29 aircraft base (in expectation that one atomic device would be delivered by air), free from storms and extreme cold, and offering a protected anchorage at least six miles in diameter and thus large enough to accommodate both the large fleet of target vessels and the additional vessels that would have to be used in support of the operation.[1] Also required were distance from cities or concentrations of population, winds predictably uniform from sea level to 60,000 feet, and predictable water currents not adjacent to inhabited shore lines, shipping lanes, or fishing areas—all in recognition of the need to reduce or eliminate the possibility of radioactive contamination of the fleets or of inhabited areas.

Sites in the Atlantic, the Caribbean, and the Pacific were reviewed. In the Pacific were little islands set in great reaches of otherwise empty ocean and enjoying the warm and stable climate of the trade-wind zone. In the Marshalls, so recently captured from the Japanese, were coral atolls that had been little disturbed by the war, that were inhabited only by small communities of Micronesians, and over which an interim control was exercised by the United States through the Navy Military Government. Among these was Bikini Atoll. Bikini fulfilled all the conditions of climate and isolation. It was distant, 2,500 miles west-southwest of Honolulu, 4,500 miles by air from San Francisco, but it also was accessible to the military support facilities that still existed at Kwajalein Atoll, to the southeast, and at Eniwetok, to the west. Its inhabitants, who then numbered 162, could be moved to another atoll during the period of the tests.

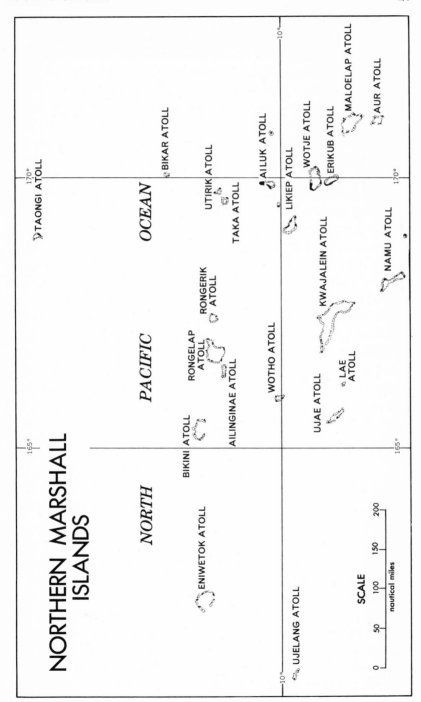

NORTHERN MARSHALL ISLANDS

NORTH PACIFIC OCEAN

SCALE

nautical miles

0   50   100   150   200

UJELANG ATOLL

ENIWETOK ATOLL

BIKINI ATOLL

AILINGINAE ATOLL

RONGELAP ATOLL

RONGERIK ATOLL

WOTHO ATOLL

UJAE ATOLL

LAE ATOLL

KWAJALEIN ATOLL

NAMU ATOLL

TAONGI ATOLL

BIKAR ATOLL

UTIRIK ATOLL

TAKA ATOLL

AILUK ATOLL

LIKIEP ATOLL

WOTJE ATOLL

ERIKUB ATOLL

MALOELAP ATOLL

AUR ATOLL

170°

165°

10°

Before the selection of Bikini was confirmed, it became necessary to satisfy spokesmen for the United States fishing industry
that the detonation of atomic bombs would not inflict important
damage on fisheries resources. The concern was that the explosions would kill millions of fish, including tuna or whales that
might be abundant in the mid-Pacific area. The Fish and Wildlife Service of the U.S. Department of the Interior reported that
Bikini was far from the migratory routes of whales in the season
under consideration, that the area was not critical for tuna or
other fish of commercial importance, and that it was not a spawning ground for West Coast tuna.[2] The inquiry, in a curious way,
was prophetic. But there seems to have been no concern for the
possibility of radioactive contamination of fisheries resources, a
matter that in subsequent years would so occupy the attention of
people in the United States and Japan. The question of the
fisheries industry answered, Bikini was selected for the atomic
tests and preparations for them were pressed forward, in the spring
of 1946, by Joint Task Force One.

Before World War II had ended and when captured islands
and atolls were coming one by one into American hands, management and rehabilitation of the native peoples had been undertaken by the Navy. There had been a momentary uncertainty
as to the status of the inhabitants. For more than a quarter of a
century Japan, having moved into Germany's Pacific possessions
at the outbreak of World War I, had administered the islands
under a League of Nations Class C mandate in which she had
been confirmed on December 17, 1920. The mandate, however,
had failed to make clear the civil position of persons for whom
Japan was responsible and, when the war ended Japan's authority,
there was a period in which the Marshallese and other peoples
were regarded as captured Japanese subjects.[3] A subsequent inter-
pretation made it possible for Navy Military Government units
to care for the natives as liberated persons, and under this view
the rehabilitation of war-disturbed island areas was proceeding
pending the establishment of a more permanent administrative
framework. In 1946, accordingly, arrangements for the use of
Bikini were worked out by the Navy.

The agreement for the use of Bikini for nuclear tests was made
with Juda, *iroiji*, headman and magistrate, of the community.

In this the agreement was said to have the sanction of ancient Marshallese custom wherein the *iroiji* held authority over community property, although acceptance of the 1946 agreement was confirmed, however, by members of the atoll council composed of *alaps,* or heads of families. The Bikini people were offered a choice of alternate accommodations, at Ujae or Lae, smaller atolls to the south, or Rongerik, the eastern neighbor of nearby Rongelap Atoll. But Ujae and Lae already were inhabited, while Rongerik not only was closer to Bikini but, as a property of the Rongelap people, who had landrights there, was used principally for the production of food and copra. The Bikini Council named Rongerik as its first choice for resettlement, and the proposal was approved by Lajrwe, the *iroiji* of Rongelap. A village was constructed on Rongerik by the Seabees, and the Bikini people were transported to their new home on a Navy LST on March 6 and 7, 1946.

II

The Pacific Ocean not only is the largest of oceans but it is twice as large as the Atlantic and larger in area than the total land surface of the world. It also is the deepest of oceans, its depth averaging almost three miles. At its widest part it extends 12,000 miles from Panama to the western reaches of the China Sea, almost halfway around the globe. In this expanse are the Marshall Islands, which are among the island groups composing Micronesia, and within the Marshalls are twenty-nine atolls and five single islands, the thirty-four bits of land arranged in two chains—the Ratak, or sunrise, eastern chain and the Ralik, sunset, chain to the west—that trend northwesterly in the North Equatorial region of the Central Pacific within the parallels of latitude 4° 30′ N. and 15° N. and the meridians of longitude 161° E. and 174° E. Bikini is in the Ralik chain at approximately 12° N.

The geographical area of the Marshall Islands group, calculated within the boundaries of its outlying points, is approximately 180,000 square statute miles. Yet the 34 islands and atolls, which include more than 1,150 separate island units, contain a total of less than 70 square statute miles of dry land.[4] Kwajalein, perhaps the largest atoll in the world, contains 97 islands distributed about a lagoon 75 miles long and 30 across and with a total area

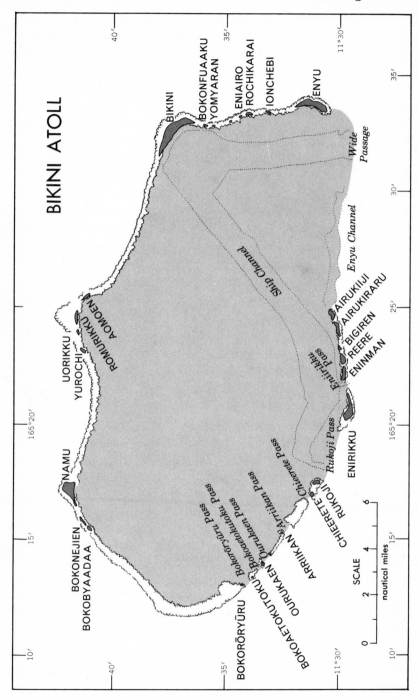

BIKINI ATOLL

of 839 square statute miles. Kwajalein's land area, however, totals only 6.33 square miles. This relationship of water to land is repeated with local variations in each of the atolls. Mili Atoll, far to the southeast in the Ratak Chain, has 102 separate islands with only 6.15 square miles of land about a lagoon of 294 square miles. Likiep Atoll contains 64 islands with less than 4 square miles of land. The 5 separate single-island units of the Marshalls together represent only 1.72 square miles of land area.

The opening of the Pacific to European influences, like the ancient movements by which the islands were populated, was a process of centuries. The atolls of the Central Pacific, small in land area and empty of resources tempting to explorers and adventurers, lay almost unnoticed in the expanse of ocean during much of the long Spanish period that began with Magellan, who sailed across the Pacific without sighting any of the islands that flanked his route. After de Saavedra, de Legaspi, and de Nayra, who followed Magellan, the atolls were only *recifes*—reefs—to the captains of the Spanish galleons. Drake may have visited atolls of the Ratak chain in 1579, although almost two hundred years then would elapse before the little islands began to be noted and placed with reasonable accuracy on charts of the European admiralties. In 1767, Samuel Wallis, commanding H.M.S. *Dolphin,* found and later reported islands believed to have been Rongelap and Rongerik Atolls. In 1787, the East India Company chartered two merchant vessels, the *Charlotte,* commanded by Captain Thomas Gilbert, and the *Scarborough,* commanded by Captain William (or John) Marshall, to transport convicts to the British penal colony at Botany Bay and then to proceed to Canton to load tea for the British market. From New South Wales the two captains wandered circuitously north and west to China, making landfalls at a number of Pacific islands, and on their return to England the story of the voyage was told in two books, one by Gilbert, published in London in 1789, the second containing in an appendix an abstract of Marshall's log.[5] The islands reported by the Captains began to be called by the English the Gilberts and the Marshalls, and ultimately they were so designated on the maps of other nations.

A Pacific atoll is a roughly oval coralline reef surmounting, at the surface of the sea, a conical structure composed principally of masses of dead coral polyps and calcareous algae and resting on a base of basaltic rock, the whole rising perhaps 15,000 feet or more above the ocean floor. The reef, lifted only slightly above the surface of the water and awash except at low tides, encloses a lagoon rarely deeper than 180 feet and characteristically cut bypasses and points of outflow on the protected leeward rim. The islets and islands of the atoll are sandy dunes bearing vegetation which varies from windswept scrub to stands of coconut palms and other tropical plants. The land averages little more than seven feet in elevation, and it is only their vegetation that gives the islands any appearance of vertical dimension. The people of the Marshalls, who in earlier times made long voyages in vessels pieced together from native woods and fibers, had a term for the distance at which the tops of the coconut palms could be seen from the mast of a sailing canoe. This distance they called *djellad-ai,* and it was about ten nautical miles. The atoll is a product of the ocean: alive, growing, its shape and character adjusted to the movement and circulation of ocean waters and regulated by tropical light and heat. Above the surface of the sea, the atoll reef curves away over the horizon. Below, among the masses of reef-building coral and the marine plants and animals that inhabit the waters, is a ceaseless competition for food and space. To windward, where buttresses have been built against the pounding pressure of the ocean, are raised lines of jagged coral that form what has been called the Lithothamnion or algal ridge because it is composed of rich growths of the calcareous algae, the *Lithothamnia,* whose existence is dependent upon the materials brought by the sea. The ridge is cut by surge channels, grooves extending down below the level of the breakers on the seaward slope and forming a sea wall and on which the rollers spend their force. At high tide, the seaward reef flats are covered by water to depths of two to four feet, but when the water recedes the flats are revealed as expanses of algal limestone cut by crevices and dotted by pools in which are the small fish, the eels, the snails, the crabs, and other creatures of the reef.

It was in such a theater that Operation Crossroads was placed, and the activities that surrounded preparations for these early nuclear tests would have effects of great importance in the advancement of understanding of an ocean about which so little yet was known. It was by chance, however, that in designating Bikini for the tests the staffs of Joint Task Force One selected an atoll that had been associated more than a century before with the earliest observations of geology and biology of the Pacific, observations of the kind that Crossroads would itself enlarge.

Bikini was discovered in 1825 by Otto von Kotzebue, then making his second voyage through the Pacific. As a young lieutenant in the Russian Navy, Kotzebue had sailed into the Pacific in 1815 in command of the *Rurik*,[6] a 180-ton brig sent out under the Imperial war flag to explore areas of the South Seas and to search for a northeast passage through Bering Strait to the Arctic and Atlantic Oceans. Within the *Rurik's* complement of thirty-one were three remarkable young men—Louis Choris, an artist then only twenty years old; Johan Friedrich (Ivan Ivanovitch) Eschscholtz, an Estonian of twenty-two who was a zoologist and physician and who shipped aboard the *Rurik* as surgeon; and Louis Charles Adelaid (Adelbert) de Chamisso, thirty-six-year old scion of a noble French family who had been a page boy in the Prussian court, a soldier in the Prussian army, a botanist, a poet, author of a classic romantic narrative, *Peter Schlemiehl*, and who accompanied Kotzebue as "naturalist."* Eschscholtz and Chamisso observed the flora and fauna of the ocean and of the places visited by the *Rurik*, and Chamisso made extensive examinations of the atolls. Chamisso was said to have been the first to note that an atoll reef usually is more extensively developed on the windward and swellward side, that major passages into the atoll frequently

*Choris had been to the Caucasus in 1813 as draftsman for a botanical expedition and he wrote and illustrated several reports of botanical work. On a journey to America in 1828 he was assassinated by bandits near Vera Cruz, Mexico. Eschscholtz, a native of Dorpat, in the Baltic provinces of Russia, ultimately published a number of scientific works and became a professor of zoology at Dorpat, where he died in 1831. Chamisso, who was nine when his family fled the French Revolution, is said to have begun his study of botany when he spent a year, 1811-12, as a companion of Madame de Stael and her son in the Swiss canton of Vaux. In 1815, a friend, Julius Edward Hitzig, mentioned to Chamisso the projected search for the northeast passage, which presumably would take Kotzebue to the polar regions, and Chamisso is reported to have exclaimed, "I wish I could go to the North Pole with those Russians!" Hitzig apparently was acquainted with August von Kotzebue, father of Otto, and Chamisso's application went to the Russian Admiral Krusenstern. Chamisso received his appointment to the *Rurik* as a substitute for a Professor Ledebour, who was in ill health. Chamisso's knowledge of languages made him interpreter when the *Rurik* visited the Spanish settlement at San Francisco in 1816. Eschscholtz and Chamisso became close friends during their voyaging and it was in honor of Eschscholtz that Chamisso named the California poppy *Eschscholtzia californica*.

appear on the protected lee side, that on seaward projections of
the reef loose sand usually is piled up, creating islands, and that
the lagoon of the typical atoll is from twenty-five to thirty-two
fathoms in depth. The *Rurik* voyage was concluded in 1818 and
Chamisso's observations were published, with Kotzebue's account,
in 1821. Chamisso was not a member of Kotzebue's company
when the second cruise was begun in 1823 aboard another vessel,
the *Predpryatic*. Eschscholtz, however, returned to the Pacific,
and a physicist, O. Lenz, conducted physical oceanographic observations. The *Predpryatic* was in the northern Marshalls in 1825,
visiting a number of atolls including Rongelap and Ailinginae.
There Kotzebue came upon Bikini, which he named Eschscholtz.[7]
In the period of nuclear testing, a century and a quarter later, the
charts of the Pacific identified Bikini as "Bikini or Eschholtz Atoll."

The forces and circumstances that put Operation Crossroads at
Bikini would become the forces and circumstances producing the
first comprehensive assault on the mysteries of the Pacific. Charles
Darwin had seen the Pacific atolls as living evidences of vast terrestrial readjustments worked out over eons of unrecorded time. It
was his hypothesis that the organic growth of the atolls first had
appeared on rocky foundations lying near the surface of the sea,
but that the slow sinking of the earth's crust had caused the coral
and algae to build upward on themselves, thus maintaining life.
Darwin enunciated his theory in 1837, and in 1842 he published
a map reflecting his calculation that certain areas of the Pacific
were characterized by submergence, others by stability or emergence.[8] In 1838, the United States Exploring Expedition, led by
Lieutenant Charles Wilkes, began extensive observations in the
Pacific, and by 1841 the expedition had visited the Northern Marshalls, charting Rongerik under the name Bigini and sighting
Rongelap and Ailinginae. While political changes swept the
Pacific and exerted modifying pressures on the structures of primitive societies, knowledge of the surface features of the ocean grew
increasingly detailed. Such developments were accompanied,
although largely without realization, by a deepening curiosity
about the ocean and its resources. In the Marshalls, Germany was
entrenched at Jaluit by 1870 and by 1885 would assume a protec-
torate over all of the islands as a means of managing the developing
copra trade. In this period, in 1872 and 1873, the U.S.S. *Tuscarora*,

making a general survey of the Pacific, was sounding the ocean floor and taking bottom samples several hundred miles north of Bikini. In 1881, Darwin, still intrigued by atolls, expressed in a letter to Alexander Agassiz the wish that the depths of coral growths beneath an atoll reef could be tested by drilling,[9] and the first such drillings were made by the British in 1897 and 1898 during the second and third Funafuti expeditions to the Ellice Islands. Later others were made at other places in the Pacific, including, but in another age, Eniwetok and Bikini. Germany's Pacific empire was extended to the Carolines and the Marianas in 1899 when Spain, defeated in the Spanish-American war, ceded to Germany all of the islands except Guam, but in that year the U.S.S. *Nero*, surveying the Pacific cable route, was exploring the ocean floor north of the Marshalls, and two years later Agassiz was in the Marshalls with the United States Fish Commission ship, the *Albatross*, making collections and observations and taking deep bottom samples south of Rongelap. The Japanese, including Japanese scientists, were active in the Central Pacific in the period between world wars, but the *Carnegie* oceanographic expedition of 1929 was the only major non-Japanese scientific group to obtain data in the area. When Japan's withdrawal from the League of Nations began a final period of concentration on military objectives, the islands of the mid-Pacific were closed to the outside world and remained so until their capture in World War II.

Bikini escaped most of the violence of the war. The Japanese maintained a meteorological station there until its six-man garrison was killed during sweeping air and sea operations launched by American forces in January, 1944. When the war ended, Bikini was marked only by the wreck of a U.S. Navy PBY aircraft, the rusting fragments of a crashed Japanese bomber and, toward the northwest tip of Bikini Island, a small stone shaft, cemented above a pile of coral rocks, bearing a memorial inscription to two Japanese airmen.

III

Operation Crossroads was a military-scientific program of a kind never seen until that time. Joint Task Force One took to the northern Marshalls, in the spring and summer of 1946, 250 naval vessels of various types (some seventy of them the ships and smaller craft that would be placed in the atomic target area in Bikini Lagoon), more than 150 aircraft for transport, liaison, observation, and drone use, and 42,000 military, scientific, and technical personnel and observers.

Operation Crossroads unquestionably was the most thoroughly documented, reported, and publicized peacetime military exercise in history. The official records filled volumes. Coverage by the press was authorized by the White House on recommendation of the Joint Chiefs of Staff, and the task force was accompanied by a press headquarters ship, the transport *Appalachian*. Also with the approval of the President, observers from eleven nations having memberships in the United Nations Atomic Energy Commission were invited to go to Bikini aboard the transport *Panamint*. Such concentration of attention, quite apart from the sheer size of the operation, gave Crossroads the quality of the spectacular. The tests were necessary, it was explained, to examine the effects of nuclear blasts on naval vessels. The tests were necessary to the further evaluation of the atomic bomb as a strategic weapon. These reasons would do. The tests were, indeed, full of portent, as the literature of the period so copiously pointed out. Yet the unique contribution of Crossroads was its mobilization of scientific interests. It managed to bring to bear on an obscure atoll not only the interests so suddenly enlarged by the physical sciences but by those of virtually the whole range of scientific disciplines. Crossroads provided a reason and a theater for studies that would have been impossible at any earlier time. Thousands of scientists took part, many of them still in uniform and fulfilling a final military obligation before returning to their universities and laboratories. The impact of this shared and concentrated effort was somehow greater, in the end, than the impact of the atomic detonations themselves, shattering as they proved to be.

Admiral Blandy originally had established a target date of May 15 for the beginning of the tests and preliminary work in the Bikini area had been authorized in January, 1946.[10] The destroyer *Sumner* (DD 692) first was dispatched to Bikini to conduct hydrographic surveying, and she was followed by vessels carrying scientific teams carrying out preliminary oceanographic, biological and geological surveys for which the headquarters ship was the

U.S.S. *Bowditch* (AGS 4).* The field work thus begun in March was continued through the summer until the operation was concluded in August. Meantime, however, on March 22, as a construction battalion arrived at Bikini to prepare the extensive shore facilities, a delay of the tests was ordered by President Truman to permit Congressional observers to attend. A new target date of July 1 was established. Whatever its other effects, the delay provided additional time for measurements and observations of a variety and intensity never before focused on an atoll.

Bikini lies in the path of the North Equatorial Current, a product of a wind system of the Pacific, which moves west across the ocean from the coast of North America to a region east of the Philippines, where it divides and doubles back as the Japan Current, circling the north rim of the Pacific basin, and the Equatorial Countercurrent, flowing eastward just north of the Equator. The trade winds maintain their most constant velocity, about 18 knots, during the winter months, but at other seasons their streams of wind of the northern and southern hemispheres shift to the north —the zone of the southeast trades extending in some areas to 10° N. latitude, almost as far north as Bikini—and in these periods the Northern Marshalls lie in an area of lighter, variable winds. Storms are not frequent, but they occur occasionally in summer and autumn, striking from the southeast, the direction of a seasonal ocean swell generated by winter storms in the southern hemisphere. The average monthly mean temperature varies throughout the year only from 80 to 83 degrees.

Bikini is an atoll of irregular outline, roughly oval in shape and exhibiting many of the classic characteristics of atoll growth—the strong reefs built to windward, the protected leeward entrances,

*Institutions and agencies involved in the surveys were the Geological Survey, the Smithsonian Institution, the Fish and Wildlife Service, the Military Intelligence Division of the Office of the Chief of Engineers, the Woods Hole Oceanographic Institution, the Scripps Institution of Oceanography, the Division of War Research, and the University of Michigan. Among scientists conducting segments of the work were J. I. Tracey Jr. and H. S. Ladd, surface geology of coral reefs and islands; K. O. Emery, submarine geology; C. C. Bates, beach studies; W. H. Munk, Gordon Riley, W. S. von Arx, and W. L. Ford, lagoon currents and diffusion and water exchange between lagoon and ocean; Leonard Schultz, lagoon and reef fishes; J. C. Marr and Vernon Brock, pelagic fishes; J. P. E. Morrison, mollusks, birds, and land animals; M. W. Johnson, plankton; W. R. Taylor, land and marine plants; and M. C. Sargent and T. S. Austin, organic productivity. (Roger Revelle, Foreword, "Bikini and Nearby Atolls: Part 1, Geology," *Geology of Bikini and Nearby Atolls,* Washington, D.C.: Government Printing Office, 1954, p. iv.)

the lagoon having a maximum depth of about thirty-two fathoms, and the principal islands linked by the long stretches of sandy reef which trace the edges of the coral cup. Bikini Island, largest of the twenty-six islands and islets, is two and one-half miles long and one-half mile wide, with about 540 acres of dry land. It rests on a reef whose outer edges, cut by surge channels, stretch outward toward and into the ocean in the direction of the prevailing winds. Southward from Bikini Island the long line of reef sand contains only patches of islet vegetation until the reef widens out at Enyu Island, the second largest island of the atoll, which flanks the wide southeast entrance called Enyu Passage. Westward from Bikini Island is the long northern reef of the atoll, a meander line of coral sand unmarked for almost twenty miles except, at its mid-point, by a northward pointing reef projection supporting an island cluster which includes Aomoen (Amen) Island.*

Bikini's lagoon is about twenty-six miles long from east to west and fifteen miles wide from north to south. The lagoon covers two hundred and forty-three square miles and the land, omitting inter-tidal areas, totals 3.4 square miles.[11] Most of the islands are only eight to twelve feet above the low tide level (mean spring high tides rise 5.5 feet), but points on Bikini Island were sixteen to nineteen feet high, and on Romurikku Island, west of Aomoen, a dune had risen twenty-three feet above the reef flat.

Bikini's coral rim is penetrated by a number of passes, the largest of them Enyu Passage, which is nine miles wide and which hides a characteristic atoll entrance sill only four to ten fathoms below the surface of the water. All of the other passes are on the protected southwest curve of the atoll, none wider than about a mile and the deepest of them thirty-fathom Enirik Pass, between Eniirikku and Eninman Islands.

In the preparations for Crossroads the imminent release of unprecedented amounts of radioactive materials was a consideration given attention at every turn. There was an appropriate attention to radiation measurement and radiation safety. Because the mili-

---

*To facilitate communications involving island sites the task force substituted simple code names for the Marshallese names of the islands. Bikini, Enyu, and Namu Islands retained their native names, but Aomoen became Amen, Ionchebi became Ion, and so on. Because a new set of code designations was assigned when Bikini became a part of the proving ground, the Marshallese names (most of them determined by a 1944 Decision List of the Board on Geographic Names) are used herein, the code names given, where appropriate, in parentheses.

tary problem obviously required assessment of the effects of blast and of thermal and nuclear radiations on living organisms, test animals were to be stationed on twenty-two vessels of the target fleet under various conditions of nearness to and shielding from the explosions.* The Radiation Safety Section took to Bikini more than 25,000 counters, film badges, and other devices. The studies of the Oceanographic Group were directed at determining lagoon currents so that postdetonation upwellings of contaminated water could be anticipated and plotted. In all of these preparations there was realization of the need to extract from the tests all possible information concerning the radiation factor. There is no evidence, however, that Crossroads was then considered the possible starting point of long-term research in radiobiology or that Bikini might offer means of discovering how radionuclides were caught up and circulated in a biological system. Although the concept of such circulation was not altogether new, its relevance in the Bikini situation seems not to have been realized.

Admiral Blandy's letter of appointment directed him to include civilian scientists in the task force organization, to arrange tests to note "the effects of atomic explosives against ground and air targets and to acquire scientific data of general value if this is practicable," and to collaborate with the test evaluation board to be appointed separately by the Joint Chiefs.† The Joint Chiefs also indicated an interest in air detonation and in underwater detonation "if the latter is considered feasible."[12] Blandy was assisted by a staff including two deputy task force commanders, Rear Admiral W. S. Parsons, the Deputy for Technical Direction, having in turn a staff of four special assistants, including John von Neumann, Scientific Adviser, two technical administrators, and two technical

---

*Studies of test animals were under the direction of Captain R. H. Draeger, of the Naval Medical Research Section, whose executive officer was Captain Shields Warren, later the first Director of the Division of Biology and Medicine of the U.S. Atomic Energy Commission. Animals taken to Bikini included 200 pigs, 60 guinea pigs, 204 goats, 5,000 rats, and 200 mice.

† The Evaluation Board, created by the Joint Chiefs of Staff on March 28, 1946, was headed by K. T. Compton, President of the Massachusetts Institute of Technology, and included six scientific and military representatives. The Board was to be available for advising the Commander of Joint Task Force One on test planning and to prepare for the Joint Chiefs an evaluation of test results. There was, in addition, a President's Evaluation Commission headed by Senator C. A. Hatch, of New Mexico, and on which President Compton also served. The Commission was to cooperate with the Secretaries of War and Navy during the test period and to submit to the President a final report of its conclusions and recommendations.

advisers. One of the technical advisers was Stafford Warren, who was both Radiological Safety Adviser and head of the Radioactivity Group. With Warren, assigned as radiation monitors, were representatives of the Applied Fisheries Laboratory: Donaldson, Welander, and Clarence F. Pautzke, a biologist with the Washington State Game Department, who had assisted in the selection of salmon for the Laboratory's X-radiation studies. They went to the Pacific aboard the U.S.S. *Haven,* a hospital ship employed in the operation because of the facilities it provided for laboratory work, and they were in the Bikini area from June 12 to August 16.

The first Bikini explosion, Test Able, the air drop of an atomic bomb of nominal yield, took place at approximately 9 A.M., July 1, 1946 (Bikini time). The bomb was dropped from a B-29 aircraft, *Dave's Dream,* and the aiming point was the battleship *Nevada* stationed in the center of the target fleet. Near the *Nevada* were two Japanese warships, the battleship *Nagato* and the light cruiser *Sakawa,* and other major vessels including the destroyer *Hughes,* the aircraft carrier *Independence,* the cruiser *Pensacola,* and the submarine *Skate.* The bomb burst as planned some 500 feet over the target array, but the burst was approximately 1,500 feet to the west of the *Nevada,* the intended zero point.[13] The result was surprising, perhaps, only to those who had expected something near total elimination of the target fleet. The destruction, although far short of total, was awesome enough. Five ships were sinking. The attack transports *Gilliam* and *Carlisle,* vessels of approximately 450 feet in length, sank immediately—the *Gilliam,* closest of all target ships to the actual point of detonation, within one minute, and the *Carlisle* about forty minutes later. The destroyers *Anderson* and *Lamson,* vessels of 338 and 344 feet, were mortally stricken, the *Anderson* going down almost at once. The *Sakawa* was in flames astern and would sink on the morning of July 2 after she had burned for twenty-four hours and despite efforts to tow her to a beach. Other vessels were badly mauled and burning or made unapproachable by irradiation. The hull of the *Independence* was buckled and wrinkled, the remnants of her superstructure hopelessly tangled, and her 600-foot flight deck broken in several places. The *Arkansas,* oldest vessel in the United States fleet, was heavily damaged and burning, although she lived through the test. The carrier *Saratoga,* the cruisers *Salt Lake City*

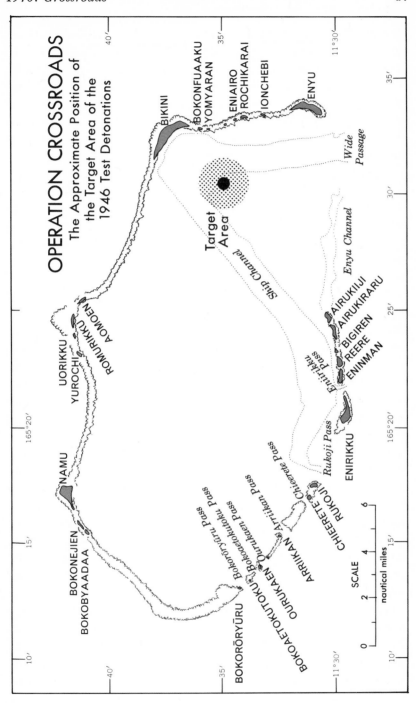

OPERATION CROSSROADS
The Approximate Position of
the Target Area of the
1946 Test Detonations

and *Pensacola,* and destroyers such as the *Hughes* were hit hard. Other ships, including the *Nevada,* the target vessel, escaped with only moderate damage. Surviving ships showing signs of irradiation were washed down in the course of fire-fighting and salvage operations, which began as soon as radiological patrols had scouted the target area. By 2:30 P.M. on July 2 Admiral Blandy had declared the lagoon safe for re-entry by all ships, and by the evening of Able Day eighteen of the target ships had been reboarded by special teams assigned to recover scientific instruments and to bring off test animals that had been placed throughout the target fleet.

The second device was exploded in Test Baker at 8:35 A.M., July 25 (Bikini time). The intervening days had been devoted to assessment of damage sustained by target vessels, to salvaging and re-equipping ships not too badly damaged for use with the underwater test, and to making preliminary examinations of test animals. Test Able had been observed by 114 representatives of press, radio, news picture services, and magazines. Before Test Baker, thirty-nine of these, and eight members of the Congressional delegation, returned to the United States. The preparations for Test Baker included rearrangement of the target ships about the small landing craft, the LSM 60, beneath which, at a depth of ninety feet— approximately half the distance to the lagoon bottom—the atomic device would be suspended.[14] Elaborate arrangements were made for measuring water pressure and wave height. A final rehearsal was held on July 19. Although a weather front threatened on July 24 to disrupt the projected detonation schedule, the chance seemed good that the front would move away and Admiral Blandy decided early on the morning of that day to order the test program to proceed. Most of the support ships evacuated the lagoon on the evening before Baker Day, standing off Bikini at a distance of a dozen or so miles. The last vessels moved out through Enyu Passage shortly after 6 A.M. on July 25. In the center of the target array was the LSM 60 bearing a tall antenna designed to receive the line-of-sight electronic signal that would detonate the device beneath her hull.

Test Baker was the first occasion in which an atomic device was exploded in such a way that fission products were mixed with water and thus returned in great measure to the area of detonation.

The Test Baker underwater detonation of 1946 as recorded at an island camera site *(U.S.A.F. Lookout Mountain Air Force Station)*

Aerial view of Test Baker, 1946, the base surge spreading toward outer edges of target array *(Joint Task Force One)*

The air burst of July 1, despite the damage it had inflicted, scarcely had prepared observers for the wrath of sound, light, and volcanic shock that erupted within the lagoon. At the moment of explosion a giant bubble, brilliantly lighted within by incandescent materials, burst from the surface of the water to be followed by an "opaque cloud" which quickly covered about half of the ships of the target fleet. Within seconds the cloud had vanished and a hollow column 2,200 feet in diameter and containing some 10 million tons of water rose from the surface of the lagoon to a height of more than a mile. The 26,000-ton battleship *Arkansas,* broadside to the LSM 60 but more than 500 feet away, was lifted and upended in the column before she was plunged to the bottom. At the base of the column was a tumult of foam several hundred feet high, and the descent of the water back into the lagoon set up a base surge from which rolled waves eighty to one-hundred feet high. The waves subsided rapidly as they proceeded outward, and the highest wave recorded at Bikini Island, three miles away, was seven feet, not sufficiently high to pass over the island or to cause damage there. The victims of the explosion, beyond the *Arkansas,* included the carrier *Saratoga,* which sank after seven and one-half hours; a landing ship, a landing craft, and an oiler; submerged submarines, including the *Apogon;* and the already-damaged battleship *Nagato,* which went down five days later. The destroyer *Hughes* and the transport *Fallon,* seriously crippled and listing, were beached.

Radioactivity in the waters of the lagoon was intense. The volume immediately after the burst was estimated in the round, by the Evaluation Board, to be the equivalent of "many hundred tons of radium." The target ships were drenched by radioactive substances as the tremendous pillar of water crashed back into the lagoon. As the weight of the column subsided, the target area became a maelstrom of radioactive debris, and at the bottom of the lagoon was a shallow basin half a mile wide from which the force of the explosion had scooped hundreds of thousands of tons of sludge and coral-algal sediment. The upper levels of the lagoon waters remained highly radioactive for days and large areas were impenetrable by the small craft engaged in attempting to outline the swirling areas of contamination. After four days it still was not safe for inspection parties to spend any useful time at the target area or to board surviving ships floating there. Within the waters, and particularly in the tons of sludge again settling to the lagoon floor, were radioactive contaminants whose disposition would present problems of greater complexity than anyone at that point in time might have guessed.

Before the Baker test, all discussions of probable effect were theoretical. Questions relating to underwater shots apparently had been debated at length while the Operation Crossroads plan was in the process of development. The debate, however, had turned principally on questions of physical effect and on the creation of a test that would yield new information on force and pressure. One view seems to have been that a detonation only slightly beneath the surface of the water would be particularly ineffective because, as was stated in a subsequent report, "neither the air pressure wave nor the water pressure wave would be maximized, and it is possible that a curtain of spray might be thrown up which would actually screen off a large part of the pressure wave in air and nearly all the thermal radiation, gamma radiation, and neutron radiation."[15] In an approximate sense, this is what actually happened at Test Baker, in which the atomic device was exploded at a medium depth in the lagoon, but in the Baker case a major percentage of the long-lived fission materials also was mixed with water and suspended minerals and was captured and retained by the lagoon. The pre-Crossroads expectation may have been substantially correct, for the water erupting into the stupendous column did screen and dampen the effect of radioactivity at the instant of the detonation, but the possible long-term result either was utterly unforeseen or placed in such conjectural terms that its relevance, even to strategic considerations, was not understood.

For a week after Test Baker the radiological teams patrolled Bikini lagoon. The work of the biologists, however, soon turned from monitoring to sampling and analysis. Among the teams on the *Haven* were representatives of other laboratories who were beginning to share a curiosity about the disposition of radioactivity in a biotic system. Warren, still interested in the problems that had produced the program at Hanford, was eager to see the problems pursued at Bikini. Accordingly, there was formed informally within the Radiological Safety Section a "Division of Radiobiology."

U.S.S. *Haven,* headquarters ship of the Radiological Safety Section, in Bikini lagoon, 1946 *(Joint Task Force One)*

Members of Radiobiology Division aboard *Haven,* 1946: from left, Bradner, Welander, Pautzke, White, Donaldson *(Joint Task Force One)*

Autoradiograph of wrasse (75 mm) collected August 8, 1946, near Aomoen and Bikini Islands *(Laboratory of Radiation Biology)*

The Division was setting itself to investigate the presence of radioactivity in an aquatic biological web of extreme complexity.* At the base of the ocean food chains are the plankton—phytoplankton and zooplankton, vegetable and animal—and the algae. Most of the marine plants are in the phylum Thallophyta, composed of primitive plants having no true root, stem, or leaf, and which includes the algae and fungi. The simplest forms of the invertebrates begin with the Protozoa, single-celled organisms which include the Dinoflagellata, a borderline group having characteristics of both animals and plants, and the Foraminifera, which are planktonic in life and whose rudimentary skeletal structures ultimately sink to the bottom of the ocean where their fossil remains are found in geological strata. There are more than 1,200 species of Foraminifera, and 18,000 living and extinct species have been catalogued. In the waters are thousands of groups and species of invertebrate organisms, multicellular animals such as the sponges, of which there are some 2,500 species; the Arthropoda, including the copepods, which comprise about 70 per cent of the zooplankton; the gastropods, which are shelled creatures, using a foot for creeping; and the cephalopods, which include the octopi. The vertebrates include the primitive fishes, the sharks, and the rays; the true fishes, predominantly carnivorous; the reptiles, including the sea turtles; and the Cetacea, among whose members are the whales and dolphins.

In the mid-Pacific, as in the vicinity of Bikini, the identifiable species of fish total more than 600 and in the open ocean the number has been estimated at more than 1,000. Most species are carnivorous, but some, like the goatfish, the mullet, and the surgeonfish, are herbivorous, feeding on marine vegetation and plankton, and a few, the parrot fish, the triggerfish, and the puffer, are omnivores. The food chains may be short and relatively simple. The surgeonfish, for example, is an herbivore feeding on algae, but he in turn is preyed upon by sharks and grouper, the larger, far-ranging carnivores. The simple protozoa are fed upon by gastropods, which become the prey of small carnivores such as the cardinal fish. The carnivorous goatfish feeds only on organisms found in the shallower areas of the ocean, and this also is the habit of the wrasse. But the food chains may not only be infinitely more com-

*Names of pertinent scientific species are listed in Appendix II.

plicated but further confused by the seasonal character of the feeding habits of some of the species. Along each of the strands of this ecological web are species of plants and animals important to man, species of plants that live in the ocean-conditioned soils of the islands and of molluscs, crustacea, and fish—sharks, tuna, barracuda, herring, tarpons, jacks, mackerel, pike, and snappers—that are elements in the diet of people who live on the Pacific or on the lands about its rim.

In such an environment, Bikini's lagoonal contamination, after the first days, was comprehensible only in relation to the biological uptake of fission products. In waters containing such a variety of biological forms, only ingested radioactivity—activity within the organs and tissues of living creatures or assimilated by aquatic plants—could provide clues to the condition of the atoll. Fish or other creatures killed by blast, heat, or massive doses of external radioactivity were not to be found in large numbers because they had been lost in the waters or consumed by the rapacious life of the lagoon. It was with the question of biological uptake that the Division of Radiobiology became concerned. The investigations were crude and, by later standards, wholly inadequate. It was not without significance, however, that the group achieved so early a measure of identity. Nowhere in the tables of organization of Joint Task Force One was there a specific radiobiological section. The Division of Radiobiology of the Radiological Safety Section was, in fact, a commissioned-in-the-field group composed of members of the Applied Fisheries staff and others who, under Warren's direction, organized themselves to pursue biological evidence of Test Baker radiation phenomena.

Early in August, Welander reported:

> On and after Baker Day, 25 July 1946, the Radiobiological Survey party under the leadership of Dr. L. R. Donaldson has taken biological specimens consisting of fish, clams, sea cucumbers, coral, and algae from various parts of the lagoon and the surrounding area for the purpose of determining the amounts of radioactive substances in these animals and plants. Tissues or parts of the above specimens were analyzed in the Tablet Counting Laboratory on board the U.S.S. *Haven* under the direction of Dr. W. Langham and Mr. J. Martens.
>
> In no case were any of the biological specimens taken within the lagoon entirely free of radioactive contamination. In general, the algae proved to have the highest activity and in consequence fish and other animals

feeding on the algae also show high activity. Such analyses included beta and gamma measurements which presuppose the presence of alphas. However, the current low beta and gamma counts do not indicate any reduction in alpha activity.

Because of the highly poisonous nature of the fission products, and the increasing difficulty of detecting alpha emitters in the tissues of these marine animals, it is recommended that no fish, mollusk, or other marine animal taken within 100 miles of Bikini lagoon be used as food.[16]

Plotting boards were used on the *Mount McKinley,* the task force flagship, to maintain records of the outlines of radioactivity developing within the lagoon. The biological dispositions of radioactivity could not be so outlined, but they had a bearing, nevertheless, on considerations of interest to the Navy. Support vessels returning to the lagoon after the underwater test had reported almost immediately the presence of radioactive contamination in water systems, in marine growths attached to the ships' hulls, and even in shipboard areas presumably inaccessible to contamination. The levels of radioactivity in the lagoon were found to be rising at night and falling in daylight hours, a circumstance later realized as attributable to the vertical movement of lagoonal plankton in response to light. Hulls of the vessels showed so much evidence of contamination that orders were issued two days after Baker for all personnel to move back from them, to sleep and work away from possibly contaminated bulkheads. Scrubdowns and changes of clothing had been ordered in the posttest period for persons returning from off-ship duty, yet contamination was found on handrails, in the galleys, and in the shipboard laboratories where scientists worked with instruments and samples. The necessity for frequent changes of clothes and boots exhausted Navy supplies. The monitor boats became contaminated as they worked long hours at surveys conducted among the units of a Bikini fleet that included the empty, battered, untouchable survivors of atomic explosion. The task force attitude was one of alert interest in every facet of the problem on which the scientific staffs could possibly shed any light, yet the biological base of many of the contamination problems was not yet fully realized.

Between June 14, when the Applied Fisheries group arrived at the atoll, and June 29, two days before Test Able, members had collected a total of 1,926 fish to be used as controls and in subsequent studies of the normal Bikini fish population. From July 2

to July 24, between the Able and Baker tests, an additional catch
of 1,819 fish was made, this both to note the effects of the Able
explosion and to extend the general knowledge of lagoon fauna.
After Baker day, from July 25 to August 13, the group collected
an additional 1,407 fish, and these provided materials for further
counting of activity and for future analysis of radiation effects.[17]
By the end of the Crossroads period, the staff had made counts of
activity in 1,021 samples of tissue from 119 fish, the date and place
of the capture, the date of radioanalysis, and the record of radioactive content being noted in each instance. A large proportion of
the work remained to be done and more exact radioanalysis attempted in laboratory conditions.*

The collections of fish and other specimens were made by members of the Laboratory staff working as teams in the waters and on
the reefs. The method was slow, yet none of the collections made
in succeeding years resulted in fundamental improvement because
of the need to take samples by type and place and with a considerable attention to selectivity. The early Crossroads plan had anticipated the use of commercial fishing gear for sweeping up fish in
the lagoon and in the waters outside the atoll, but this arrangement was abandoned. Collections of fish were made in the lagoon
by poisoning tide pools with derris root, which stunned the fish
and permitted them to be picked up at the surface or by diving.
The larger fish were caught, inside or outside the lagoon, by hook
and line, although this system was, in fact, acknowledged to be
"too selective for good sampling."[18] Algae, coral, and reef forms
were taken from the reefs at low tide or by diving near the lagoonal
coral heads or, occasionally, with a dredge. Visits to collection
points were made in one of the U.S.S. *Haven's* whaleboats, the
landings on the beaches being accomplished by rubber rafts. Landing craft were used when they were available, but the rubber raft
demonstrated its superiority in beach landings made over rough
coral or in turbulent waters.

The team method of collection forced selectivity of sample and
location. In a lagoon twenty-six miles long and presenting a water
area of almost 250 square miles, the sampling of aquatic life could

*Field determinations of the presence of radioactivity were made with a Victoreen
X-263 scaling counter, and all samples in which activity was detected were reserved
for further analysis in X-327 counters. Values were made comparable by reducing
all to counts in 0.01 gram of material.

be accomplished only at those points that were presumed to hold materials of interest. The points had to be chosen with as much knowledge as possible of the organic composition of the atoll and with some sensitivity, however rudimentary, to the ways the presence of radiation in the biological system might be revealed. The process of picking the collection points thus was directly related to radiobiological understanding which, in Bikini's aquatic environment, came to embrace the idea of radiation cycling in the biological system. If a collection point proved to hold contamination in unexpected amounts, it was apparent that the original expectation was wrong. The adjustment of the expectation involved searches for clues and reasons and new hypotheses.

IV

The movement away from Bikini began early in August, and by mid-September most of the support vessels would have departed. The pressure to conclude the operation was checked, however, by the need to determine the disposition of the target vessels, many of which still were dangerously radioactive, and to complete the observations that had to be made in the field.

Within Bikini lagoon, the intensity of residual radioactivity had been reduced to low levels by dilution and decay, but the diminution permitted a clearer view of the extent to which the residues had been taken up by the environment of the atoll and were behaving in response to biological influences. From August 2 to August 9, members of the Radiobiology Division made collections of fish and other samples at all previously determined stations and at several other points within the lagoon. In fish, the highest concentrations of radioactivity were in digestive tracts, and the highest activity counts were in those fish which feed on algae. In general the activity per unit of weight was greater in algae than in fish taken from the same station. Clams *(Tridachnas)* collected at the northeastern rim of the atoll, near Bikini Island, contained an abundance of radioactivity in digestive glands, but clams taken at Airukiiji (Arji) Island, flanking Enyu Passage to the west, contained only trace amounts. Coral samples containing living polyps held greater amounts of activity than samples from the same location where the corals had died. A number of organisms were beginning to die on the north reef between Bikini and Aomoen

Islands, although the cause was unknown.[19] By August 12 members of the biological team visiting the reef were picking up dead or weakened fish and dead sea urchins and clams. Notably, too, the fouling organisms on the ships' hulls were continuing to build up amounts of activity which seemed to be the result both of the direct absorption of materials and of the accumulations caused by the nightly surface migration of planktonic forms.

The radiobiological phenomena being revealed, whatever their relevance to military considerations, were of importance because of their bearing on the question of how soon the Bikini people could be returned to their atoll. The question was cited by Donaldson and his associates in their preliminary Radiobiology Division report to Warren and Joint Task Force One. In this the biologists said:

> 1. The material gathered to date needs additional study along the following lines:
>
> (a) A number of activity counts on the material available, using better techniques, would provide quantitative and qualitative results.
>
> (b) Studies of the tissues of controls and fish exposed to activity should be completed.
>
> (c) The materials in the collections should be identified and the proper nomenclature used in reports.
>
> 2. Additional collections should be made at Bikini.
>
> (a) Collections in a period of about six months are needed especially from the northeast portion of the atoll. The collections would provide information on population changes, activity retention, and a distribution of active materials.
>
> (c) Collections the year after the blast might be made to further the studies of population changes and provide information on genetic problems.[20]

The Division also said that additional laboratory work was needed, particularly on the radiation absorption-retention relationships among acquatic organism and of the role of fouling organisms in the accumulation and retention of radioactivity in the aquatic environment. The recommendations seem peculiarly prescient. It is probable, however, that they reflected only a normal curiosity about an entirely new scientific problem that obviously needed very much more work but which was not apt to be examined further in the Crossroads context. In August, 1946, there was no reason for members of the Applied Fisheries Laboratory staff to believe that the problems of Bikini would be enlarged at Eniwetok and would continue to occupy their attention for many years. They were, in fact, expecting to return to the University to take up the X-radiation studies begun three years before.

In October, four Navy and Marine Corps lieutenants, members of the Radiological Safety Section, reported the results of a late-September survey of migratory fish—tuna, jacks, mackerel, and barracuda—caught in the waters off Ailinginae, Rongelap, Rongerik, and Wotho atolls.* Sixty such fish were caught, their organs monitored with an X-263 G-M counter, and liver sections preserved in formalin for later and more accurate assessment of beta activity. None of the fish showed the presence of ingested radioactivity.[21]

---

*The four were Lieutenants C. Carter, David Bradley, T. J. Madden, and F. C. Larson. Bradley later was the author of the Bikini diary, *No Place to Hide*.

Chapter Three

1947: THE BIKINI RESURVEY

I

THE POSSIBLE USEFULNESS of a re-examination of Bikini Atoll at some point in the future occurred to members of the staffs of Joint Task Force One before Operation Crossroads was concluded. From the standpoint of the Navy, much obviously yet was to be learned, and in the broader fields of scientific investigation the momentum of inquiry was far from exhausted in a single summer. The fact that the atoll had been measured, sounded, and catalogued so thoroughly before Crossroads made almost irresistible a further, similar study after the tests. In the introduction to the subsequent technical reports it was recalled that at the time of Crossroads

> certain questions necessarily had to remain unanswered, either because post-test radiation made desired inspections hazardous, or because the questions were concerned with long-range effects. For example, the problems of how long and in what ways abnormal radioactivity affects the flora and fauna of a region could not be solved immediately.[1]

The preliminary statement of the Crossroads Evaluation Board, filed shortly after the close of the 1946 tests, noted that:

> Although lethal results might have been more or less equivalent, the radiological phenomena accompanying the two bursts were markedly

50

different. In the case of the airburst bomb, it seems certain that unprotected personnel within one mile would have suffered high casualties by intense neutron and gamma radiation as well as by blast and heat. Those surviving immediate effects would not have been menaced by radioactivity persisting after the burst.

In the case of the underwater explosion, the airburst wave was far less intense and there was no heat wave of significance. Moreover, because of the absorption of neutrons and gamma rays by water, the lethal quality of the first flash of radiation was not of high order. But the second bomb threw large masses of highly radioactive water onto the decks and into the hulls of vessels. These contaminated ships became radioactive stoves, and would have burned all living things aboard them with invisible and painless but deadly radiation.

It is too soon to attempt an analysis of all of the implications of the Bikini tests. But it is not too soon to point to the necessity for immediate and intensive research into several unique problems posed by the atomic bomb. The poisoning of large volumes of water presents such a problem.[2]

Joint Task Force One went out of existence on November 1, 1946. It was succeeded on that date by a Joint Crossroads Committee of five members and thirteen supporting officials.[3] The chairman was Rear Admiral Parsons, who had served as Deputy Task Force Commander for Technical Direction. Members of this committee, already familiar with the character of the Crossroads problem, pursued the question of a resurvey of Bikini Atoll. They believed that the radiation problem should be assessed after some time had passed and after residual contamination had had opportunity to decay or to produce observable effects. Other factors also suggested the desirability of a return to Bikini. The Navy desired to obtain detailed observations and photographs of the ships sunk in Test Baker, including the *Saratoga* and the *Nagato* and the submarines *Pilotfish* and *Apogon* lying at the bottom of Bikini lagoon; to recover ionization, pressure, and damage gauges from the *Nagato*; to search for any existing fragment of LSM 60, the landing craft beneath which the Baker bomb had been suspended; and to attempt to make a comprehensive estimate of Bikini's physical condition after the atomic tests.[4] Plans also were made to send drills into the Bikini Island reef to make a new study of the depth of the coral above the atoll's rocky base, a project that Darwin would have applauded. Oil-rig crews were to accompany the expedition for this purpose.[5]

Members of the Joint Crossroads Committee made preliminary inquiries into the feasibility of a survey and eventually appointed a subcommittee under the chairmanship of Rear Admiral T. A. Solberg, Navy member, and including Roger Revelle, then a Commander in the Navy and head of the Geophysics Branch of the Office of Naval Research, and Commander E. S. Gilfillan, Jr., technical director of the committee.[6] A proposal went at length from the committee to the Joint Chiefs of Staff and on May 16, 1947, the Joint Chiefs, in a memorandum signed by Fleet Admiral W. D. Leahy, U.S.N., asked the Navy Department, in cooperation with the War Department, to conduct a Bikini Scientific Resurvey in the summer of 1947. A target date of July 15 was set for the start of operations at Bikini.[7] The plans were being developed, necessarily, without specific reference to the existence of the new U.S. Atomic Energy Commission, which was in its first and formative months after taking over the facilities and the residual functions of the Manhattan District at the first of the year. The Joint Chiefs of Staff memorandum asked, however, that technical direction of the resurvey be assigned to the Joint Crossroads Committee or its successor organization, the Armed Forces Special Weapons Project, created with the Commission to represent the continuing interests of the three armed services in atomic developments. Revelle served as project officer of the resurvey until he was succeeded by Commander C. L. Engleman on June 13. Commander Gilfillan, who had participated in Crossroads as a member of the technical staff and as executive officer of the *Nagato*, was made Technical Director of the new operation. The Task Group commander was Captain T. A. Hederman U.S.N.[8]

II

The Bikini Scientific Resurvey was conceived as a concluding phase of Operation Crossroads and it was organized as a full-scale effort to follow up, a year after the tests, the geological, biological, and oceanographic investigations that had been started months before Crossroads and continued throughout the testing period. Donaldson and other members of the Applied Fisheries Laboratory staff, who already had expressed interest in further examinations of Bikini materials, were invited to participate as members of the Radiobiology Group. By 1947, the Laboratory program had been shifted to sponsorship by the Atomic Energy Commission, and F. H. Rodenbaugh, Sr., consultant to the Medical-Legal Board of the Commission, was a member of the radiobiology staff for the resurvey. Donaldson remained a Commission consultant in connection with the Hanford work.

The resurvey, placed under the operational control of the Commander in Chief, Pacific Fleet, employed as its flagship the U.S.S. *Chilton* (APA 38), which was to be supported by the *Coucal* (ASR 8), the LSM 382 and, later, by the LCI (L 615). Additional small craft were taken along for lagoon and landing operations. The scientific and technical staff included about eighty persons, most of them grouped as members of teams concerned with geology, biology, fisheries, radiobiology, radiochemistry-radiophysics, radiological safety, radiological health, engineering, and aerology. Total personnel taken to Bikini numbered some 700, including officers and crews of the resurvey vessels, service staff officers and representatives, and members of special project groups.

Scientists participating in the new Bikini operation were representative of the disciplines in which interest now was focused. Those who would continue the examinations of island and reef geology included the U.S. Department of the Interior geologists, H. S. Ladd and J. I. Tracey, who had taken part in the comprehensive pre-Crossroads studies of Bikini, and associated with them were J. Harlan Johnson, of the Colorado School of Mines; J. W. Wells, of the Ohio State University; and G. G. Lill, of the Geophysics Branch of the Office of Naval Research.

In the fisheries group were R. W. Hiatt and V. E. Brock, of the U.S. Fish and Wildlife Service, reef and lagoon fishes; O. R. Smith and J. C. Marr, aquatic biologists of the Fish and Wildlife Service, and G. S. Myers, professor of biology and curator of the Zoological Collection, Stanford University, pelagic fishes; and L. P. Schultz, curator of fishes of the U.S. National Museum, population and taxonomic studies.

Experimental biologists included three representatives of Stanford University, D. M. Whitaker, of the Department of Biology, L. R. Blinks, director of the Hopkins Marine Station, and G. M. Smith, professor of botany; P. M. Brooks, associate plant physiologist of the Stanford Research Institute; and W. A. Gortner, associate scientist, and T. F. Goreau, assistant oceanographer, Scripps

Institution of Oceanography. Ecological and morphological studies
were conducted by J. P. E. Morrison, associate curator of mollusks,
and F. M. Bayer, assistant curator of marine invertebrates, U.S.
National Museum; and A. C. Cole, professor of zoology and ento-
mology of the University of Tennessee.

With the radiochemistry and radiophysics group were W. H.
Hammill, associate professor of chemistry, and R. R. Williams,
assistant professor of chemistry, of the University of Notre Dame,
who were interested in fission products chemistry; Jack Schubert,
assistant professor of physiological chemistry, University of Minnesota, plutonium chemistry; L. F. Seatz, assistant professor of
agronomy, University of Tennessee, soils chemistry; and J. H.
Roberson, physicist, Clinton Laboratories, Oak Ridge, radiophysics.

Revelle, who had been the resurvey's first project officer, was
to join the resurvey at Bikini on July 15.

The radiobiology group was headed by Donaldson and included
Welander, Pautzke, Rodenbaugh, and seven associates and assistant
scientists drawn from the University of Washington and the Applied Fisheries Laboratory. Among these was Foster, supervisor
of the laboratory at Hanford, Allyn H. Seymour, then a biostati-
cian with the International Pacific Halibut Fisheries Commission;
and R. C. Meigs, assistant chief biologist of the Washington Department of Game.

The *Chilton,* berthed at the San Diego Naval Station pending
her departure for the Marshalls by way of Pearl Harbor, was provided with survey facilities which included two radiochemistry
laboratories, a radiation counter room, a laboratory for the use of
Donaldson's radiobiology group, a fisheries laboratory under the
direction of Brock, and an experimental biology laboratory which,
when moved ashore at Bikini Island, became two laboratories—
one devoted to morphological and physiological studies of plants
and the other to studies of marine invertebrates. In addition to
these, three scientific group centers subsequently were established
on Bikini Island to facilitate studies of low-level radiation, of geology and aerology, and of the relationship of marine organisms to
the chemical content of sea water.[9]

The character of the preparations reflected the general interest
in the levels of residual radioactivity that might be found at Bikini.

The *Chilton*, decks piled high with equipment, en route to Bikini, 1947 *(Bikini Scientific Resurvey)*

Landing craft alongside the *Chilton* during preparations for lagoon collections, 1947 *(Bikini Scientific Resurvey)*

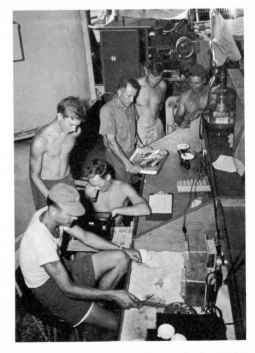

A laboratory aboard the *Chilton* during Bikini Resurvey, 1947 *(Bikini Scientific Resurvey)*

The question of radioactivity was, in fact, uppermost in the minds of the scientists and members of the Navy staffs even though the Bikini Scientific Resurvey program also was set up to satisfy, so far as possible, curiosity about both the general scientific questions and the more specific matters such as types of structural damage sustained by the sunken target ships. In Admiral Leahy's original memorandum to the Secretary of the Navy on May 16 the purposes of the resurvey had been stated thus:

> The resurvey would entail the collection of biological specimens, diving on target ships to recover specific instruments and to make certain structural examinations, the taking of water and bottom samples and cores, and radiological studies of the lagoon, the surrounding islands and organisms with particular reference to analysis of hazards from alpha radiation and from possibly contaminated food organisms.[10]

The concern about alpha radiation, undoubtedly reflecting concern expressed in discussions of members of the Joint Crossroads Committee, revealed the presence of the thought that the field surveys necessarily performed hastily after Test Baker, and under conditions which permitted only gross measurements of beta and gamma radiation, had been inadequate to disclose the potential ingestion by Bikini's biological system of the low-penetration alpha emitters. Such concern with radiation formed a large element in the planning, for the character of the work at Bikini would be governed by what was found at the atoll when the *Chilton* and her little fleet moved through Enyu Passage into the lagoon on July 15.

Operation Crossroads had been conducted in a spotlight of world attention. The Bikini Scientific Resurvey claimed no such general interest. The resurvey, on a scale infinitely smaller than that of Crossroads, was a mixture of military and scientific interests and objectives translated into action under security conditions which made it necessary to filter information through official channels. The conditions were inevitable and they would continue to exist throughout the subsequent Pacific test operations, but they reduced almost to zero the possibility that the public or, for that matter, the scientific community, would have access to information making the qualitative distinctions that would be necessary thereafter in reports of radiation effect. As for the immediate public information question, the Navy task group included a public information officer whose small staff operated under a carefully prepared plan, but matters relating to atomic programs bore security classifications and the responsibility for clearance and release rested with the Navy Department's Director of Public Information in Washington, D.C. In addition, the very nature of the project made impossible the release of any information having conclusive meaning.

For all this, there was an atmosphere of inquiry about the proceedings that was altogether genuine. The resurvey was, after all, returning to an atoll which had last been seen in the rush of evacuation after Test Baker and which not only held scientific problems of interest but which had the appeal of association with events of epoch-making dimensions.

The *Chilton* departed San Diego on July 1, 1947, and from then until her arrival by Bikini on July 15 members of the scientific groups were organizing their laboratories and working, formally or informally, to plan their operations. On July 2 the project officer, Commander Engleman, appointed an advisory board under the chairmanship of Whitaker and including Donaldson, Ladd, Roberson, Schultz, and Richard D. Russell, of the Navy Electronics Laboratory (E. H. Shuler and Tracey were to act for Russell and Ladd until their arrival at Bikini) to provide counsel on such administrative matters as use of space and equipment, and at a meeting of the board on the same date Whitaker and Donaldson were named cochairmen of a seminar series designed to inform all members of the scientific groups of the purpose and methods of the Bikini studies. Engleman opened the series by reviewing films of Operation Crossroads, and subsequently, as the *Chilton* cruised to Pearl Harbor and then westward toward the Marshalls, seminar lecturers included Wells on Pacific geology, Tracey on the geology of Bikini, Morrison on the invertebrates, Schultz on fishes of the Pacific, Brock on reef collecting, Welander and Rodenbaugh on the effects of radiation, Commander H. S. Etter and Lieutenant Colonel C. E. Grant on operation plans for radiological safety, and—when the *Chilton* reached Bikini—Revelle on the phenomena of the Baker explosion.

The *Chilton,* accompanied by the *Coucal,* entered Bikini lagoon at 10:30 A.M. on July 15. To starboard lay the curved reef leading from Enyu Passage to Bikini Island, the *Chilton*'s objective. The *Coucal,* from which were to be conducted the diving operations

(Left) Advance party taking first readings on Bikini beach in the Bikini Resurvey, 1947 *(Bikini Scientific Resurvey)*

(Below) Marine hydroids, mildly irradiated, on boat frames left floating in Bikini waters, 1947 *(Laboratory of Radiation Biology)*

Juda, Bikini magistrate, with one of his *alaps* on Rongerik, 1947 *(Bikini Scientific Resurvey)*

for further examination of the target ships, was stationed in the former target area near the position of the sunken *Saratoga*. When the *Chilton* had dropped anchor off Bikini Island, Engleman led ashore the landing party that was to make preliminary reconnaissance, the group including Donaldson, Rodenbaugh, and L. B. Marquiss, of the radiobiological team. All members of the initial group were required to wear long-sleeved shirts, full-length trousers, and heavy boots. All also wore film badges. Counters and film badges carried inland showed no beta or gamma radiation substantially above normal background, and the only significant counts of activity were found at the scraps of Crossroads gear—old life rafts, planks, fenders, and such—which littered the lagoon beach and which probably had been washed ashore from the target vessels. Samples of miscellaneous materials were collected from scattered parts of the island and returned to the *Chilton* to be counted for possible alpha contamination. Members of the landing party were monitored on their return to the *Chilton* to preclude any possible contamination of the ship, and a change station was set up for handling work clothing and gear. After the initial landing on Bikini Island, Commander Gilfillan took another group to Eninman (Prayer) Island, on the south rim of the atoll and adjacent to Enirik (Erik) Pass, for further monitoring of the reef and beach at a point of outflow of waters from the lagoon. Surface counts of radioactivity there were at the same levels as those encountered on Bikini. By the following day, July 16, the offloading at Bikini Island was under way and members of the scientific groups were readying their shore stations and laboratories and beginning their collections and samplings.

It would be hazardous, years after the event, to attempt to suggest, much less to evaluate, the interests that must have hovered about the activities of the Bikini Scientific Resurvey. It would be difficult to endeavor to recreate the atmosphere of carefully regulated anticipation in which the resurvey groups approached their tasks. Diverse moods, purposes, and scientific and military points of view were fused, it may be imagined, by a common feeling that this small postscript to Operation Crossroads might contain the substance of the matter—that whatever radioactive residues of Test Baker now existed would reveal, in their amounts and distributions, circumstances more deeply significant than had yet been realized, or that the absence of meaningful quantities of radio-activity would constitute a showing, on the other hand, that a problem had ceased to exist. It certainly would have been im-possible to participate in the return to Bikini without sharing a sensation of excited recollection, for Bikini was so well known that even those who were visiting the atoll for the first time could experience a sense of recognition. Bikini was empty and silent, but out where the *Coucal* was anchored, a mile-high column of water had erupted in the lagoon, less than a year before, in a moment so awesome that many members of the Crossroads crews, watching on vessels a dozen miles away, had become violently ill. The ghost of that column still inhabited Bikini—the column certainly would stand there forever in the picture records of the atomic age—but if the ghost were to be laid it was necessary to get at the truth about the unseen forces of which it was the manifestation. The Bikini Scientific Resurvey went to the Pacific to face the ghost, perhaps to lay it. But first it had to be hunted out.

The consciousness of the resurvey's association with Operation Crossroads was reflected, quite naturally, in press releases trans-mitted by the Navy through Washington, D.C. On July 15, the day of the landing, the press section noted:

> The Navy reoccupied Bikini Island today, just 355 days after the underwater atomic bomb blast sent a mile high column of radioactive sea water crashing down on the Operation CROSSROADS target fleet.
>
> .   .   .   .
>
> Geiger counters indicated some radioactivity on the beach. However, CDR. E. S. Gilfillan, Jr., U.S.N.R., technical Director for the project, said the amount recorded was not dangerous. Stronger amounts of radioactivity were noted on life rafts and other gear cast up on the beach. It is believed some of this material may have been blasted loose from ships of the target fleet last year. . . .[11]

Later, on July 17:

> Below the surface of Bikini lagoon Navy divers today walked up and down the flight deck of the gallant old aircraft carrier SARATOGA.
>
> They reported that the 33,000 ton ship, sunk last July 25 by an under-water atomic bomb explosion, is resting on nearly even keel. The top of her mast can be seen a few feet beneath the surface of the lagoon.
>
> .   .   .   .
>
> Waterproof Geiger counters were lowered in the water ahead of the divers while radiological safety monitors topside kept a careful watch on

the meters. As an additional safety precaution, each diver carried three photographic film badges and a gauge that tabulates cumulatively the amounts of radioactivity to which it has been exposed. . . .[12]

There would not be, either during the course of the survey or at the end, when the results were being compiled, disagreement as to fact. The levels of residual radioactivity were low and, as Commander Gilfillan said, they were not dangerous. The Navy originally had forbidden task group personnel to eat coconuts or other fruit growing on Bikini Island or fish caught in the lagoon. Even samples of fish, vegetation, or other materials could be taken aboard the vessels only by scientific personnel and then only with attention to proper care and packaging. By July 24 the ban against eating coconuts had been lifted, although fish still were proscribed, and this on the advice of a three-man medical-legal board which included Rodenbaugh.[13] The concern about the immediate hazards of radiation was beginning to subside. Scientists and technicians patrolling the islands and beaches, navy divers probing about and photographing the sunken target ships, and drillers sinking shafts into Bikini coral were working long hours on a six-day-a-week schedule, but on July 25 the Navy information office reported:

> Sun-tanned sailors and scientists observed the anniversary of the world's first underwater atomic bomb explosion today by going swimming in the clear blue-green 84° warm waters of Bikini lagoon. They swam from beaches that one year ago were lashed by high and angry waves thrown outward from the explosion point.
>
> .   .   .   .
>
> One year later the scientists and military personnel now engaged in an intensive six week resurvey of Bikini Atoll can find few visible effects of that blast. Except for activities of the 700 man Bikini Scientific Resurvey Task Group, Bikini is the same placid palm ringed lagoon on which King Judah and his subjects sailed in outrigger canoes.
>
> .   .   .   .
>
> Fish and other forms of marine life still inhabit Bikini's teeming tropical waters. On the islands, coconut palms, pandanus, papayas, and other forms of vegetation threaten to obscure man-made installations left from last summer.
>
> Only the scientists and military technicians now engaged in a painstaking examination of the atoll can complete this picture of Bikini one year after Baker Day, and 37 days of hard hot field work and laboratory analysis lie ahead of them before they will have obtained sufficient data

to piece together the study of long range effects of last summer's two atomic explosions.[14]

The field work of the Radiobiology Group was performed at some fifty-five collection stations on the rim of the atoll and in the waters between Bikini Island and the target area. The stations were selected for the probable relevance of the samples to be obtained in each. The studies in radiobiology were designed to assess the incidence of radioactive materials in organisms taken from various geographic locations, to determine the quantities of radioactive substances in certain tissues and organs, and to gather materials for later histological studies relating to possible presence of anomalies or radiation-induced genetic effects. The selection of the sampling stations necessarily was made, therefore, with appropriate consideration of all the factors which might bear upon the results. Collections were made in the target area and in the vicinity of Bikini Island and along the northeast reef between Bikini and Aomoen Islands, over which the wind of 1946 had carried the fallout from Test Able. Attention was given to Enyu Passage, where the inflow of waters to the lagoon was accelerated seasonally by the arrival of swells originating in the southern ocean. Collections also were made at Namu Island, far to the northwest of the atoll, and along the southwest and southerly curve where deep passes—Bokororyuru (Boro), Bokoaetokutoku (Boku), Ourukaen (Oruk), Arriikan (Aran), Rukoji (Ruji), and Enirik (Erik)—permit the escape of lagoonal waters cycling and circulating under the steady pressure of the surface winds.

The problem was to obtain, even in six weeks of unremitting effort, collections of biological specimens sufficiently large and diverse to be meaningful, and to obtain such collections at fifty-five stations spotted about an atoll of 243 square miles. Samplings of similar kinds were being made by the groups studying reef and lagoon fishes, the pelagic or ranging fishes, the marine invertebrates, the reef and lagoon algae, and classifications of atoll life. Collections were made independently at independently established stations, although there was a considerable amount of cross-checking of data and exchange of specimens.

The collections were made, as in 1946, by hand or by the use of small gear. Nets were employed to gather plankton, and occasionally improvised dredges for bottom specimens. The larger species

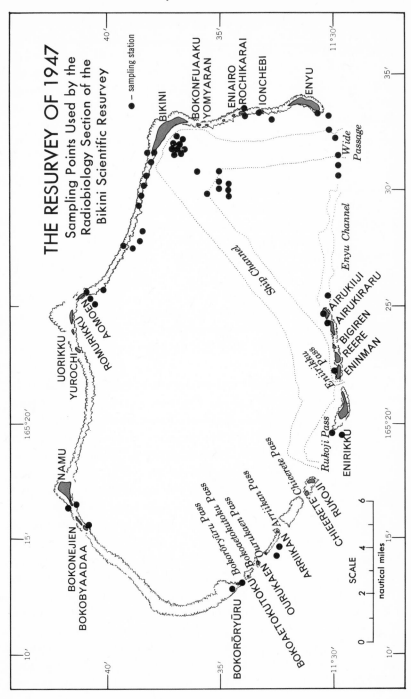

THE RESURVEY OF 1947

Sampling Points Used by the
Radiobiology Section of the
Bikini Scientific Resurvey

● – sampling station

of fish were taken by hook and line, but for the smaller varieties some less haphazard method of capture was required. The result was that most of the collecting, and the collecting that proved the most fruitful, was accomplished by day after day of swimming and diving about the reefs and lagoonal coral heads and walking along the miles of sandy beaches to examine the life in the shallow waters and the tide pools. The Navy report described the activity:

> On the average working day, a geological party would be out studying one of the reef structures and taking samples which were duly returned to the Laboratory on Bikini Island for further study. Meanwhile, drilling operations designed to furnish additional geological information would be proceeding on Bikini Island . . . , and the Submarine Geologists would be taking cores and samples from the bottom of Bikini Lagoon.
>
> On the same day, two or three groups of scientists, including members of the Radiobiology and Fisheries Groups, would be at different locations along the reefs of Bikini Atoll, either collecting sample specimens for purposes of determining the existing degree of radioactivity, or conducting studies concerned with the habitats, food chains, and taxonomic relationships. Many of the localities where such studies were carried on proved to be relatively inaccessible because of the coral growths beneath the surface; in such cases rubber boats and wherries proved to be invaluable items of equipment.[15]

On August 6, Juda, the Bikini magistrate, and three of his *alaps* were brought to Bikini from Rongerik by courier plane to spend several days visiting islands of the atoll to determine if they could note changes in their home environment. The visitors, with the help of an interpreter sent from Kwajalein, contributed to the scientific record the Marshallese names of certain plants and fish, but the only change they professed to notice was the presence of a new plant, papaya, the seeds of which may have been introduced during Crossroads. Juda and his associates were returned to Rongerik on August 11.

The Radiobiology Group's collections of 1947 were made against the relatively thin background of information assembled in the midst of the atomic test operations of the year before. Some of the 2,000 samples harvested in the Crossroads period had been taken before Test Able, when Bikini was free of contamination, but the others had been gathered between Tests Able and Baker or, in haste, while high-level Baker radioactivity still moved about in the waters of the target area. In 1946, some of the sampling had been done at Rongelap Atoll, to the east, and at Kwajalein, to the southeast, so that after the Bikini shots the counts of Bikini radioactivity could be compared to those of specimens from radiologically uncontaminated atolls. In 1947, to continue the studies of comparative values, sampling was accomplished again at Kwajalein and at Rongerik, Rongelap's eastward neighbor. Samples of algae and other marine organisms also were taken by divers from the sunken target ships which had rested for a year on the floor of Bikini lagoon.

The determination of the gross levels of radioactivity in samples of tissue was made by reducing to ash, on a steel plate placed in a muffle furnace, a tissue sample of convenient size, usually one gram, and then obtaining a count of radiation in one of the argonalcohol Geiger tubes in the *Chilton's* laboratory.* The reduction to ash eliminated tissue bulk and left on the plate only the tissue residue and any radioactive materials which might have been present therein. In the process of counting, corrections were made for the presence of normal background radioactivity, for the effect of the geometry of the radiation emission, and for the absorption of emissions by even the small sample residue. It was necessary for the counting of samples to be in sufficient number to establish a general pattern, if any existed, of the presence of radioactivity in the various organs of the fish—the skin, bone, gut, spleen, liver, or other—or in the organs or components of the other marine specimens, animal or vegetable, taken from Bikini waters.

In all, 5,883 specimens were assembled by the Radiobiology Group, including those contributed by other teams. Of these, 735 specimens were processed in the field (2,562 samples were counted) and the others preserved for later analysis. Principal attention was given to gross beta-gamma radioactivity counts, although some counts for alpha radiation also were made. The data indicated an exceedingly wide distribution of radioactive substances in organisms collected in and about Bikini Lagoon.

The collection of fish at Kwajalein was near the stern of the dead hulk of the former German cruiser, the *Prinz Eugen*, a target vessel

*All samples were counted in an aluminum shelf sample holder, with a thin window, argon-alcohol Geiger tube, and a Tracerlab autoscaler circuit. The geometry of this arrangement was about 22 per cent. Total absorption, exclusive of self-absorption, which varied widely for different samples, was approximately 6 mg/cm^2. Counter background averaged 18.5 c/m.

that had capsized on a coral shelf at Kwajalein Island after being towed from Bikini the year before. The thirteen fish gathered there were ashed and counted whole, but radioactive materials were present only in trace amounts. Samples of liver obtained from thirty-five fish caught at Rongerik by the Fisheries Group also were subjected to radioanalysis. The liver of an ocean skipjack and liver samples from several tuna yielded counts of radioactivity substantially above normal levels, and it could only be guessed that these particular ocean rangers had obtained active substances by feeding at Bikini before they were captured at Rongerik.

The derris root method was not suitable for capture of the larger fishes. For these trolling gear operated from 45-foot picket boats was used. To obtain its samples for studies of the pelagic fishes, the Fisheries Group employed three such picket boats, each under the direction of a commercial fisherman. Some forty-eight boat days were fished at Bikini and twenty-three at Rongerik. In these operations, 506 fish were caught near Bikini and 185 in the Rongerik area. These specimens were identified, catalogued as to sex and degree of maturity, and examined for stomach content and the presence of gross abnormalities. (Stomach content data was sought from all animal specimens as a means of determining more precisely the place of the organism in the Pacific food chains.) Routine data also included notes on the length and weight of the specimens and on color patterns, ecology, and behavior.

Work proceeded simultaneously on a dozen fronts. Hiatt was studying reef and lagoon fishes to determine the food chains represented on Bikini reefs. Marr and his associates not only were seeking the pelagic fishes but were collecting small or larval fishes of pelagic types that could be caught in young-fish trawls towed at various depths. Schultz was concentrating on taxonomic studies of the fish population. Whitaker was working with invertebrates, particularly the great slate pencil sea urchin *(Heterocentrotus trigonarius)*, which was found flourishing on that section of the Bikini Island reef over which radioactive waters had flooded after Test Baker. Myers, in a program complementing Whitaker's, was endeavoring to discover if there were ascertainable effects within the vertebrate population, which included the lizards. Cole studied insect populations, finding posttest comparative data impossible to assemble because no similar studies had been made prior to Crossroads and before the atoll had been sprayed by DDT as a health and safety measure. Examinations of land snails, reptiles, birds, and mammals were directed by Morrison, who had made the survey of Bikini's land animals before the 1946 tests.

In such a survey, in which teams of specialists attacked in a compressed period of time specific elements of a total problem, a final answer could by no means be expected to come clear at once. Even though the sampling necessarily was far from complete (and frequently, as in the trolling for the larger pelagic fishes, frankly miscellaneous), the very numbers and varieties of specimens made the task of observation, dissection, data-recording, radioanalysis, and reporting an enormous one. The *Chilton*'s laboratories and the shore equipment and installations, fixed or portable, were in use for long and tedious hours by sweating men who returned from the field, loaded with gear and sample bags, to attempt to add bits of information to the records for which they were responsible. In such a survey, only the immediate and obvious really could be grasped, and almost every group was forced to put off until some later time the final statement of conclusions that were significant. But in the immediate view was the conclusion that, a year after Crossroads, no deleterious effects attributable to radioactivity, no biological abberations or departures from the known norm, were observable. There were qualifications. There were frequent doubts. There were suggestions that additional evidence was needed. Occasionally, there were reports of situations in which radioactivity might, indeed, have played a part—unless, as was possible, some other factor was present and, in the year since Crossroads, had produced the observed result. There was no doubt that decay and dilution had reduced residual radioactivity to a low level, but certain questions persisted, nevertheless.

For example, there was the question of an unexplainable turbidity of Bikini lagoon's eastern waters, the waters about the target area and near Bikini Island. In 1946, before Test Baker, the waters had been clear and transparent, so that the bottom could be seen at depths of more than one hundred feet. In 1947, even as the *Chilton* moved through Enyu Passage on the return to Bikini, it was noted immediately that the lagoonal waters were opaque and obscure, so much so that objects were visible in the water at little more than thirty feet.[16] There was an initial suspicion that the increase in opacity indicated a significant change in the biological condition of the atoll, but what change was likely to produce such a result no one was prepared to say. Whatever the condition, the scientists thought, plankton would be participating.

Plankton studies had not been projected in the original planning for the Resurvey. Late in July, however, after the groups had been at work about ten days, it was decided, at a meeting including Revelle, Gilfillan, Brock, Marr, Schultz, and Myers, that the difference in appearance in Bikini waters (as compared to the appearance in 1946, when pre-Crossroads sampling had been performed by Martin Johnson, of the Scripps Institution of Oceanography) made perfectly logical some effort to obtain quantitative data on plankton, not only to see what quantitative changes had occurred since 1946 but to permit comparisons with the situation at Rongerik, where the waters were clear and sparkling. Accordingly, seventeen surface tow-net hauls (two to four feet in depth) were made in various sectors of Bikini and Rongerik lagoons between July 29 and August 14.[17] Because the plankton work had not been anticipated, equipment was inadequate or improvised and thus the results were not exact. Nevertheless, "reasonable" conclusions could be enumerated. In plankton content, the upper waters of Bikini at the target area and of Rongerik, at a comparable distance from the main island and reefs, appeared about the same. Amounts of plankton in the shallow waters (a quarter of a mile or more off the beach of the main island) were greater at Bikini than at Rongerik, where the water was much clearer. Amounts of plankton diminished as hauls were made west and south from Bikini Island and away from the target area. Inexplicably, apparently, representatives of one variety of plankton, the ctenophores—jellylike animals, two to four inches long—were found in numbers in the vicinity of the *Chilton* throughout the period of the Resurvey, yet only rare specimens were observed or captured in other parts of Bikini lagoon or at Rongerik. In short, plankton were flourishing most prolifically, and in one instance almost uniquely, in the waters between Bikini Island and the target area.

None of the plankton work was related in any specific way to the radioactivity question. Qualitative evaluations were not attempted at Bikini. In 1947, it was suggested that the turbidity of the Bikini water was the result of some seasonal effect (a suggestion that subsequently was rejected) or that the increase in plankton near Bikini Island was the result of the deposits of nitrogenous waste products by personnel of Operation Crossroads in 1946. It was agreed that the Bikini turbidity was unique, but no one could assert that the two atomic explosions, whether by blast effect or radiation, had set up a condition that would encourage an increase in plankton.[18]

Below the waters of the target area, however, was a condition which was more familiar to the Navy divers who continued to explore and photograph the sunken target ships but which also was of great importance to members of the scientific task groups. This was the condition of the bottom of the lagoon about the point at which the LSM 60 had been disintegrated by the detonation of the atomic device suspended beneath her hull and where there now was a vast area of radioactive mud.

Ladd and Tracey and their associates continued in 1947 the studies of island, reef, and ocean geology undertaken in connection with Crossroads. These included studies of the seaward reefs outside Bikini Island and of the geological zonations outside and inside Bikini lagoon. Traverses made by dredge or other methods in 1946 were re-examined during the Resurvey and in the course of these particular attention was given to that part of the lagoon bottom that had been disturbed by the Baker test. One of the major objectives was to investigate, by taking bottom cores and samples of sediment, the effects of the explosion on the lagoon floor, including the persistence and disposition of radioactivity. Work toward this objective was conducted by Russell and Shuler who, using core equipment, bottom samplers, heavy rock dredges, and underwater cameras operated by special winches and other gear installed on a landing craft, obtained 240 bottom samples, thirty-three cores of the lagoon floor, thirty dredging hauls, and a number of photographs of the bottom in the vicinity of the target center.[19] They also took about 350 pounds of the mud from the site of Test Baker for examination by the Atomic Energy Commission. Duplicate samples of all bottom cores were turned over to the Radiochemistry Group for plutonium and fission products analysis and for recording of alpha, beta, and gamma radiation counts. Interest was not exclusively geological, and other mem-

bers of other groups—among them Donaldson and the radiobiologists, and Morrison, Whitaker and others studying marine
invertebrates—were curious about the levels and kinds of radioactivity to be found in the deeper waters of the target area and
in the organisms there. The bottom samples and cores, and the
biological specimens collected by or for the scientists studying
Bikini's invertebrate inhabitants, showed that the target area still
held, as the technical report phrased it, "large amounts of radioactive material."[20]

The geologists reported that, although the Baker Test had
stirred up the bottom of the lagoon to distances of 1,000 to 1,500
yards, the maximum disturbance was limited to radius of some
300 yards. The center of blast intensity actually seemed to be,
they said, 100 to 150 yards southwest of the former position of
LSM 60.[21] Test Baker, the geologists found, "not only increased
the depth of the lagoon bottom in the immediate vicinity of the
explosion point, but also produced an area of mud which is quite
distinct from any other sediment found in Bikini lagoon."[22] The
thirty-three cores taken during the Resurvey showed that the
bottom at the target area consisted essentially of four layers of
materials—a top of target area mud grading into a layer of silt and
sand, which rested on a layer of clean, white algal debris, which in
turn rested, usually without a transitional zone, on darker, brown-
ish algal debris mixed with mud and sand. The bottom layer was
believed to be the original sediment of the bottom prior to Test
Baker. Most of the radioactivity at the target area was found in
the top layer of mud, although streaks and overlaid deposits were
found in the second and third layers. The thickness of the three
top layers varied considerably. The coring had to be accomplished between the hulks of the sunken target ships and amid
diving operations from the *Coucal,* and thus the distribution of the
core samplings was not ideal in number or pattern. Nevertheless,
it was established that the layer of mud which contained the bulk
of the radioactive materials was about 5 feet, 3 inches thick at the
point below the LSM 60 location, was at a thickness of 8 feet at
core No. 33, 125 yards to the southwest, and was thicker than
10 feet—the length of the longest core—at one point near the
center of the target area. The average depth of mud was put at
about 5 feet. From the data on depths it was calculated that there

were "about half a million tons . . . of radioactive mud on the lagoon bottom. . . ."[28]

The radioactive mud was at the bottom of Bikini lagoon, 180 feet below the surface of the waters. The waters hid the target ships and the radioactive substance in which they lay, however, and elsewhere the presence of radioactivity at what could be considered significant levels simply was not evident. There was so much of Bikini without apparent disturbance, and so few instances of possible deviation from the expectable, that any questions tended to appear academic. Practically everywhere Bikini seemed too normal to be otherwise, and might, in fact, have been scarcely distinguishable from any neighboring atoll except for the presence of the shacks and towers on the principal islands and the litters of sun-scoured flotsam on the beaches. The Radiological Safety Section, which monitored most of the islands, found few places (except in the patches of tar on the coral and in the beach debris) where beta-gamma readings indicated the presence of radioactivity that would exceed the 24-hour tolerance limit of one-tenth of a roentgen unit. Certain corals were discovered to be dying on the reef between Bikini and Aomoen Islands, corals that had been known to be healthy shortly before Test Baker, yet it was not possible to determine whether these coral clumps had been injured by radioactivity, by oil from the ships of the target array, or—although improbably—by the fresh water of heavy rains during exceptionally low tides. Whitaker's studies of the sea urchins and other invertebrates led to the observation that the specimens examined in the shipboard laboratories—whether taken from places showing no more than normal background radiation or from the most radioactive of Bikini's reefs—were healthy, abundant, and reproducing normally without evidence of aberration or ill effect. One specimen of an unknown species of sea urchin, a specimen brought up by the Navy divers from the flight deck of the *Saratoga*, was by far the most radioactive invertebrate studied, a Geiger counter reading of its shell and exposed viscera producing a reading of twenty times background.[24] This sea urchin, it was believed, had spent its whole life on the sunken vessel—one of the ships which after Test Baker had been described as a "radioactive stove"—yet dissection disclosed ovaries filled with full-sized eggs altogether usual in number and character.

What, then, could be decided about Bikini a year after Crossroads? If the atoll were considered as a whole, reassurance was there. On the floor of the lagoon, beneath the former target center, lay half a million tons of radioactive mud. But on the islands and reefs and in the waters of the lagoon—even where there existed a mysterious turbidity—life still appeared to thrive and flourish. Even where the faint footprints of the Bikini ghost could be detected they apparently were being dimmed by sun and wind and water. Tiny hermit crabs continued to haul their shells across the sands, making small traces. Big blue and brown coconut crabs stalked as usual through the fallen husks on Namu Island or stared in beady solemnity from the recesses of their burrows amid the roots of palm trees. Moray eels darted about the rocks of the tide pools, and schools of round herring passed in clouds among the coral heads, and with them could be observed fleetingly, now and then, the plump and colorful parrot fish, or the grouper, or the shark. It could not be said that Bikini was sick or that the shocks of 1946 were not being shaken off by the bursting life of a mid-Pacific atoll. Yet doubt lingered. And the difficulty was that no one knew for certain that some insidious malady was not actually at work, in some as yet undetectable way, in the apparently healthy body of Bikini. No one was prepared to certify Bikini as safe for human habitation.

Late in August, the Bikini Scientific Resurvey prepared to evacuate Bikini. Preparations were begun on August 22 when members of the Advisory Board met to discuss logistical problems. In following days the land-based laboratories were put aboard the *Chilton,* the gear from the officers' and enlisted men's clubs was stowed, drilling and diving operations were suspended, the buildings on Bikini Island were cleaned, closed, and secured, and a final inspection was conducted by Commander Engleman, the project officer. The task group of the Bikini Scientific Resurvey departed Bikini on August 29.

III

The Radiobiology Group, as did the others, prepared a preliminary report to be incorporated into the 1947 report of the technical director. Also like the others, the Radiobiology Group later developed additional material in its home laboratory, the results to be submitted to the Atomic Energy Commission and made available to the Armed Forces Special Weapons Project. If there were any substantial difference in the Radiobiology Group's view of Bikini in 1947 it is not revealed in specific recommendations or conclusions. There undoubtedly was, however, a difference in the group's interest in Bikini as a field laboratory. In its preliminary report the Radiobiology Group said:

> The data . . . indicate a very widespread distribution of radioactive substances in the organisms in and about Bikini Lagoon. In fact, some activity was found in organisms taken from every part of the Bikini area that was sampled. . . .
>
> Fission products were found to occur in fish and in invertebrates such as clams, snails, oysters, corals, sponges, octopods, crabs, sea urchins, sea cucumbers, spiny lobsters, and shrimps. They also were represented in the algae found about the lagoon.
>
> Concentration of active substances in fish was greatest in spleen, liver, and feces. Average gross beta-gamma counts per minute per gram of wet tissue for the three above-mentioned materials were 23.5 c/min/gm, 18 c/min/gm, and 14.5 c/min/gm respectively. The kidney and gonads were next in order of active-substance content, exhibiting respective averages of 11.6 c/min/gm and 8.2 c/min/gm. Other tissues extensively sampled, including gills, skin, bone, and muscle, contained fission products in lesser amounts.[25]

The point of view of the Radiobiology Group reflected an interest in the possible values of Bikini as an area, the only such area in the world, in which it would be possible to observe the subtle processes by which small over-amounts of radioactivity were being distributed about a biotic system. The radioactivity to be detected at Bikini in 1947 was at levels low enough to be manageable yet sufficiently high to be traceable through the food chains. When low arounts of radioactivity were found, as the group reported, in "organisms taken from every part of the Bikini area that was sampled," Bikini continued to hold out opportunities for observation. The source of Bikini's irradiation undoubtedly was the target area. If there were, as there seemed to be, a continuing uptake and transfer of fission products from the silt of the lagoon bottom, and if long-lived radioactivity were captured and retained by the tissues of animals and plants, then there was spread out in Bikini a set of problems whose answers lay beyond the scope and period of the 1947 Resurvey.

The report of the technical director of the Bikini Scientific Resurvey, which contained the summary reports of all scientific and technical groups, was published in December, 1947, by the Armed Forces Special Weapons Project. It appeared as Volume II of a set of Resurvey reports to which were appended four annexes incorporating the field data, photographs, and tables covering the work on the sunken target ships and the radioanalyses of soil and biological samples.*

The report contained a comprehensive preliminary statement of the results of the 1947 field work, a statement which touched in turn the principal findings of the scientific groups. In the preparation of a summary statement, however, a certain amount of reconciliation undoubtedly was inevitable. There also was, from the Navy point of view, a primary interest in the condition of Bikini as a peacetime equivalent of a military target. The summary statement thus put emphasis on over-all quantitative elements of the situation even though portions were devoted to descriptions of the probable behavior of radioactivity in the food chains and, in a section based on the result of the radiochemistry analyses, of the processes of disposition of fission products in the target area after Test Baker. In its introductory paragraph the statement said:

> The principal result of the BIKINI SCIENTIFIC RESURVEY was to show that the atomic explosions caused only minor, transient disturbance to the plant and animal populations of the area, the effects of which have almost completely disappeared after one year's time. Some plants and animals in the immediate area of the underwater explosion were killed and some highly radioactive plants, fish and invertebrates of impaired vitality were found in the three weeks following Test Baker. One year later, a most careful search of the islands, reefs, and lagoon by some twenty very well-qualified and well-equipped and well-supported biologists, over half of whom had made extensive studies of the same areas before the explosion, revealed no changes in population, numbers, or composition, and no physiological damage which definitely could be ascribed to the explosion. The nearest thing to a case of definite damage from the products of the explosions is furnished by some dying corals on the reef between Amen and Bikini Islands. These corals *(Heliopora)* were observed to be in fine condition a few weeks before Test Baker. At the time of

---

*All published items were classified as Confidential except Volume I, *Operations,* which bore a security classification of Restricted and Annex IV, the annex to the *Report of the Technical Director,* which covered the work of the Radiochemistry Group and which was classified as Secret.

the explosion the tops of the coral clumps were about a foot under water, and the tide was rising. They may have been killed by radioactive fission products definitely known to have washed over the reef after raining down from the base surge. More probable causes of their death are contamination by oil from the sunken ships . . . or by heavy rain during one of the lowest tides. Corals are easily killed by fresh water. The question of what happened to these particular corals remains open.[26]

The matter of the future habitation of Bikini was approached in a manner far less conclusive than earlier evaluations of evidence might have suggested. Of this the report stated:

Large amounts of radioactive material still exist on the lagoon bottom. Above the water, the external radiation is appreciably greater than background only on the sand spit at the northern end of Bikini Island and the adjoining reef, and near debris from the target ships cast upon the various beaches. Even there, it provides no physiological hazards. In the habitable portions of the islands, any radiation from fission products is so weak as to be completely lost in the normal background. In the waters of the lagoon, the residual radioactivity from the bomb is similarly lost in the radioactivity normally present in sea water the world over. Of approximately a thousand plant and animal samples, mostly fish, which were counted or analyzed, the average radioactivity per unit weight was approximately fifty per cent more than that of the body of a man who has had no exposure to radium, fissionable material, or fission products; and in only one sample, a sponge, was the energy per unit volume being received from radioactivity as much as it would have been from the accepted tolerance of external radiation, 0.1 R/24 hours. Other than fish, no food product was found which contained more than twice the normal radioactivity of human flesh. The maximum amount of plutonium found in any part of any fish was 3×10^{-10} grams per gram of wet tissue. When it is remembered that two of the dangerous long-life fission products, strontium and cesium, are not now present at Bikini and that the fission product activity still present there will have decayed to about 30 per cent of its present value after one more year, and that from food eaten, somewhere between 1 and 10 per cent of the radioactive material is retained by the body, it becomes obvious that after a few more years these islands will constitute relatively slight radioactive hazard to any one. Nevertheless, definite predictions cannot yet be made as to whether the radioactivity will soon become sufficiently diluted to permit permanent reoccupation of the atoll. The primary considerations in such relocation would be medico-legal.[27]

The report recounted in some detail the processes by which, in the Baker explosion, the fissionable material, plutonium, and long-lived fission products—yttrium, zirconium, columbium, antimony, praseodymium, element 61, and europium—were adsorbed and carried to the bottom of the lagoon, where as was pointed out, "all but an insignificant fraction" remained.[28] The report noted, however, that the radiochemists had found interesting absences of radioactive elements. Thirty-three year cesium had not been adsorbed because large quantities of sodium, chemically similar, already were present. Similarly, radiostrontium was not carried to the bottom because neutral strontium, chemically identical, had saturated the surfaces of the adsorbents. "After six months," the report stated, "more than 99 per cent of these soluble elements had been carried off to sea by the normal flushing processes occurring in the lagoon."[29] Of what was happening at the bottom of the lagoon it was said:

> At the present time worms and sea cucumbers are burrowing actively in and eating the highly radioactive bottom mud. Most of this passes right through them, and some of the feces are left on top, where bacteria compost them, returning most of the active material to the mud. However, some is left available to plants, which grow on the altered material. These plants are eaten by small fish, which pass almost all of the altered material through the gut. Small fish with the small fraction of radioactive material they have retained in their tissues are in turn eaten by large fish, which again eliminate most of the radioactivity, carrying some of it to distant parts of the lagoon and even outside. Plants remote from the explosion center get traces of radioactive material in this way, and the cycle is continued. The net tendency is to spread the material evenly over the lagoon bottom and to carry a certain amount of it out to sea.[30]

Then, of the possibility that radiation had caused mutations in Bikini organisms:

> One of the most discussed effects of radioactivity is the possibility of producing genetic changes. At Bikini more than 1000 species of organisms have been exposed to radioactivity, and many have reproduced through at least one generation. A careful search of the area by competent biologists, including ichthyologists, botanists, invertebrate zoologists, and entomologists, in the course of which tens of thousands of specimens were examined, failed to reveal definite evidence of aberrant forms. Since it is known that mutations produced by radiation almost invariably have negative survival value, this result was not unexpected. No interference with the reproductive functions of sea-urchins taken from the most heavily irradiated portion of the reef could be detected. . . .[31]

The meaning of Bikini in 1947 depended, perhaps, on the nearness to the eye of the viewer of the immediate objectives of the Resurvey. For military purposes, even for a major share of the scientific purposes, Bikini had contributed all that could be expected. As all scientific reports testified, no radiation-induced genetic or other effects had been positively identified in six weeks of work at the atoll. The question of further habitation by the Bikini people was reserved as "medico-legal," but the records of 1946 now contained new data, laboriously assembled, comprising a useful sequel to the investigation for which the Bikinians had surrendered their homes. Further, the damage to target ships had been reassessed, and the drilling of Bikini reefs had extended knowledge of atoll structure. If problems remained, they were biological and only to be solved by the future.

Chapter Four

1948-1949: THE ATOLLS

I

THE UNITED STATES Atomic Energy Commission was created by
the Atomic Energy Act of 1946, which stipulated that the new
agency was to conduct a program of atomic energy development
"subject at all times to the paramount objective of assuring the
common defense and security." By August, 1946, at the conclusion of Operation Crossroads, five atomic weapons had been
detonated, one at Alamogordo, two over Japan, and two at Bikini,
and an overwhelming proportion of the world's experience with
atomic energy had been invested in the effort that produced those
explosions. The Commission, in taking over the nuclear program
from the Manhattan District on January 1, 1947, had inherited a
task far broader than the development of bombs but one which,
since it would encompass activities for the improvement of nuclear
weapons, seemed also of necessity to include a program of proof
testing in the field. In July, 1947, the Commission announced that
it was "establishing proving grounds in the Pacific for routine
experiments and tests of atomic weapons."[1] The place selected
was not Bikini. It was, as would be revealed after the Operation
Sandstone tests the following year, Eniwetok Atoll.

The year 1947 was a year of fearful examination of the atomic problem by both scientists and laymen, of review of the records of the first reverberating months of the atomic era, and of emotional adjustments to the fact of mankind's new capacity to release energy at unprecedented levels of magnitude. The task force of the Bikini Scientific Resurvey, even though its members, seven hundred strong, had "reoccupied" and swarmed over Bikini for six summer weeks, had contributed what was on balance only a paragraph in the larger annals of the immediate postwar period. Within the Atomic Energy Commission the spring of 1947 was a time of preparation for new responsibilities. Chairman of the Commission was David E. Lilienthal, whose appointment had been confirmed by the Senate after a protracted committee inquiry. His associates on the Commission were Robert F. Bacher, Sumner T. Pike, Lewis L. Strauss, and William W. Waymack. Among the others participating in the determination of policy and program, however, were many whose experience extended far back beyond the Manhattan District operations or, in some instances, into the period of the earliest theoretical approaches to the atomic problem. The Atomic Energy Act of 1946 provided for the creation of the General Advisory Committee, to be appointed by the President; of the Military Liaison Committee, whose service representatives were to be appointed by the Secretaries of War and Navy; and of a Joint Congressional Committee on Atomic Energy. The Advisory Committee of nine members, whose function was "to advise the Commission on scientific and technical matters relating to materials, production, and research and development," was under the chairmanship of J. Robert Oppenheimer, Director of the Institute for Advanced Study at Princeton University, and included such other distinguished scientists as Enrico Fermi, professor of physics at the Institute for Nuclear Studies at the University of Chicago; Lee A. Du Bridge, President of the California Institute of Technology; James B. Conant, President of Harvard University; I. I. Rabi, Chairman of the Department of Physics at Columbia University; and Glenn T. Seaborg, professor chemistry at the University of California. The Military Liaison Committee, on which General Groves replaced Major General L. E. Oliver, was headed by Major General Lewis H. Brereton and also included in its initial membership Colonel John H. Hinds, of the Army, and three Navy representatives, Admiral Parsons, who had been commander of the Technical Task Group at Bikini and chairman of the Joint Crossroads Committee, and Rear Admirals Thorvald A. Solberg and Ralph A. Ofstie. Admiral Solberg had been a Navy member of the Joint Crossroads Committee and Admiral Ofstie, as senior Navy member of the U.S. Strategic Bombing Survey, had been a member of the Crossroads Evaluation Board.

With the General Advisory and Military Liaison Committees, as with the Joint Congressional Committee on Atomic Energy, then headed by Senator Bourke B. Hickenlooper, of Iowa, the Commission was maintaining an active and continuous relationship. Commission plans and problems were outlined in several formal meetings with the Joint Congressional group. The Advisory Committee held four meetings between January and July, 1947, and established subcommittees to provide uninterrupted assistance on special matters. The Military Liaison Committee became an agency for the coordination of Commission programs with plans and requirements of the War and Navy Departments.[2] Within the Commission, such requirements were transmitted through the Division of Military Application.

It was in this period of program development that Eniwetok was designated as the Commission's proving ground. The Los Alamos Scientific Laboratory, now the Commission agency for weapons research, had reported that it was becoming necessary to conduct field tests of new devices. The test recommendations were approved by the Commission and by "a majority" of the new Military Liaison Committee. Thus prepared for executive scrutiny, the proposal was submitted to President Truman, who authorized the program. "Thereupon," as the Commission reported, "a site was selected, and the Commission asked the National Military Establishment to prepare the proving ground and to provide necessary logistic support."[3]

The selection of the site had occasioned the same kind of review of possibilities that had proceeded in the Bikini case except that, in the search for what might prove to be a more permanent establishment, a location within the continental United States was initially considered. Assembly of data on possible ocean sites was the responsibility of Captain James S. Russell, U.S.N., Deputy Director of the Division of Military Application, and Darol K.

Froman, who would become Scientific Director for the Proving Ground. A return to Bikini apparently was not contemplated at any time, not only because Bikini was in an interim status and scheduled for further observation but because the land areas were neither large enough nor properly oriented to the prevailing winds to permit construction of a major airstrip.[4]

Sites in the Indian Ocean and in Alaska were studied, and some thought was given to Kwajalein. The review convinced Russell, as it convinced Froman, that Eniwetok, with which he was familiar from wartime experience, offered all of the advantages found earlier at Bikini plus the presence of established airstrips and facilities. Westward, in the direction in which the prevailing winds might carry radioactive particles, lay hundreds of miles of open sea. As for the matter of control, Eniwetok was in a custodianship status as a United States base although islands formerly under Japanese mandate were being moved into a new framework of United Nations trusteeship. Under the agreement which would create the Trust Territory of the Pacific Islands, the United States was to take all appropriate measures to advance the interests of the people of the Territory, but it also was authorized "to establish naval, military, and air bases and to erect fortifications" and "to station and employ armed forces in the Territory."*[5] The tentative selection of Eniwetok was followed by an inspection of the atoll and conferences with native leaders, including Abraham, the Eniwetok *iroij*, who were taken by the Navy to Ujelang to inspect the atoll as a site for their possible relocation. The site was approved by President Truman on December 2, 1947. The Eniwetok people, about 120 in number, were moved to Ujelang while planning went forward for testing at the new proving ground.

The atoll selected as the site for further nuclear operations lies some 165 nautical miles west of Bikini, a unit of the Ralik chain

*The process of repatriation of Japanese and other nationals had been completed in June, 1946, and in November President Truman announced that the United States was prepared to place the liberated islands under trusteeship. Copies of a draft agreement, transmitted to the United Nations Security Council, were approved there with minor modifications on April 2, 1947. The Trust Territory of the Pacific Islands came into being on July 18, 1947, when the President, with Congressional authority, approved the agreement and assigned to the Navy the responsibility for civil administration pending enactment by Congress of organic legislation for the Territory.

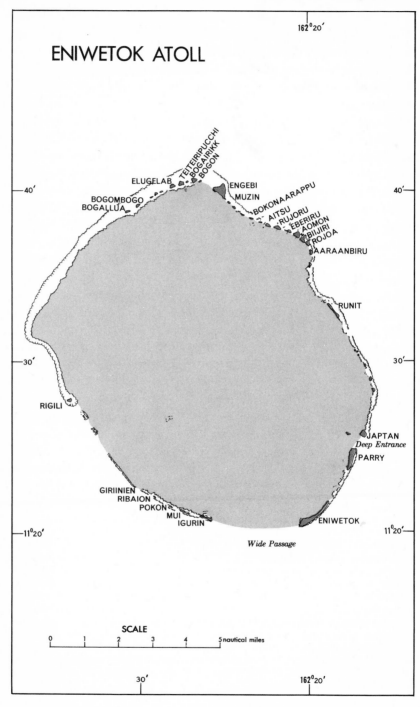

ENIWETOK ATOLL

of the Marshalls but further west, actually, than Kusai, in the eastern Caroline Islands.* Eniwetok, however, already had lost the relatively unspoiled quality of Bikini in 1946. It had been the scene of a bloody, difficult, and climactic assault by United States forces in World War II and a base of naval operations in the later phases of the war, and before that it had had an even longer record of association with the events of Pacific history.

Eniwetok was discovered on December 13, 1794, when Captain Thomas Butler, commanding the British sloop *Walpole*, encountered uncharted coral reefs lying approximately 12 degrees north of the Equator in the Central Pacific.[6] Butler, who was engaged in the China trade, called the reefs Browne's Range, a Mr. Browne being the factor of his firm at Canton. The discovery followed by only six years the cruise of Gilbert and Marshall, and Butler was following a similar route.† Browne's Range also is said to have been visited in 1798 by Captain John Fearn, of the British snow *Hunter*, who surveyed and charted the atoll for the first time, and the location of the range was noted on a chart published in 1799 in an account of the voyage to the South Pacific of the London Missionary Society ship, the *Duff*.[7] For many years Browne's name clung persistently to Eniwetok even after the final "e" was lost. In World War II, the Japanese frequently referred to Eniwetok as Brown, and on recent U.S. Hydrographic charts Eniwetok is identified as "Eniwetok or Brown Atoll." The meaning of Eniwetok, in the Marshallese, apparently is unknown.‡

*A comprehensive oceanographic and geological survey undertaken in 1950 by the Mid-Pacific Expedition determined that Eniwetok Atoll is the single surface manifestation of what actually is a third chain of the Marshalls, a chain of *guyots* or underwater sea mounts to the west of and roughly paralleling the Ralik and Ratak chains. This hidden archipelago was found sufficiently distinct to be designated an "Eniwetok Chain." (Kenneth O. Emery, J. I. Tracey Jr., H. S. Ladd, "Bikini and Nearby Atolls: Part I, Geology," *Geology of Bikini and Nearby Atolls*, [U.S. Government Printing Office (Washington, D.C., 1954)], p. 19.)

† A John Cary map published in London in 1806 locates Browne's Range with considerable accuracy and notes that Walpole Island, off the tip of New Caledonia, was discovered by Butler in 1794. A Cary globe of 1830 traced Butler's route through the Pacific.

‡ The Marshallese names for the islands and atolls seem usually to have been descriptive—Jaluit, "Something Lying Across," Ailinginae, "Atoll of the Current," and Likiep, "Bottom of the Basket." In response to an inquiry by the author, the Bernice P. Bishop Museum, at Honolulu, pointed out that in Marshallese the word *enin* means an island in an atoll and that *wetok* apparently referred to some characteristic of the atoll or its islands.

In the century and a half between its discovery and World War II, Eniwetok remained little known although involved in copra production for German interests and its tiny society modified, doubtless, by contact with the successive waves of German and Japanese. Even in the early years of the war Eniwetok escaped many of the Japanese defense operations going forward at more exposed points. But when, by the end of 1943, American forces had fought their way through Makin, Apemama, and Tarawa, in the Gilberts, and Majuro and Kwajalein, in the Marshalls, Eniwetok assumed a new importance. With the fall of Kwajalein, the Americans' northward movement across the Equator was ready to turn toward Truk, in the Carolines, and Saipan, Tinian, and Guam. Eniwetok lay to the northwest, a flanking threat to American air and sea operations and a point which, in American hands, might be a base for further strikes. Japan, already facing the realization that she could not hold the Pacific islands, was preparing nevertheless to make their conquest as costly as possible.

In January, 1944, Japanese troops in the Marshalls and on Wake Island totaled 13,721, including members of Army units called from the home islands, the Philippines, and Manchuria, and distributed as amphibious brigades. Only Kusai had more of these troops than Eniwetok, where a fighter strip had been built on Engebi Island, on the northeast rim of the atoll, and where the reinforced garrison was composed of 2,686 armed troops and about 1,000 laborers and other noncombat personnel.[8] Against the atoll so recently strengthened the Americans sent a task group, called the Eniwetok Expeditionary Force (Task Group 51.11), under Admiral Harry W. Hill, who was equipped with intelligence reports indicating that the Japanese strength was concentrated on Engebi. The Battle of Eniwetok opened on February 17, 1944, when the task group moved into Eniwetok lagoon to begin bombardment and assault to the north. Engebi was secured by the afternoon of February 18, by which time 1,276 Japanese had been killed and 16 taken prisoner at a cost of 85 Marines killed and missing and 166 wounded. Most of the Japanese, however, were not on Engebi but on the major southern islands, Parry and Eniwetok, where the defender of the atoll, General Yoshima Noshida, had made the best possible use of meager terrain and facilities and where he had ordered his troops to die in battle. The capture of Parry and Eniwetok took an additional four days, for even naval shelling and bombing had not driven the defenders from the networks of trenches and strong points dug hastily in the shallow sands. The Battle of Eniwetok was the last assault against a defended atoll in World War II. In it the American forces lost 169 killed in action, 521 were wounded, and 26 missing; 2,661 Japanese were killed and 41 taken as prisoners.

After Eniwetok's capture, its reefs and lagoons were recharted by the Navy in preparation for use of the atoll as a base of operations, but the war moved on toward Hiroshima and Nagasaki and Eniwetok became a station in the support area. In this period, several scientific studies of atoll geology were made in connection with military activities. With the end of the war, Eniwetok was left for a time in the care of a small housekeeping force. The respite, however, would be brief.

II

The agency created to prepare the Eniwetok proving ground and to conduct the first Atomic Energy Commission test series was Joint Task Force Seven, a combined Army-Navy-Air Force-AEC organization headed by Lieutenant General John E. Hull, U.S.A., task force commander.

Joint Task Force Seven came into being on October 18, 1947.[9] A number of military agencies had been invited to participate in the test program and to supply technical or other personnel, these including the Armed Forces Special Weapons Project, the Naval Ordnance Laboratory, the Naval Research Laboratory, the Navy's David Taylor Model Basin, and the Army's Aberdeen Proving Ground. The new task force differed, however, from the Joint Task Force One of Operation Crossroads in that it had a Scientific Task Group composed primarily of civilian scientists who were to conduct the tests. The military groups were to prepare the proving ground, to provide logistic and operational support, and to assist the scientific group in technical and administrative aspects of the program.

The scientific group was led by Captain Russell as Test Director. Froman was Scientific Director for the proving ground and headed the Task Unit of scientists within the Scientific Task Group. The scientific unit, through Russell, operated technically under the

Commission, and the Los Alamos Laboratory was represented at the administrative-command level by Alvin C. Graves, Deputy Director to Froman, and John C. Clark and Robert W. Henderson, Assistant Scientific Directors. As General Hull said later, "This (Scientific) Task Group, by common consent, did not work through my staff. The channels between Captain Russell, Dr. Froman, and myself were direct."[10] The military staff included Admiral Parsons and Major General William E. Kepner, U.S.A.F., as Deputy Commanders, and Brigadier General Claude B. Ferenbaugh as Chief of Staff. Military service units of the task force were commanded respectively by Rear Admiral Francis E. Denebrink, Brigadier General David A. D. Ogden, U.S.A., and Major General Roger M. Ramey, U.S.A.F.

Joint Task Force Seven was preparing in the winter and spring of 1947 and 1948 for Operation Sandstone, in which three atomic devices would be detonated at Eniwetok in April and May, 1948. Preparation of proving-ground facilities was started late in December, 1947, by army units under General Ogden, although some of the construction was performed under civilian contract and one of the most complex of the projects, the laying of almost a million feet of submarine cable, was performed under the direction of the U.S. Coast Guard. The main elements of the task force, including particularly the scientific personnel, sailed from Pearl Harbor on March 8, 1948, in ships of a Naval Task Group whose flagship was the U.S.S. *Mount McKinley*, which had similarly served the commander and the staffs at Crossroads. The Eniwetok tests were to be clearly distinguishable in concept, the Commission emphasized, from the tests at Bikini, conducted under conditions as close as possible to those of laboratory control and with extensive instrumentation.[11] Also unlike the Crossroads tests, the new experiments were to be conducted in secret. No press ship accompanied the task force, and the observers were limited to members of the Joint Congressional Committee and representatives of the Commission and of the armed forces. The total strength of the task force, including the civilian employees of the contractors and all others who had participated in the preparations, was 9,800 persons.

The symmetry of Eniwetok's outline is, in the broad view, the atoll's most obvious physical feature. Between Eniwetok Island at the south and Engebi to the north is the twenty-five mile thread of the brilliantly colorful windward rim, a rim edged in white by the breakers foaming on the ocean side and streaked, between the scattering of islands, by the blues, the greens, and the reds of the living coral. On this rim, north of Eniwetok, are Parry and Japtan Islands, which flank the Deep Entrance to the lagoon, and further to the north are such islands as Runit, Aomon, Biijiri, Eberiru, and Aitsu. Others mark the wide reef west of Engebi, but on the long curve to the leeward West Spit and along Eniwetok's southwesterly side, are only stretches of white sand, occasional patches of vegetation, and now and again another island—Rigili, Mui, Igurin—that seems to be placed only tentatively on the reef. In such a setting the Battle of Eniwetok had been fought, and long before their removal to Ujelang the members of the Eniwetok community had left their homes on the southerly islands and were living on Aomon and Biijiri to escape the activity swirling about them. It was on these islands of the eastern reef that the Sandstone shots would be detonated.

Three devices were tested during Operation Sandstone, each on a 200-foot tower for control of elevation, timing, and measurement of blast and thermal effect. The first shot was on Engebi at 6:17 A.M., April 15 (Eniwetok time), the second on Biijiri at 6:09 A.M., on May 1, and the third on Runit at 6:04 A.M., May 15. The second detonation, Test Yoke, was the largest of the three with a yield that was announced later as of 49 kilotons.[12] When the tests were completed, Joint Task Force Seven prepared to move home. The public announcement of the successful completion of the series was made by President Truman on May 17, two days after the final shot at Runit. No details, however, were made public. The Commission said that the tests had proved the effectiveness of new weapons designs and "confirmed a great deal of the theoretical and experimental work performed at the Los Alamos Scientific Laboratory since the war."[13]

III

No plans for radiobiological monitoring, either before or after the tests, had been incorporated into the Sandstone program. For the 1948 series there had been established a Radiological Safety Group, given the code name of "RadSafe," to advise the test commander on radiation problems, to furnish trained monitors to survey test areas, to determine radiation tolerance levels, to assure supplies of radiation detection instruments, and to do whatever was necessary to prevent undue exposure or radiation injury.* The RadSafe monitors were not, however, engaged in biological sampling. On May 16, nevertheless, the day following the Runit detonation and some thirty-six hours after shot time, a small collection of marine organisms was made on the reefs a mile and a quarter north of the test site—a collection that would prove to be a reference point for the radiation contamination studies conducted later in the season by the Applied Fisheries Laboratory. How this small survey happened to be made was related to the Bikini Resurvey of the previous year and to its sequel in the report of the Radiobiological Division.

On their return from the Bikini Scientific Resurvey, members of the Applied Fisheries staff spent several months making (by methods which would come to seem of the crudest possible sort) analyses of the radiation discovered in the fish and other biological specimens harvested in Bikini lagoon. The conclusions they drew from their data suggested again that Bikini should be examined further after additional time had passed. During the winter of 1947 and 1948 the Laboratory prepared for the Atomic Energy Commission an outline of proposed further studies at Bikini. This outline was received during the months when, as it proved, plans for the Eniwetok shots were maturing. In the statement of objectives the Laboratory said:

> A resurvey of the Bikini Atoll during the summer of 1948 should be undertaken to further our knowledge of the over-all biological problems of the effect of the release of energy from atomic bombs above or under water.
>
> Biological studies are of necessity long time, complex projects. The Bikini biological studies are so very complicated that only through *continuous* long time effort can we hope to understand the basic principles involved.[14]

*The RadSafe group in 1948 consisted of hand-picked officers and technicians who were trained for monitoring activities, who were given complete physical examinations before leaving the United States, and who took with them about 1,000 detection instruments and 10,000 radiation film badges and dosimeters. Monitors accompanied every team, field unit, ship, or aircraft operating near the test areas. In subsequent years RadSafe teams and communications networks operated throughout the enlarged proving ground area.

It was against this background, but before a decision had been made concerning the resumption of the Bikini work, that Donaldson was invited to attend the Eniwetok tests as an observer. As an observer, Donaldson had no function or assignment. Captain Russell, however, as head of the Scientific Task Group, was acquainted with the Bikini investigation and interested in the biological problems there. Under Russell's direction, arrangements were made for Donaldson and a small team of volunteer assistants to visit the Runit reef to collect marine specimens.

Runit Island, a narrow elevation of almost a mile and three quarters in length, had been crowned before Sandstone by a thin stand of coconut palms which straggled over into the dunes at the island's tips. The atomic explosion there had swept the center of the island clear of all vegetation for perhaps 1,000 yards in each direction, leaving at the ends the decapitated and tumbled palm trees which stood outside the region of maximum blast effect. The result was that the base curve of the blast seemed outlined in the surviving vegetation. Even the following year, when stunted and sickly plants had begun to repopulate the area, it was possible to measure between the clumps of surviving trees the approximate range of the shot's effect.

The Runit collection point, at a mile and a quarter from the center of detonation, was chosen because it was outside the area of greatest fallout but still within the general fallout pattern. Samples were collected by spreading derris root in water about isolated coral heads on both sides of the exposed reef. Specimens, first preserved in a formalin solution, later were placed in alcohol for shipment to the laboratory in Seattle because no counting facilities were available at Eniwetok. The specimens were few. Donaldson, flying from the proving ground, carried them in his personal luggage, and ultimately 118 samples of tissue were prepared and counted. The counting began on May 22, a week after the specimens were picked from the waters off Runit.[15]

As a scientific operation the Runit collection was small and altogether opportunistic. What it showed, however, when the counting was started in the Applied Fisheries Laboratory, was that on the day following the land-based Runit shot there already was a pronounced uptake of radioactive products by marine organisms at the outer edges of the fallout zone. The first counts, made in the period from May 22 to May 27, revealed the presence of relatively large amounts of beta-gamma radioactivity in the digestive tracts of the specimens. In the gut of a black surgeon fish, for example, of a species which feeds only on algae, the radioactivity on May 22 was at a level of 55,980 counts per minute per gram of wet tissue. In the gut of a red striped squirrel fish the activity counted on May 23 was at 32,542 counts per minute.[16] In an oyster the count was 14,004. The samples were few and random, but they indicated a significant primary contamination. Some of the counts of activity were beyond the capacity of the scaler (Victoreen, Model X-327). Nevertheless, what was noteworthy was the level of uptake, on the day following the test, by the organs of fish and other specimens. In the liver, skin, bone, muscle, and gills of the fish the beta-gamma counts were significantly high, the gross counts per minute in liver tissue from seven specimens averaging approximately 3,810 millimicrocuries per kilogram of wet tissue.[17]

The small collection of Eniwetok specimens continued to furnish material for laboratory work until February, 1949. Tissues counted in June, 1948, and at intervals thereafter produced data on the decay of radioactive materials taken into the bodies of the marine animals. Without the assistance of Captain Russell there would have been no radiobiological data at all.

IV

It was not until the Eniwetok series was concluded that the Applied Fisheries Laboratory learned that the Atomic Energy Commission had approved its proposed resurvey of Bikini, and that with the Bikini program was to be combined, as an extension of it, a radiological survey of Eniwetok.

With this decision there began in the Pacific, in the summer of 1948, a period of almost two years in which Bikini and Eniwetok would be the field stations of the radiation biologists. The work there had a random quality, for the atolls were not laboratories in which assumptions were tested under conditions allowing precise measurements of results. The radiobiologists had no specific knowledge either of the character of the atomic devices or of the probable quantities of fission products introduced into the environments they studied. From the beginning, the problem of tracing radioactivity at Bikini and Eniwetok was akin to hunting

The Bikini Island lagoon beach in 1949, three years after Operation Crossroads *(Laboratory of Radiation Biology)*

The east reef of Bikini Atoll, Enyu Island in the distance, 1949 *(Laboratory of Radiation Biology)*

invisible clues in a game without rules. No one really knew which clues were valid, which were not. The problem became infinitely more complicated when the bits of evidence, by mechanisms no one understood, began to be transported from one place to another. Somewhere in Bikini and Eniwetok, however, lay information that seemed altogether worthy of pursuit while the opportunity remained.

The hunt for evidence actually only began, however, in 1948, when the first phase of the postwar testing was finished and the Pacific entered a quiet period that would not be broken until the beginning of the Korean War. Joint Task Force One had passed into history and Joint Task Force Seven, its mission at Sandstone completed, awaited the further evolution of the atomic program. The Bikini Scientific Resurvey, having done its work, was contributing to the enlargement of scientific literature but without further examination of the Bikini radiation problem. Juda and his Bikini people still clung to the hope that they would be permitted to return to their native atoll. Members of the Eniwetok community, now also the special wards of the Navy-administered Trust Territory, were at tiny Ujelang Atoll. Bikini and Eniwetok, restricted zones in the beautiful, troubled, hopeful, postwar Pacific, awaited the future and the decisions that would be made in Washington.

The Applied Fisheries Laboratory made Commission-sponsored surveys at the test sites in 1948 and 1949. These were unlike any of the previous activities at the atolls. The virtual impossibility of estimating quantitatively the effect of atomic radiation on natural marine populations had been demonstrated. There remained, essentially, the qualitative problems that could be solved, if ever, only by the most painstaking examinations of the amounts and processes of radiation uptake in a marine environment. These problems were of long-range implication. But they also were of immediate and practical relevance, or so it seemed then, to the matter of what was to be done with Bikini. In the case of Eniwetok, the atoll had been claimed for use as a proving ground for as long as it should be needed, but the Bikini case was different, morally and legally. Bikini had been borrowed from its inhabitants by the Navy for what was presumed in 1946 to be only short-term use. But could the inhabitants, the owners, who subsisted on the fish of the lagoon and the vegetation of the islands, be returned to an atoll even slightly contaminated by radioactivity? Could the Bikini people live in health and rear new generations of children on an atoll in which layers of lagoonal silt held "large quantities" of residual radiation? The historian of Crossroads had written in 1947 that the Bikini people, "convinced that the tests would be a contribution to world peace, indicated their willingness to evacuate."[18] The Navy military government, early in 1946, had not asked permanent possession and the Bikini people had been in no doubt that they would be repatriated once the atomic tests were over. Still the question remained: When was Crossroads finished?

After fifteen months on Rongerik, an atoll much smaller than Bikini, members of the Bikini community were in serious straits for want of food. On June 2, 1947, even before the Bikini Scientific Resurvey had taken to the field, a Navy Board of Investigation recommended that the community be transferred to some more suitable place, and Juda and three members of his council set out once more, with Navy help, to find an alternate home.[19] It was in this period that Juda was taken to Bikini itself to consult with the scientists there. Between June and September, 1947, Juda and his companions visted Ujae, Wotho, and Ujelang atolls and Kili Island, in the southern Marshalls, but none of these seemed satisfactory. J. E. Tobin, anthropologist of the Marshall Islands District, later quoted in translation a letter finally transmitted to the Navy authorities by the Bikini group:

> To the Office at Kwajalein.
> Gentlemen:
>   We, the council, have held a meeting to find the best place to go. We have been to some other places to inspect and have considered them. In moving we find it quite a problem. The place we all agree to stay on is Ronrik Atoll.
>
> We
The Council[20]

The Board of Investigation decided in September, however, that in its own interests the Bikini group should be moved to Ujelang. Preparations for the move were being made when word was received that Ujelang had been designated for the Eniwetok people. In January, 1948, the Navy called in Leonard Mason, professor of anthropolgy at the University of Hawaii, to make a study of the

Bikini group on Rongerik, and Mason found, quite simply, that the Bikinians were not getting enough to eat. By March, 1948, the community was moved to Kwajalein, and the following autumn, after a further review of sites, to Kili, a single coral island that once had been a copra plantation during the German period in the Marshalls. Kili became, then, the permanent home of the people who had surrendered their atoll for the test of 1946. Kili had the capacity to produce fine crops of coconut, papaya, breadfruit, and pandanus, but it had no lagoon and fishing there, on the ocean reefs, was almost impossible. Juda and his people continued to long for Bikini. They had the attention and assistance of the officials of the Trust Territory.

V

The Bikini-Eniwetok Resurveys of 1948 and 1949 were conducted by the Applied Fisheries Laboratory with the support and communications-transport services of the Navy. In 1948, instead of the scores of scientists and technicians who had composed the 1947 field groups, the Laboratory took to the Pacific just twelve men, half of them junior staff members and promising students. Instead of the *Chilton*, the *Coucal*, the drilling and diving gear, and the shore laboratories and facilities of the Bikini Scientific Resurvey, there were only the LCI (L) 1054 and three small landing craft, LCVP's, to be used as work boats within the lagoons. The expedition, like most of those that would follow in the next decade, was compact and geared solely to making collections that would provide clues to the operation of the radiobiological mechanisms. The group was small, and the survey vessel was no more than a dot in the Bikini lagoon that had held with ease the two hundred and fifty ships and small craft of the Crossroads fleet. But, large as were the questions involved, the answers lay now in the tissues of the minutest forms of aquatic life.

The 1948 expedition, transported by air to Kwajalein, arrived at Bikini aboard the LCI on July 3, and worked there until July 20, when it moved to Eniwetok. The Eniwetok sampling was finished by July 30. The party was headed by Donaldson, whose assistant and executive officer was Allyn H. Seymour, the research associate who had participated in the 1947 resurvey and who was both bio-statistician and plankton specialist. Other senior members of the

(Top) The LCI(L) 1054 off Bikini Island, 1948 *(Laboratory of Radiation Biology)*
(Center) The LSI(L) 1091 in Bikini lagoon, 1949 *(Laboratory of Radiation Biology)*
(Bottom) The LSI(L) 1091 showing temporary laboratory and sampling pump *(Laboratory of Radiation Biology)*

group included Welander, ichthyologist; Asher A. White, lecturer at the University of Minnesota College of Medicine, medical consultant; George Hollenberg, professor of botany at the University of Redlands, marine algologist; Theodore Bullock, associate professor of zoology at the University of California at Los Angeles, specializing in marine invertebrates; and Spencer W. Tinker, director of the Waikiki Aquarium of the University of Hawaii, marine biologist. Staff members and students were Edward E. Held, U.C.L.A., marine invertebrates; Frank G. Lowman and Richard H. Osborn, radiobiologists; John J. Koch, in charge of sample processing; and John R. Donaldson, son of the survey director, a fisheries biologist assisting the plankton studies.[21]

Bikini had not been visited since the *Chilton* had departed the year before. The vegetation which by 1947 had begun to erase the traces of Crossroads activity on the islands had closed even more tightly about the empty buildings, and storms and sunlight had rotted even further the wood and canvas flotsam on the beaches and had added layers of rust to the hull of the LCT 816, a target ship lying on the Enyu Island beach. In the eighteen days of field work the 1948 team made collections of samples at eleven major stations—on the land and reefs of nine major islands, in the target area, and on the reef northwest of Bikini Island—seeking representative specimens of floral and faunal systems. A total of 1,918 ashed samples were prepared in the shipboard laboratories (in subsequent years ashing in the field would be discontinued), and large numbers of specimens were preserved for later study. Field counts also were made by Geiger counter to determine whether contamination were detectable on land, this in the thought that there might be some contamination of land plants and animals by the transfer of fission products from the lagoon.

The methods of collecting fish were similar to those used at Bikini in 1946 and 1947. The 1948 Bikini resurvey concentrated on obtaining specimens occupying specific and easily recognizable places in Bikini ecology. Of the fish, 187 specimens selected from twelve groups ultimately produced 1,152 ashed tissue samples for radioanalysis. Beyond the fish, however, attention was directed to algae gathered within the lagoon and on the inner and outer reef areas; to the invertebrates, including the sea cucumbers, slugs, clams, oysters, snails, sponges, and sea urchins that had been of interest in previous years; and finally, within the waters, to the plankton, whose possible role in the accumulation and transfer of radioactivity had only begun to be suspected in 1947.[22]

Bikini radioactivity, because of natural decay and dilution, was at levels even lower than those of 1947. In the fish, as subsequent laboratory work demonstrated, radioactivity in the tissues usually was not higher than twice the normal background count. But slightly higher levels were found in samples taken from parts of the lagoon where little residual radiation would have been expected. For example, Crossroads studies of the circulation of Bikini's lagoonal waters had produced calculations that the volume in Bikini lagoon was replaced by new water from the ocean every thirty-nine days.[23] By July, 1948, two years after Test Baker, the waters presumably had been exchanged eighteen times. Yet radioactivity remained. The cleansing of Bikini of radioactivity obviously was being delayed and protracted far beyond any pre-Crossroads expectation by the biological uptake of radioactive elements released by the mud of the target area.

Additional bits of such evidence appeared. In 1947 the radio-biologists had noted that rough wooden boat frames floating in the water at the *Chilton* anchorage had picked up during the Bikini Scientific Survey clusters of marine hydroids which contained measurable amounts of radioactivity.[24] The same experiment was tried in 1948. Twelve eight-foot floats made of scrap lumber were anchored in July 5 in and near the waters of the target area. After fourteen days, just before the departure on July 20, the floats were lifted and the hydroid samples and algae removed. Counting of the samples in the laboratories revealed that in two weeks hydroids and algae had brought to the floats small but significant amounts of long-lived radioactivity. The residual contamination was a positive aspect of the Bikini environment, affecting even objects newly introduced into the waters.

Another intriguing circumstance was observed when the data of 1948 were compared to those of earlier years. The new surveys seemed to be indicating that increasingly higher concentrations of radioactivity were appearing in the coral and vegetation along the easterly rim of the atoll, east of the target area and upwind from the detonations of 1946. For some reason, minute amounts of Baker fission materials were being deposited, two years later, in that portion of the atoll which should have been relatively free of contamination. This phenomenon also was produced by the circulation of waters within the atoll. The "lake" of the lagoon, while protected by the encircling reefs from the westward-driven ocean swells, still is subject to complex forces resulting from the inflow and outflow of ocean waters and from the action of the tides. On their surface, however, the lagoon waters are pressed constantly by the east winds, which set up a westward moving surface layer of a thickness that varies, according to the strength of the wind, from five to twenty meters.[25] The volume of this surface water moving west in the lagoon is too great to be carried out to sea through the leeward passes or over the leeward reefs, and some of this excess water sinks to the bottom and returns to the east end of the atoll on the lagoon floor. The bottom current is thicker and slower than the surface current, but it represents the lower elements of an endless lagoonal circulation system. These lower waters, moving along the lagoon bottom, were crossing the radioactive silt of the target area and transporting to the eastern reef the radioactive materials and current-borne organisms which had ingested them. Thus, on the inner edge of the windward reef, where radioactivity had been almost totally absent before, a general distribution of low-level activity now was detectable.

Aquatic samples from each station showed in 1948 the presence of small amounts of residual radiation. In each of the biological categories—fish, algae, invertebrates, plankton—analysis revealed that there had been uptake of radioactivity in amounts which, while expressible only in fractions or multiples of normal background levels, indicated that life at Bikini was proceeding in a slightly altered environment. The Geiger counter surveys of land areas apparently confirmed this. On Bikini Island, teams surveyed the lagoon side for two and a half miles, one team on the beach and another about 50 yards inland. The beach crew found sand and rock virtually free of radioactivity, but on the land the counts of activity in the vegetation ranged from two to four times background all along the two and one-half mile course.[26] The living grass, palm and pandanus roots, foliage, and the trunks of trees produced counts averaging 80 per minute, twice background, while dead leaves, grass, and fronds, which form a brittle matting at the bases of the trees, showed counts averaging 150 per minute, four

(Top) The lagoon beach of Likiep village, where control collections were begun in 1949 *(Laboratory of Radiation Biology)*

(Center) An Operation Crossroads marine dispatch tower on Bikini Island, 1949 *(Laboratory of Radiation Biology)*

(Bottom) The World War II Japanese memorial, Bikini Island, 1949 *(Laboratory of Radiation Biology)*

times background. On Rokar Island, south of Bikini and east of the target area, Geiger readings increased from background at the water's edge to two and a half times background at the vegetation line. On Enyu Island, dead vegetation averaged 400 counts per minute, about ten times background.[27] Surveys of Aomoen, Uorikku, Airukiiji, Eniirikku, and Bokororyuru islands—key points about the rim of Bikini—told similar stories. Radioactivity in Bikini vegetation was low, but it was found everywhere and at approximately the same levels.

After Bikini there remained Eniwetok—the same procedures of collection, the same questions. There was not yet at Eniwetok the complication of a Baker shot or even of a Test Able, in which a bomb had been exploded over a fleet. The land shots of Eniwetok nevertheless had touched the lagoon and the ocean and had set up, as Donaldson's samplings of Runit had shown, questions of the same kind as those at Bikini. The LCI (L) 1054, having departed Bikini on July 20, moved into Eniwetok lagoon on July 21 and by the following day the radiobiology team was beginning its sampling, slightly more than two months after the Runit test. Six stations were used for the collection of specimens, three near the sites of the spring detonations and three on Japtan, Igurin, and Rigili islands, even to fourteen miles to the south and west and, in the case of Rigili, downwind from the test reefs. As was by now the standard procedure, samples of fish, algae, invertebrates, and plankton were taken. The digestive systems of the specimens from the regions of the bomb sites showed clearly that the fish had been ingesting radioactive materials. There were peculiarities in the data, as when the values of radioactivity in the invertebrate samples were found to be lower at Runit, where the final device was exploded, than at Rigili Island, fourteen miles westward across Eniwetok lagoon. But, in general, the Eniwetok story of 1948 was that low-level aquatic radiation was present at the places it might be expected.

Never before, however, had a test site been examined after such an interval of time, before certain of the scars had healed, and a visual check of the shot-island reefs proved to be almost more revealing than the biological analyses. On July 26, four members of the group, swimming with face masks and making observations from a rubber raft, surveyed an equilateral triangle of water and reef on the shore of Engebi Island north of the crater scooped out of the coral by the atomic shot. In the clear waters above the reef they could trace the "area of kill" in the skeletons of sedentary forms, such as clams and corals, littering the submerged sands. All such forms were dead to a distance of 250 yards on the northwest leg of the triangle. "Appreciable quantities of living coral and clams," they reported, "were observed 300 yards and farther from shore on the northwest leg and 150 yards on the third leg. Numbers of clams were dying or had died within the previous few days. These clams were agape, with the soft parts in various stages of decay."[28] Within this area, however, algae continued to grow. Fish were seen feeding on algae which unquestionably had absorbed radioactivity from the shot-island reefs.

VI

By 1949, although none could know it at the time, the introductory period in the chronology of the atomic era was coming to a close.

On September 23, President Truman announced the end of the United States atomic bomb monopoly—which may, in fact, have ended more than two years before—saying, "We have evidence that within recent weeks an atomic explosion occurred in the U.S.S.R."* Within six months would come the Korean War and a cessation of Pacific testing while American troops were shuttled to and from the distant combat areas. Behind the scenes had been developing for some time, within the Commission and its advisory bodies and at Los Alamos, but also within the complex of civil and military departments at the policy levels of government, discussions and determinations that would lead to the creation of a thermonuclear weapon. Yet this introductory period also had incorporated developments reflecting recognition of the need for encouragement of biological studies. An early Commission policy determination called for the appointment of advisory committees through which the Commission availed itself of the part-time services of persons having special knowledge in fields important

---

*On September 25, 1949, Tass, the Soviet news agency, issued a statement saying that Russia had possessed the secret of the atom bomb since 1947. The Associated Press reported that the statement "recalled that on November 6, 1947, Soviet Foreign Minister V. M. Molotov said the secret of the atomic bomb had long ceased to exist."

to the federal program. Shortly after assuming its responsibilities the Commission had appointed a seven-member Medical Board of Review headed by Robert F. Loeb, Lambert professor of medicine, Columbia University, to make recommendations concerning the appropriate implementation of Commission responsibilities in health and biological fields. In June, 1947, this Board submitted a report recommending rapid expansion of research and training, the creation of a permanent Advisory Committee for Biology and Medicine, and the appointment within the Commission of a medical director to assume responsibility for research and training in biology and medicine and for health protection programs. These recommendations led to the appointment in 1947 of an Advisory Committee, initially under the chairmanship of Alan Gregg, director for Medical Sciences of the Rockfeller Foundation, and in turn, with the help of the Committee, to the establishment in 1948 of a Division of Biology and Medicine under Shields Warren, its first director.* The Commission, reporting to Congress on the beginnings of its work in biology and medicine, said:

> Over the many decades during which physicians have used X-rays and radium for the treatment of disease, they have become familiar with the harmful effects of overdoses of radiation. Biologists have assisted by studying how radiation affects plants and animals. . . . By the time that atomic energy was developed, therefore, science was already famliar with the biological effects of most types of radiations.
>
> What was new to the biologist and the physician in the development of atomic energy was the massive quantity of radioactive materials created and the greater potentialities of these materials for both good and ill. The Atomic Energy Commission has the obligation to investigate these potentialities and to encourage and assist others to do so. It must explore the many benefits in prospect . . . and it must learn how to forestall the dangers to human, plant, and animal life.[29]

There was not in this time, within the Commission, among members of the advisory committees, or elsewhere, an appreciation of the potential values of the Pacific atolls as sites for studies

---

*Other members of the Advisory Committee were G. W. Beadle, Division of Biology, California Institute of Technology; Detlev W. Bronk, President, the Johns Hopkins University; Ernest W. Goodpasture, Dean of the School of Medicine, Vanderbilt University; Baird Hastings, professor of biochemistry, Harvard Medical School; E. C. Stakman, Chief of the Division of Plant Pathology and Botany, University of Minnesota; and Joseph T. Wearn, Dean of the School of Medicine, Western Reserve University.

of radioactivity in the natural aquatic environment. The Commission was supporting research programs in health physics, in the effects of nuclear radiations on living matter, in the detection and treatment of radiation injury, and, in a score of related areas. In July, 1948, the Division of Biology of the Argonne National Laboratory had established a Radiobiology Experiment Station for nonsecret types of research. The numbers of biological investigations would be increased manyfold in succeeding months and years. But the testing programs, designed to fit the requirements of weapons development, would remain distant and fundamentally separate, functions of "the paramount objective of assuring the common defense and security." The Pacific programs were curtained off from the world not only by the restrictions placed about such operations but also by their distance from the established laboratories and, in the cases of the radiobiological surveys, by the essential inconclusiveness of their results. Nevertheless, the Division of Biology and Medicine would become the sponsor and protector of the slowly emerging interest in radiobiology at the Pacific Proving Ground.

In 1949, when the proving ground was idle and Bikini continued to await a verdict, there was opportunity to follow up—without interruption, perhaps for the last time—the further biological distribution of the radioactivity already released in the Pacific. The resurveys of that year were broader than those of 1948, but their essential differences were qualitative. At the suggestion of Shields Warren, the expedition included in its samplings a third atoll, a "control" atoll uncontaminated by radioactive fallout. This was Likiep, some 75 miles northeast of Kwajalein and 150 miles east-southeast of Bikini.[30] For the first time there was an attempt to examine residual radioactivity at the test sites in relation to the levels of natural radioactivity at an inhabited atoll in the same area and where, among other things, the food habits of the native people might be observed. The results profited, too, from a refinement of instrumentation. Until 1948, measurements of radioactivity had involved necessarily only gross counts of beta activity in dry-ashed, unseparated samples. The increasing interest in alpha radiation had led to the acquisition of two gas-flow counters for alpha and beta proportional counting. Chemical analyses of biological samples also were attempted and, while the

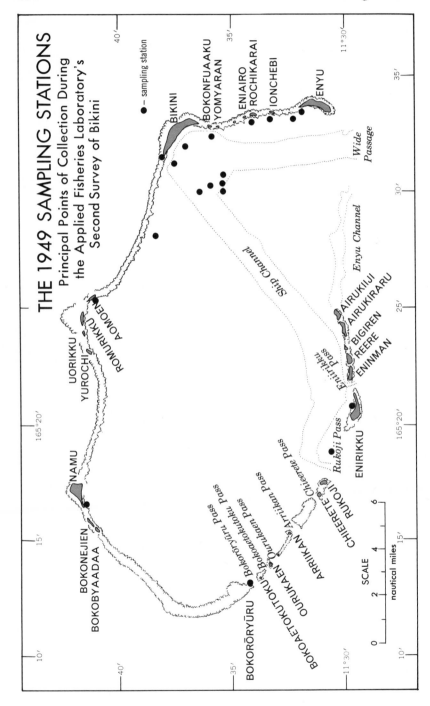

THE 1949 SAMPLING STATIONS

Principal Points of Collection During
the Applied Fisheries Laboratory's
Second Survey of Bikini

● — sampling station

processes then employed were primitive and tedious (about three months were required for analysis of ten samples for four or five radioelements), the Laboratory began to get a glimpse, actually for the first time, of the inner complexities of the biological problems it had undertaken to pursue.

The Laboratory group was in the field from July 19 to August 31, 1949. The team was no larger than that of 1948, but the cumulative experience it represented was greater. Persons with earlier work at the atolls—Donaldson, Seymour, Welander, Tinker, and Lowman—were joined by Orlin Biddulph, professor of botany at the State College of Washington, plant physiologist; and Harold St. John, professor of botany at the University of Hawaii, plant morphologist. The group also included Kelshaw Bonham, a Laboratory research associate specializing in marine invertebrates; Ralph Palumbo, of the Department of Botany of the University of Washington, an algologist; and Paul Kellogg, a student at the Massachusetts Institute of Technology, a radiation monitor.

The course of the 1949 survey took the group by ship—this time the LSI (L) 1091—from Kwajalein to Bikini, where collections were made from July 24 to August 5; to Eniwetok, for sampling from August 6 to 16; and finally to Likiep for five days of sampling and observations beginning on August 19. Supporting the team in the field was an LST, which carried additional landing craft for work in the lagoon and Navy aircraft from Kwajalein for transporting mail and supplies and, occasionally, for use in aerial photography. The LSI carried on its fantail a pump for taking samples of water from the lagoon, and on its deck had been installed benches and equipment for laboratory work.

It was three years after Crossroads, two years after Sandstone. At Bikini, the radiological pulse was fainter, but not merely detectable, clearly measurable. At Eniwetok, the same. But what did this mean? And did it matter? The answers were elusive, difficult to phrase, their significance discernible as concepts rather than as tabulations of absolutes. What good was it to know that algae seemed radiation-resistant, or that microplankton appeared to be rather more important than macroplankton in the transport of radioactivity about a lagoon? The little surgeonfish darting over the iridescent coral shallows of the reef was a quick and lovely little creature living a life attuned only to an endless search for food.

Capture him, and in his tissues would be found traces of the radio-activity created in Test Baker, long before he was born. To whom, or to what, was this important? To the fish? To a Marshallese child? To the Navy? To the Atomic Energy Commission? To mankind?

The 1949 expedition did all the usual sampling in the waters now so familiar to most of the members of the party. In 1948 only the most superficial assessments had been made of radiation uptake by plant life, but in 1949 Biddulph and St. John (the latter joining the survey by air just before it departed Bikini) were present to make detailed investigations of plants. Lowman, con-centrating on vertebrates, began that year studies of the rats in-habiting the atolls—studies which, some years later, would lead him, on Engebi Island, Eniwetok, to one of the unsolved mysteries of test-atoll animal life. In a sense, Bikini, so long under quaran-tine, was a new problem in 1949. The natural life of the atoll, still prolific whatever its degree of irradiation, had further erased the visible remnants of Crossroads. Three years before, the Seabees had bulldozed a road down the center of Bikini Island, but young coconut palms now grew along the former thoroughfare. The long-unused buildings still stood neatly back among the palms, but the screens were rotted away and profuse growth of *Ipomoea,* a plant of the morning glory variety, had sent long vines through the doors and windows and across the plank floors. Here and there, on a coral beach, a long-discarded soft drink bottle would have been captured by the growing coral and imbedded there for all time. But in Bikini's life system radioactivity of very low levels continued to circulate, constantly replenished from the supply of long-lived radioactivity in the mud of the target area. The source of Bikini's continuing irradiation was marked in another way. Even after three years, oil seeping from the sunken target vessels laid westward across the waters of the lagoon a faint oil slick which made perfectly visible, from the air, the surface element of Bikini's cycling currents.

Land surveys at Bikini produced Geiger counts averaging 30 per minute over beach sands (the counts would average 21 per minute at uncontaminated Likiep), but the counts rose to 60 per minute in living vegetation and to 120 in the dead leaves and coconut husks.[31] Patches of oil scum and litter on the beaches still produced counts up to 100,000 per minute. Biddulph's collections of plants demonstrated how significant was the role of dead vegetation in the retention of radioactivity. "It is doubtful," Biddulph reported later,

> if, within those coconuts studied, there resides any activity greater than twice that which might be found in mainland truck crops normally consumed without question as to the amount of activity present. There is, however, significant activity on the dead leaf bases and within the accumulation of debris located in the axils of the leaf bases in those areas where "fallout" of radioactive materials was to be expected. . . . The retention of the adsorbed fission products through the years of constant leaching by rains is surprising and certainly is worthy of special note. In all cases where significant activity was encountered, dead organic matter served as the carrier.[32]

These dry leaf bases of the coconut palms were producing counts of up to 8,000 per minute in amounts of approximately one gram of dry vegetable material.

After three years the residual radioactivity had penetrated further along the aquatic food chains. As early as 1947 it had been noted that tissues of the larger fish, the rangers, frequently contained accumulations of radioactivity larger than those found in the reef fish. A demonstration of this occurred by chance in 1949. Among the specimens of fish were a dozen or so groupers, barracuda, snappers, and mackerel taken with deep-sea gear near Rukoji Pass, west of Eniirikku Island on the southwest curve of the atoll. Months later, when the Rukoji samples were ashed in the University laboratories, it was discovered that the livers contained amounts of activity higher than those of fish taken from the reefs and almost half as high as in fish taken from the target area.[33] Since Rukoji is one of the principal points of outflow of Bikini waters, the fish may have found good feeding there and thus may have picked up additional amounts of radioactive materials, or they may have spent some time in the target area before moving on to Rukoji Pass. Whatever the case, these fish were of species representing the end products of the Pacific food chains, and in them had been concentrated amounts of radioactivity as large as those found in any of the intermediate links.

The return to Eniwetok in 1949 disclosed what seemed to be examples of aberrations in plant growth. By August, 1949, fifteen months after Sandstone, the craters of the test islands and the sur-

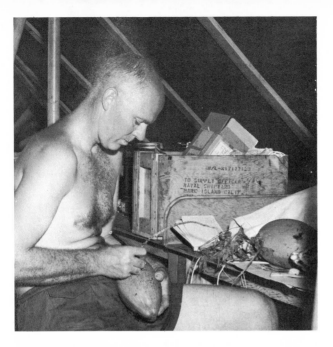

Biddulph marking coconut samples aboard the LCI(L) 109 at Bikini, 1949 (Laboratory of Radiation Biology)

Bonham in laboratory of LSI(L) 1091, Bikini, 1949 (Laboratory of Radiation Biology)

(Lower left) Coconut palm with spiraled fronds (presumed to be a naturally occurring aberration), Eniwetok, 1949 (Laboratory of Radiation Biology)

(Lower right) Specimen of Ipomoea tuba on Engebi Island, 1949, showing tumorous growth and regenerated rudimentary leaves (Laboratory of Radiation Biology)

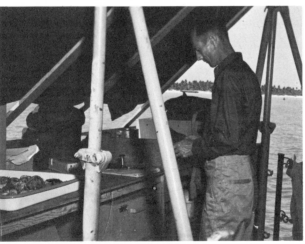

rounding terrain had been smoothed by bulldozers to reduce radio-activity and to restore as effectively as possible the natural island contours. Because of this, the results of the blasts themselves had been obscured by rearrangement of the sands forming the island's topsoil. Nevertheless, the condition of the surviving or reviving vegetation, as reported by St. John, was noteworthy. Within 200-yard circles about the blast centers only two species of living plants were found, one species, *Portulaca oleracea,* on Runit and Aomon and that and another species, *Chloris inflata,* a grass, on Engebi. There were apparently healthy plants within the central zones—the two species are annuals and certainly had grown up after the Sandstone tests—but there also were many abnormal specimens. *Chloris inflata* on Engebi showed flattened, spiral, and shortened stems. These plants, St. John believed, may have been fertile.[34] Nearly all of the larger specimens were suffering, however, what was called "die-back," in which the young stem tips turned yellow and a withering sickness progressed through the mature leaves to the stems and roots. The coral sand was dotted by the black and shriveled tatters of dead plants, yet these apparently had produced viable seeds before succumbing to die-back, for seedlings were springing up among the remnants. St. John believed that the seeds of the *Portulaca,* buried in the soil, might have survived atomic explosion only to succumb to radiation when they grew into mature plants. Possible effects on subsequent generations could not be guessed, but the illness of the plants seemed to be the result of continuing irradiation from the soil particles in the shot areas rather than from the ingestion of activity through the root systems.[35]

The farther one moved from the center of detonation, St. John reported,

> the more numerous were the species of plants found, but at all distances up to a mile there were evidences of the drastic, destructive effects on the vegetation. Also there were alternating bands or patches of well-vegetated areas and those completely bare, probably due to unequal distribution of radiant soil particles. These bare areas were found at random from 200 to 1,150 yards from the center.[36]

Stem abnormalities, atrophies, and cancerous tumors had appeared in these more distant specimens. In some the leaves showed an absence of color; in others, colors were abnormally brilliant.

A catalogue of extinct species or those in which aberrations were found was prepared by St. John as a result of his examinations of Engebi, Aomon, and Runit Islands. Engebi, as he pointed out, had been subjected for many years to disturbances of various kinds, with the result that no studies of indigenous vegetation had been made until those by E. H. Bryan in 1944 and F. R. Fosberg in 1946. In 1949, however, he found that four species of plants listed by Bryan and nine collected by Fosberg apparently were extinct on the island, and of the twenty remaining species seven "were found altered by the bombing."[37] On Aomon, nine species listed by Fosberg were missing, and of twelve species remaining three showed erratic development. Of Runit's nineteen species, three furnished "mutant" specimens. *Portulaca oleracea* appeared in all three lists of "mutant" plants.

Where tumors appeared on plants, radioactivity in the tumor tissue was low. Biddulph, in fact, found only a small absorption of fission products through the roots of plants. Where the dead leaf bases of the Bikini palm trees had produced counts as high as 8,100 per minute, those on the Eniwetok test island rose to 500,000 per minute—on Aitsu Island, to 530,000, highest on the atoll.[38] On Aitsu, also, deformities were discovered in several coconut palms, and in these trees, standing in an area of the highest surface radiation counts, the fronds were so twisted as to be curling and spiraled. There was no evidence that aberrations were caused by irradiation, and Biddulph noted that many of the conditions found in vegetation were those produced characteristically by calcium deficiency.

The essential differences between the problems of Bikini and Eniwetok were believed to be reflections of the differing characters of the nuclear tests. The Bikini bomb bursts were over and under water and, apart from the wreckage and the effects of fallout on the reef, the contamination remaining was primarily in the realm of aquatic biology. At Eniwetok, where the detonations were over land, the effects were noted most clearly on the bare, burned, bulldozed shot islands and in the nearby waters of their reefs. But none could say that the effects were radiation-induced. Where did the effects of atomic heat, blast, and soil disturbance end and the possible effects of radioactivity begin? The question presented a tangle of uncertainties.

Before the LSI (L) 1091 returned to Kwajalein, it took the expedition to Likiep for a final collection of control specimens. There the ship lay off the beach of Likiep Island while members of the survey group visited the reefs for further samples and were guests of members of the Likiep community. When the field expedition was over, the analysis of materials from the three atolls occupied the Laboratory until late in the spring of 1950.

Chapter Five

1950-1951: INTERIM

I

THE MONTHS BETWEEN the summer of 1949 and the winter of 1951 contained developments that would make necessary new arrangements in the Pacific and would set the stage for the return of Bikini into the realm of test operations.

The general state of disrepair into which Eniwetok's shore facilities had fallen was evident in 1948 and 1949. The security detachment stationed there was quartered in the temporary buildings erected during the war and these, sun-blistered and rotting in the Pacific humidity, were in need of replacement. Even though the atoll had been used for the atomic tests of 1948, provisions for scientific operations virtually did not exist. A decision regarding the more permanent occupation of Eniwetok depended, however, upon the requirements of the weapons program and on the maturing of a national policy in this field.

By mid-1949 the Atomic Energy Commission had determined to go ahead with the refurbishment of Eniwetok, to make "substantial improvements" in structures, and to "provide more adequate technical facilities."[1] The decision, which meant that nuclear testing would be resumed, had been reached in consultation with other agencies, including the Department of Defense. A new test series at the proving ground was, in fact, contemplated in 1951. In its public report to Congress in January, 1950, the Commission said that future tests would be held in the Pacific and that a new division had been created at Los Alamos to facilitate weapons work in the field. The Commission reported:

> It now appears that periodic tests of atomic weapons will be made at Eniwetok, and that construction of semipermanent facilities is justified, both for economy and efficiency. Accordingly, a contract has been let with the engineering firm of Holmes and Narver, of Los Angeles, to assist in planning and to design and construct semipermanent housing, utilities, and communications in the Atoll.
>
> As a part of the program for periodic tests at the proving ground a permanent test division has been organized at the Los Alamos Laboratory. This division is responsible for coordinating the scientific and technical activities at the proving ground, for formulating the laboratory's experimental program for full-scale tests, and for directing relevant research at both Eniwetok and Los Alamos.[2]

Preliminary surveys of Eniwetok's requirements had begun, in fact, in the fall of 1948, when the Los Angeles engineering firm was authorized, on September 16, to make a preliminary reconnaissance of the Eniwetok site. A team from Holmes & Narver was at Eniwetok from October 4 to 17, 1948, and the probable construction demands, as dictated by projections of population, utility loads, and geographical distribution of proving ground facilities, were discussed in November, 1948, at a series of meetings between Holmes & Narver representatives and Alvin Graves, now the director, and other members of the new Test Division, which was called the J Division. Construction planning was to assume a proving ground use equal to the period of two series of tests.

Holmes & Narver was one of the large engineering-construction firms of the country. The company had been founded in 1933 by James T. Holmes and D. Lee Narver, whose first job as partners was to direct the rebuilding of the business and industrial districts of Santa Ana following a disastrous earthquake, and in subsequent years the company had been identified with major engineering programs in southern California and with the development of standards for earthquake-proof construction. During World War II, Holmes & Narver had been employed on government engineering projects and in 1947 its engineering, construction, management, and planning services had been at a level of $125,000,000.[3] Holmes & Narver's reconnaissance of the Eniwetok site showed, however, how singular an undertaking the preparation of the proving ground would be. No permanent buildings were in existence and few of the decaying structures were worth salvaging. Airstrips had been bulldozed across the sands of six islands, but the 6,400-foot strip on Eniwetok would require surfacing and lengthening. Four 75-foot steel towers were standing at remote sites, but the shot islands of 1948 were stripped and bare for 1,000 feet about each former zero point and sands containing radioactive materials would need to be bulldozed away before construction could begin. Nowhere was there a supply of fresh water, and the humid climate would magnify problems of maintenance, storage, and mechanical repair. All materials and personnel would have to be transported from the United States, and certain scientific facilities would require unusual precision of installation or the use of specialized structures. There was the certainty that developments in the testing program would demand frequent changes in specifications and engineering requirements. Use of the Pacific site would be characterized by periods of intensive occupation by large populations followed by long periods of inactivity, and this would present problems of construction, maintenance, and management.

The Holmes & Narver reconnaissance produced preliminary proposals for the disposition of facilities. Parry Island, the engineers suggested, was suitable in size and situation as a base for the laboratory, scientific, and administrative functions, and for quarters for construction personnel. Military units could be quartered on Eniwetok Island. Test shots would be detonated on the northern reefs or in the lagoon itself. Holmes & Narver proposed that all possible support functions—engineering design, prefabrication, procurement, accounting—be performed in the United States to reduce personnel requirements at the site; that construction forces be self-sustaining in the operation of their own communications and water-transport facilities within the lagoon, and that military support be requested for air and surface overseas transport. As for the actual construction, the firm suggested that the work proceed in five phases—from Parry to Eniwetok to other islands—beginning in February, 1949.

The initial contract with Holmes & Narver had covered only the preliminary engineering survey. The report of this survey, submitted on January 7, 1949, was a base from which further planning was projected by the J Division. The question of a continental site again was considered, as in the period of Eniwetok's selection for Operation Sandstone, but the Commission decided that no satisfactory site was available. In April, 1949, the Commission approved recommendations for construction and the definitive contract was signed in June.

The magnitude of the proving ground program was comprehensible only in the context of the giant effort that had produced the atomic weapon. What was being undertaken was the conversion of an atoll having less than two and one-half square miles of land into an experiment station equipped with every instrument and device necessary to the conduct and measurement of atomic detonation. In this process, Eniwetok itself would be literally remade. Operation Crossroads, although it had involved 42,000 persons, had been a waterborne expedition for which Bikini's shore facilities had been altogether temporary. Operation Sandstone, also primarily shipborne, had used Eniwetok briefly, making the best of shabby facilities and concentrating on setting up only those towers and systems needed to detonate and measure the effects of three nuclear devices. The new determination meant, however, that Eniwetok would become a land base for operations that would extend at least to 1953 or 1954. Islands would be linked by utilities cables and causeways and cleared, extended, or joined as test calculations suggested. Towers, photo stations, fire control stations, and laboratories would be built. Steel, lumber, electronics components, and machine tools would be stockpiled in storage depots. The runway on Eniwetok Island would be surfaced and lengthened to accommodate volume airlifts of men and materials from the United States. A deepwater dock would be constructed at Parry Island to receive ocean shipping. Earth-moving equipment and heavy machinery would be hauled to the site and local shipping provided to haul machinery and materials to the islands of the atoll technical areas. The engineering requirements were large in concept, infinitely various in detail, and subject to sudden change to accord with the changes or enlargements of test programs. Islands and reefs sometimes

Air view, Parry Island, Eniwetok *(Holmes & Narver, Inc.)*

Eniwetok Island runway and air transport facilities *(Holmes & Narver, Inc.)*

would be loaded with equipment. For a subsequent test series 416 scientific stations were constructed. For another, Runit Island alone, only 8,700 feet long, would hold 191 separate scientific stations or installations.

Projections of personnel needs were modest, for the limitations of space and the distance from continental manpower supplies forced the most economic use of available areas. Nevertheless, Eniwetok would be occupied for long periods by construction workers, military personnel, and scientists from Commission laboratories and research agencies, and all planning had to be conducted with this in mind. Initial site platting projected housing for 600 persons on Parry Island, with temporary quarters for an additional 200 persons during tests, and on Eniwetok Island semipermanent quarters for 660 military personnel. Beyond housing, it was necessary to build extensive storage and maintenance compounds, administrative buildings, laboratories, transportation control centers, and security installations as well as the medical, dental, and hospital units and the mess halls, recreation rooms, playfields, barbershops, theaters and other facilities for the health and comfort of men spending long months at a distant, guarded station in the mid-Pacific. Chapels also would be built, one on Parry, another on Eniwetok (and another, when Bikini was integrated into the proving ground, on Enyu Island), plainly beautiful little structures in which the vaulted ceilings were supported by A-frames made of heavy wooden beams transported from the United States. The chapels would stand, amid the hot and dusty activity of the proving ground, on lawns fenced, tended, and planted with small coconut palms. Yet Eniwetok would be, and would remain throughout, a place only for men. In the beginning, Holmes & Narver had anticipated the employment of women in clerical positions and had assumed that women scientists would be participating in the laboratory programs. Two buildings to house women were included in the original Parry Island site plan, and three two-family houses were proposed for administrative personnel remaining at Eniwetok between the series of tests. The plans were abandoned before construction was started, however, and although thousands of men worked and lived there between 1950 and 1958, no woman ever was assigned to the proving ground.

The conversion of Eniwetok involved the solution of a number of problems presented by the factors of distance and climate. Logistical considerations alone were of major magnitude, even in the matter of establishing water and air transport within the atoll. Eventually interisland marine operations were conducted from an Atomic Energy Commission boat pool using equipment provided by the Navy and operated by Holmes & Narver. Navy and Military Sea Transport Service vessels hauled heavy cargo from the United States. Airlifts to Eniwetok Island, the port of entry, were conducted by the Military Air Transport Service. Communications were developed through Holmes & Narver to augment military facilities, and radio circuits linked not only the islands of the atoll but the monitoring and meteorological stations on other atolls encircling the proving ground area.

In the process of preparing the proving ground the engineers solved two problems that illustrated the specialized requirements of atoll operations. One was in the use of coral rock as aggregate in the manufacture of concrete, the other the design of a building, assembled from prefabricated aluminum elements, capable of withstanding the difficult climatological conditions of the Marshalls.

The question of concrete was critical. Concrete would be used everywhere in the proving ground, in the floorings of buildings, in the footings of towers, in instrument sites and revetments, and in thousands of large and small installations in which weight and strength were important. But no rock but coral is available in the Marshalls, and coral, which crumbles and dusts, was not considered satisfactory as aggregate where maximum strength was necessary. Nevertheless, if coral rock could not be employed at Eniwetok, the alternatives was to import by ship the thousands of tons of crushed rock that would be needed. Holmes & Narver analyzed the corals of various Eniwetok islands and experimented with materials and crushing techniques. Ultimately a method was devised for making concrete from coral and sea water.[4] The coral of Eniwetok's southerly islands was found to be inferior to that of Engebi, in the north, but the aggregate necessary for concrete at Eniwetok and Parry Islands also could be of lesser toughness than that used in the technical areas where testing was conducted. It was possible, accordingly, to use the coral available at

(Top) Chapel on Parry Island, Eniwetok, in 1957 *(Holmes & Narver, Inc.)*
(Center) Interisland marine dispatch office, Parry Island, 1956 *(Holmes & Narver, Inc.)*
(Bottom) Interisland liaison airstrip, Parry Island, 1957 *(Holmes & Narver, Inc.)*

either end of the atoll. A quarry was established at Parry and equipped with a portable rock-crushing plant. Local aggregate was used as necessary for construction of base facilities and test sites. Agitating trucks were hauled from island to island by landing craft.

The problem of providing semipermanent buildings that would withstand the humidity and salt spindrift of Eniwetok weather was solved by designing, after extensive examination of many materials, including concrete and galvanized steel, a standard unit that became characteristic of the proving ground. The building was composed of precut and die-stamped aluminum elements, the roof of double panels for insulation, the eight-foot sidewalls having panel windows top-hinged to provide shade and ventilation, and the inner partitions elevated fifteen inches from the floor for interior air circulation. The unit was adaptable to dormitory, mess hall, warehouse, power plant, office, or other community purpose. It was low in cost, easily assembled, and weather resistant. The units erected in 1950 still were sound a decade later.

The transformation of Eniwetok created still another community differing in character from any that the era of nuclear science had produced. Construction workers, military personnel, scientists, visiting officials, and engineers mingled there. Contractor employment alone would come to total more than 3,000 men in later preoperation construction peaks. The mess halls on the main islands served thousands of men, in shifts, family style. Tent cities were erected on Parry and on remote sites. Liaison aircraft, helicopters and M-boats, the 56-foot landing craft used for general water transport, shuttled endlessly between Parry and Eniwetok and the technical areas. On Parry, the administrative compound, the storage and maintenance areas, and the rows of barracks were laid out along streets carrying such names as Sandstone Avenue, Los Alamos Lane, and Oak Ridge, Hanford, and Brookhaven Roads. Contractor and military personnel and Atomic Energy Commission representatives composed a basic resident group that was augmented periodically by waves of scientists, technicians, and task force members pursuing special test-related missions. On an atoll on which security measures were enforced at all times, the identification tag was a badge of membership in a society in which the focus was on phenomena at the outer edge of atomic experiment, a society that had its diverse levels of purpose and understanding but that was bound together by association with the greatest forces yet compounded on earth.

II

Public announcement of the decision to develop a thermo-nuclear bomb was made by President Truman on January 31, 1950. He had, the President said, directed the Commission "to continue its work on all forms of weapons, including the so-called hydrogen or super-bomb." The announcement of the intention, so soon after Russia's detonation of a fission device, contained unmistakable meaning. The statement indicated not only intent, which was in the field of policy, but the confidence of the scientific-engineering staffs that the manufacture of the fusion weapon could be successfully accomplished in the near future. Tests of such a weapon could only be conducted at the Pacific Proving Ground.

The announcement was followed within months by the outbreak of hostilities in Korea. These created, literally overnight, a whole new set of conditions and problems. They also created a new atmosphere compounded of shock and urgency. To the general public, the image of atomic horror, terrifying as it had been, still had remained but an image, a remembrance of Hiroshima and Nagasaki, a photograph of Bikini. But Korea was war again—in the first chilling weeks a war of frightfully swift action—and war, for the first time, in the atomic era and when it was known that both Russia and the United States possessed atomic capability. There was a movement, far from universal and emerging in a mood of disbelief, toward accelerated civil defense training, virtually all of it built on concepts of possible atomic attack. In this movement the Atomic Energy Commission provided assistance.[5] But meantime, in the matter of weapons designs already in being, the Commission had effected a significant advance. By January, 1950, the production of weapons had been shifted from a laboratory to an industrial-type operation. The atomic devices of the kind tested at Eniwetok no longer were put together individually —literally by hand—but were being produced in numbers for stockpiling. The Los Alamos Laboratory thus was freed of weapons manufacturing problems and allowed to concentrate on developmental work while the weapons production facilities were dispersed strategically to reduce their vulnerability to attack in war. Temporary wartime structures at Los Alamos also were being replaced.[6]

Until some weeks after the outbreak of hostilities in Korea, the Applied Fisheries Laboratory had been preparing to return to Eniwetok for a further survey of Sandstone radioactivity. The general outline of the further work had been discussed by Donaldson at a conference in Washington, D.C., in February, 1950, involving Paul B. Pearson, Chief of the Biology Branch of the Division of Biology and Medicine, and George V. LeRoy, then of the Northwestern University Medical School, Biomedical Project Director for the testing programs.* By the end of February the projected survey had been approved by the Commission's Test Division at Los Alamos, and in March and April the Laboratory, on Pearson's request, developed its plan for survey operations in the proving ground—and including a further visit to Bikini— during late July and early August, 1950. The group would have been small that year, including just six men, and arrangements for support were pushed ahead by the Navy even in the midst of its Korean operations. The survey, however, could not go forward. On July 5, less than two weeks before the group was to depart for the Pacific, Pearson notified Donaldson by telephone that Navy support could not be extended into a summer that was proving increasingly critical in Korea.

In the summer of 1950 the detonation of the first thermonuclear device was more than two years away. The Eniwetok test series being planned for 1951 would be designated Operation Greenhouse, and it would include, among other things, activities related to thermonuclear research. But the war and the acceleration of the weapons development program were bringing pressures for additional testing and for more testing than could be accommodated at Eniwetok even if major problems of logistics were not inherent in the use of such a distant base. The Commission believed that the pace of weapons development depended upon the

*A research program in biology and medicine in connection with future tests had been set up in 1949 under proposals submitted by the Commission and the National Military Establishment. The program had been approved by the Joint Proof Test Committee of the Joint Chiefs of Staff and by the Division of Biology and Medicine. LeRoy, as Project Director, was on the staff of Graves, head of the Test Division at Los Alamos.

finding of an additional, and nearer, test site, and once again, even before the Eniwetok rehabilitation project was completed, the question of a continental site came under review. By autumn it had been decided to establish a proving ground in the United States for test of devices up to the nominal yield of the Hiroshima weapon. The site selected, and approved by the President for Commission use, was a 640-square-mile tract of Nevada desert, 65 miles northwest of Las Vegas and within the 5,000-square-mile Las Vegas Bombing and Gunnery Range.[7] This became the Commission's Nevada Proving Ground.

In an atmosphere so charged with urgency, the enlargement of biological studies might have been expected to suffer. But there was, in fact, a growth of Commission-supported programs, particularly in universities, attributable to the realization of how acute was the need for trained personnel. The Commission's budget estimates for fiscal year 1950 had been prepared before the outbreak of war, yet in the summary statement accompanying the estimates the Commission had said, in relation to "Program 600—Biology and Medicine":

> The development of atomic energy has brought new problems into the field of medicine and has introduced new factors into the environment of plants, animals, and man with effects yet to be determined. The Division of Biology and Medicine has the responsibility, among others, of maintenance of health in the operations of the AEC and its contractors, the provision of adequate safeguards for controlling hazards to health of populations adjacent to the facilities, and to safeguard all forms of life from the special hazards involved in the many and varied possible applications of atomic energy. In addition, it is essential to stimulate research. . . .
>
> The newness of this field is such that relatively few are acquainted with it or have confidence in its possibilities. This situation is found aggravated by the fact that the general scientific population became sharply reduced during the war, particularly among the young and active scientists who would be of special value in the development of the research programs in atomic energy. Consequently, there is a serious need for training programs, fellowships, development of special training facilities. . . . It has been helpful to develop cooperative arrangements with universities to provide personnel on a loan basis to Commission activities.[8]

During World War II few universities had been involved in the contract programs of the Commission's predecessor organizations. These institutions had included the University of Rochester, the

University of California, the University of Chicago, Washington University of St. Louis, the University of Washington, and Columbia University. By 1949, the Commission reported in that year there were "more than one hundred projects in unclassified biological and medical research being carried out in more than sixty universities, hospitals, and institutions . . . under sponsorship of the Commission."[9] The three national laboratories then operating, Argonne, Brookhaven, and Oak Ridge, were serving as centers of research and training in biology and medicine. For the fiscal year 1950, funds for research and development in these fields totaled $17,600,000, about 45 per cent for biological research alone. Total support would rise to approximately $22,000,000 in 1951, $23,800,000 in 1952.[10] In comparison to the $202,000,000 then being allocated to weapons work, the amounts spent for biology and medicine were small enough, but the measurement had to be made on a different scale. The educational and other institutions were themselves contributing facilities and talents that could not by any means have been assembled or purchased by federal appropriation. The interaction between the Commission and the research interests was providing a variety of investigations in the life sciences that probably could not be reflected at all in budgetary terms.

Within the spectrum of programs in biology, those of the Applied Fisheries Laboratory were infinitesimal. They occupied, nevertheless, a place of singular interest because of their relationship to problems of radioactivity in the natural aquatic environments of the Columbia River and the Pacific test atolls. For the fiscal year 1950 the basic Laboratory program was budgeted at $50,000, with an additional $40,000 proposed to cover the Laboratory costs of the Navy-supported Bikini-Eniwetok survey that did not, after all, materialize. Yet within this small unit, whose basic staff did not exceed a dozen persons until many years later, there were generated and developed a number of programs that represented at that time practically the whole of the Commission-sponsored investigations in aquatic radiobiology.

III

The first test explosion at the Nevada Proving Ground was detonated on January 27, 1951. By February 6, four more tests had been completed. The series of five comprised what was called Operation Ranger. In Nevada, as in the Pacific, the technical responsibility rested with the J Division of the Los Alamos Scientific Laboratory. Eniwetok would be reserved for tests of greater magnitude, and Eniwetok was to be used again almost immediately.

Operation Greenhouse was the first program at the reconstructed Pacific facility. The tests—four tower shots, two from towers 300 feet high and one having a yield announced later as a 47 kilotons —were detonated between April 7 and May 24, 1951, in a series conducted by a new test organization, Joint Task Force Three, under the command of Lieutenant General E. R. Quesada U.S.A.F. The operation, like Sandstone, involved a force of about 9,000 men, and for it, despite the pressures on transport created by the Korean war, the Military Sea Transport Service and the Service Force of the Pacific Fleet jointly carried to the proving ground 250,000 measurement tons of cargo.

A major objective of the series, as General Quesada said in a statement the following June, was "to contribute to research on thermonuclear weapons."[11] The Greenhouse shots were not themselves thermonuclear. No new weapons of the larger yields had been tested, however, for three years and, in the context of the deepening solemnity of the international situation, the program certainly was viewed as important to the development of information for defense planning, including planning by the Civil Defense Administration. Studies related to the detonations were various and detailed. Nine hundred measurements were made on twenty-seven structures of diverse design to examine methods of minimizing the effects of blast on military and industrial facilities. Also incorporated were studies of weapons performance and phenomenology, of atomic cloud physics, and of blast effects on aircraft. A radiac instrument evaluation program field-tested new models of radiation badges and dosimeters and radiation detection devices. Observations were made of fallout patterns and of blast and contamination effects on military equipment. Finally, although no aquatic radiobiological monitoring was planned before or after the test series, an extensive biomedical program was incorporated.[12]

The scientific aspects of Greenhouse were directed by Graves, who headed a task group which at its peak had a strength of 2,580 men, including the Holmes & Narver force that had built the facilities. The biomedical program was headed by LeRoy. Preparations for it had included the construction at Eniwetok, long before the tests, of animal quarters in which mice, dogs, and pigs were bred and raised for use in studies of the effects of nuclear detonations on skin tissues, glands, and circulatory systems. The primary purpose was to develop information helpful in devising treatment of atomic bomb casualties, and work with glands and tissues of exposed animals subsequently was continued at Los Alamos, Oak Ridge, the University of Rochester, the University of California, the California Institute of Technology, and at other institutions and agencies. In his public statement summarizing the results of the Greenhouse tests Quesada said:

> We have again operated in and around radioactivity. Our operations have indicated to us clearly that the mysterious ghost of lingering radiation should be dispelled. The immediate radiation, blast, and heat kill and destroy. Fear of lingering residual radioactivity must not confuse or delay prompt disaster operations in the event we are attacked.[13]

In these months of enlarging weapons efforts and determinations the Applied Fisheries Laboratory, which was but one of scores of laboratories conducting biological or medical research under Commission contract, had no new responsibility in the Pacific and only marginal contact with the programs at the Nevada Proving Ground. In the Nevada area, radiobiological surveys were conducted by teams from the Atomic Energy Project of the University of California at Los Angeles, where the director was Stafford Warren.

Members of the Applied Fisheries group—Donaldson, Lowman and others—visited Nevada as consultants and observers during the spring tests of 1951 and the Laboratory was involved incidentally in monitoring activities during the second Nevada series, Operation Buster-Jangle, conducted between October 22 and November 29. This series, opened with a shot from a 100-foot tower, included four air bursts, a 1.2 kiloton surface detonation, and the first underground explosion of an atomic device, a 1.2 kiloton shot seventeen feet below the surface of the earth. But the problems of the desert were far different from those of the Pacific atolls in which the Applied Fisheries group had compiled its experience. This experience would be used again, but not, as it proved, until the hydrogen device had come upon the scene.

By 1951 the Laboratory had reached a period of consolidation and one in which the necessity for its continued employment in the Pacific would come under critical review. The abandonment of the surveys projected in 1950 and the absence of planning related to Greenhouse left the Laboratory, for the first time since 1946, without specific commitment there. At the same time, the Laboratory now had opportunity to pursue in more detail the X-radiation studies of the kinds launched during World War II and to re-examine its experience at the atolls. The Laboratory turned to the tabulation of all data accumulated between May, 1946, and June, 1951, on the effects in succeeding generations of X radiation applied to rainbow trout. A new experiment was started on the relative sensitivity of rainbow trout exposed to various amounts of X radiation. Studies begun in 1947 on the effects of X rays on algae and invertebrates were summarized and reported.[14] Second-generation returns from the Chinook salmon stock originally liberated in the Samish River in 1943 were captured in the autumn of 1951 and studied for the presence of possible delayed effects of parental exposure to X radiation. To supplement the Chinook salmon X-radiation studies, the Laboratory initiated a new study of the effects of temperature on the salmon during their first year of life. But, among these projects, the residues of the Pacific studies still occupied a place in Laboratory thinking. On June 13, Donaldson attempted to summarize, in a letter to Pearson, of the Division of Biology and Medicine, the current condition of the Laboratory's efforts with particular reference to work that remained undone. The radiation absorption studies, Donaldson said, were suffering from lack of active material, and he suggested:

> The work on absorption of bomb fission products by aquatic flora and fauna could be accelerated if 100 pounds ± of active coral sand from the shot islands of Eniwetok and about the same amount of control coral sand from Japtan or from Parry Island could be shipped to us.[15]

But the letter also included a suggestion concerning a new line of inquiry and one that eventually would become a major Laboratory program. Of this Donaldson said:

> We should like to explore an area—new for us—the use of specific isotopes for tagging foods and in natural food cycles by aquatic animals. These studies would take two general directions:

a. The role of essential food elements such as phosphorous, calcium, iron, etc., in the food cycles of natural waters and the possibility of dilution of radioactive materials by the addition of non-active salts.

b. The exploration of the synthesis of vitamin B^{12} by insects and its subsequent absorption by fishes using Co^{60} as a tracer.[16]

In that summer of 1951, with a war in progress and in a time of developing certainty that Eniwetok would be used for new and more frequent test programs, there was arising within the Division of Biology and Medicine a doubt concerning the advisability of pressing for continuance of the Pacific radiobiology work. The Division wanted, at least, to be absolutely certain that field work was necessary and that work at Eniwetok was essential to the search for information on long-term fallout effects. Pearson had visited the Laboratory in August, 1950, when the discussion turned largely on the question of publication of program results. Pearson was planning to visit the Laboratory again, and on August 15, while his visit was awaited, the Laboratory drafted a more extensive summary than had been possible in Donaldson's letter of June.[17] The Laboratory noted that, while it had made quantitative measurements of the residual radioactivity at the test atolls, no studies of the long-range effects had been possible. Edward E. Held, the Laboratory reported, was being added to the permanent staff, to begin to approach these physiological problems.* In addition, work had been started on analysis of alpha radiation in the Bikini-Eniwetok samples—analysis that had not been possible because of the priority of other studies and because of the absence of adequate chemical facilities—and of the fission products, still clearly measurable, in the samples brought back from Eniwetok in 1949. Eniwetok, the Laboratory thought, held information that should be obtained while it still was available. Of these matters the summary said:

> The Korean War interrupted the continuity of studies at Bikini and Eniwetok scheduled for the summers of 1950 and 1951. The tests conducted at Eniwetok during the spring of 1951 have further complicated the studies.
>
> The radiation products in the Bikini Lagoon have, we believe, now decayed and have been diluted to the extent that little trace of radioactivity

*Held, who had been a member of the Bikini-Eniwetok Survey group of 1948, was being brought to the staff from the Atomic Energy Project at U.C.L.A., where he had been in charge of metabolic studies of the Alamogordo Section.

remains. A survey looking toward repopulating the atoll should be conducted. If it is found that our calculations on the biotic contamination are essentially correct, then the Bikini natives should be allowed to return.

The repeated testing of atomic weapons at *Eniwetok* makes finite studies impossible. *We do, however, believe that the general pattern of radiation contamination can be determined at field testing plots, such as Eniwetok. . . .**

The field studies . . . can point the direction laboratory work should take. . . .[18]

On August 20, 1951, Pearson was at the Laboratory for the discussion with Donaldson and other members of the staff of the probable directions of future work. To focus discussion, Pearson presented to the group seven questions, the answers to which, he said, would be important in later determinations of the course and nature of aquatic radiobiological studies for the Commission. The questions were these:

1. What data of importance are to be gained by the Laboratory and by the Division of Biology and Medicine from new resurveys?
2. What advantages have field studies over laboratory studies?
3. Why use mixed fission products in preference to known isotopes?
4. What are the advantages of working at Eniwetok rather than in continental sites?
5. Is the radiation level sufficiently high to be of interest to the Commission?
6. In recurrent tests, how could revegetation be studied?
7. Could some of the conclusions you are seeking be drawn from a trip possibly this next summer (1952)?

The answers to the questions were contained, in part, in the summary already prepared. Members of the Laboratory staff reviewed their findings after three resurveys of Bikini and two of Eniwetok, citing the persistence of significant amounts of radioactivity at Bikini and the more obvious effects noted at Eniwetok in 1948 and 1949 even before the more recent Operation Greenhouse series. Two of the questions seemed critical—the second, "What advantages have field studies over laboratory studies?" and the fifth, "Is the radiation level sufficiently high [in the Pacific] to be of interest to the Commission?" In the one case, the Laboratory could only urge its view that, as Donaldson later put it,

*Laboratory emphasis.

Laboratory experiments in themselves cannot substitute for direct observations in the field.* The total ecological situation is of such a complex nature that only comparatively minute segments can be duplicated under controlled laboratory conditions. Which segments deserve priority can and should be determined from results obtained in field studies. It is essential . . . that studies evaluating biotic contamination keep pace with the changes in weapon design, materials used, and efficiencies obtained.[19]

As for the fifth question—whether the levels of activity were sufficiently high to be of interest—the Laboratory said, with what seems an unnecessary asperity, that it had no information on the levels of contamination that were of interest to the Commission. The implication was clear enough, however. The Commission, the Laboratory believed, should be interested in any level of radioactivity that promised to have significant or continued biological impact. The difficulty was that no one really knew what this level might be.

The challenge of Pearson's questions, however, led to the preparation in the autumn of 1951 of a further statement of the Laboratory's views of the urgency of continued, rather than "spot check," studies of biological contamination in the Pacific. The summary, completed early in 1952, set out as completely as possible the case for going after information when and where it existed—information which the Laboratory felt was of such importance "that it is worth any amount of effort" to assemble it.[20] The seven questions were used as topics in an outline in which the Laboratory set out what amounted to a statement of how little yet was known and what needed to be learned.

What data were to be gained from new surveys? The most important contribution of repeated surveys, the Laboratory said, was understanding of living processes developed by studying flora and fauna tagged with identifiable materials. It was important to see if time produced changes or balances:

> Quite unlike physical measurements, which have a definitive end point that can be measured at a single observation, biological processes are constantly changing and it is only through continuous or repeated observations that the changes can be evaluated.
>
> The time factor . . . is often little appreciated, and it is only after a lapse of sufficient time that many effects become obvious.
>
> The data collected over a period of years will determine if the selection

*Original emphasis.

and retention of radioactive material in a natural environment . . . are transitory phenomena or if there will tend to be a balance at some level with these materials in equilibrium.[21]

The Laboratory suggested that studies of "the so-called soluble, non-available" isotopes should be made. It cited the finding, in another study, of Zr^{95} in the soft parts of fish even though the principal fission product, ZrO_2, is insoluble except in sulphuric or hydrofluoric acid. It pointed out that plutonium was being discovered in plants and animals of the New Mexico area five years after the first nuclear detonation at Alamogordo, and that soluble fission products with long half-lives, "such as Sr^{90} and Cs^{135}," still were present at Bikini and Eniwetok.* Broadly, the Laboratory repeated, water areas not only provided shifting biological problems but were incapable of assessment in ordinary ways. "Small amounts of any radioactive material in a water environment," the Laboratory said,

> are of greater importance from a contamination standpoint than like amounts on land. The ease with which they are transported in this medium, with a greater chance of being taken up by living organisms, results in a monitoring problem which cannot be effectively measured with field-type monitoring instruments.[22]

The Laboratory already had presented its case for field studies. No laboratory could duplicate, it said, the field situation in which all biological influences—and all unknowns—were present. As for using mixed fission products rather than the selected isotope, more work with mixed products was needed because so little had been done. Studies of contamination, whether from tests or accidental release, were of mixed fission products, not single isotopes. On the question of work at Eniwetok rather than at continental sites, the Laboratory pointed out that the test atolls represented the only sites where water contamination was involved, that base lines for further work already had been established there, and that climate and isolation made Eniwetok an advantageous field site. Levels of radiation were sufficiently high at the test atolls for biological analysis; vegetation might be studied at Eniwetok by following (as had been started in 1949) the re-establishment of the vegetation of

---

*The Laboratory's typed report refers specifically to cesium 135. This can only be an error, however, for this isotope would have been present, if at all, only in minute and undetectable quantities. Undoubtedly cesium 137 was meant.

the shot islands. Would a further field trip permit "conclusions"? Not necessarily, but "another point could be placed on the scale of studies. . . . The amounts and kinds of contamination in the biotic forms could be measured and their distribution mapped."[23] In sum: "The basic problems of contamination of aquatic and terrestrial areas from an atomic bomb detonated at a low elevation need constant study, and Eniwetok is the logical place for such a study."[24]

In such terms the Laboratory addressed itself to the questions of the Division of Biology and Medicine. Behind the Division's question was, without doubt, the single question of how best to assess the biological implications of weapons tests. If testing were to continue, the opportunity for learning should not be missed, but was it, after all, the best use of scientific manpower to send expeditions of biologists into the distant arena of Eniwetok to pursue radioactivity on the islands and along the reefs? If not, how else? The answer, in the winter of 1951, was in suspense.

Meantime, events had moved forward on the larger stage. In October, 1951, two more atomic devices had been detonated successfully by the U.S.S.R.

Chapter Six

1952: IVY

I

BY 1952 the secret effort to build the hydrogen device was nearing
fulfillment. The year opened, however, with a third series of test
shots at the Nevada Proving Ground, a series of eight detonations
beginning with an 800-foot airburst on April 1 and ending on June
5 with a 17.6 kiloton shot from a 300-foot tower. The series was
designated Tumbler-Snapper, and it included a 3,450-foot airburst on April 22 that was witnessed by 200 representatives of the
news media and some 60 officials of federal and state civil defense
organizations who were stationed at an observation point about
10 miles from ground zero. With the permission of the Commission, Lowman and Held of the Applied Fisheries Laboratory were
transferred for the period of the series to the staff of the U.C.L.A.
Atomic Energy Project group that was conducting radiobiological
monitoring. By the time the series was concluded, the United
States had detonated in all, in the seven years after the first shot at
Alamogordo, thirty-two atomic fission devices, twenty-three of
them within the continental limits of the United States. Including
the three shots by Soviet Russia, thirty-five atomic weapons or test
devices had been detonated by June, 1952.[1]

The construction of a hydrogen device—or, more exactly, the devising of a way to release immense amounts of energy by fusing together four atoms of hydrogen into one atom of helium—had been recognized by scientists as theoretically possible for many years, even before the discovery in January, 1939, of the phenomenon of uranium fission. But fusion could only be achieved by the production of heat at levels seemingly unattainable by manmade means, and it was not until the first successful atomic detonation at Alamogordo that there existed the certain knowledge that it was possible to provide heat of such an order. With the end of the war in Japan and the subsequent testing and development of the fission weapon, new doors were opened into wholly unexplored labyrinths of nuclear technology. J. Robert Oppenheimer, Albert Einstein, and Professor Hans A. Bethe, of Cornell University, were among the several distinguished scientists who had indicated publicly between 1945 and 1950 that it now was within the realm of possibility that the release of energy at levels hundreds of times greater than that of the Hiroshima atomic weapon could be accomplished. But the dark rooms of the hydrogen age were those which many were reluctant to enter. It was argued that the effort to build the "super-bomb" could only be viewed as necessary in relation to the need to produce a weapon even more destructive than the atomic bomb, the potential of which, as an instrument of war, already exceeded comprehension. There had developed sharp and diverse views, too, on the continued imposition in peacetime of secrecy, as prescribed by the Atomic Energy Act of 1946, of the kind that had been necessary in war years. Such secrecy, it was pointed out, made virtually impossible the development of informed discussions in the shaping of public policy. Between 1950 and 1952, nevertheless, while work on the thermonuclear project continued, the news media and the general literature contained quantities of information on the possibility of hydrogen fusion and speculative comment on the probable imminence of its achievement.

Many of the details subsequently were revealed concerning the operation in which the United States exploded the first hydrogen device. On February 18, 1952, the Department of Defense and the Atomic Energy Commission announced jointly that preparations for a new series of tests were being conducted by Joint Task Force

132 but that "full security restrictions of the Atomic Energy Act apply to preparations for and the time of the test."[2] Commanding the new task force was Major General Percy W. Clarkson, deputy commander of U.S. Army Forces in the Pacific. Graves was Deputy for Scientific Matters. Within the Commission, the weapons program was augmented during the spring of 1952 by the establishment of a new research laboratory at Livermore, California, under the direction of Ernest O. Lawrence, head of the University of California Radiation Laboratory, and Herbert York. By summer, the Livermore Laboratory, occupying former Navy facilities acquired by the Commission, was employing 1,500 persons. In the Division of Biology and Medicine, John C. Bugher, who had served as deputy director since 1951, had been appointed director to succeed Shields Warren.

The 1952 series at the Pacific Proving Ground was Operation Ivy. It was to include the thermonuclear detonation and a subsequent "high yield" explosion, Test King, in the vicinity of Runit Island. The thermonuclear shot, first in history, would be accomplished in Test Mike on Saturday, November 1, a surface explosion detonated at 7:15 A.M., in an elaborately engineered setting at the extreme north end of Eniwetok Atoll.

II

The decision to bring back into the field work at Eniwetok the experience of the Applied Fisheries Laboratory was made on Pearson's recommendation in the spring of 1952. Pearson had reviewed the Laboratory's responses to his questions and had examined the necessarily generalized proposals for future surveys at Eniwetok. On March 26, 1952, Pearson addressed the first of two memorandums to Bugher, then newly installed as director of the Division, suggesting approval of surveys from which land studies were omitted. Of the possible relevance of the studies Pearson said in part:

> In the long run, the role of the oceans in the maintenance of populations will undoubtedly increase. Furthermore, it may be expected that eventually a large proportion of radioactive materials used therapeutically, in research, and possibly for certain industrial purposes will reach the ocean.
>
> As the population of the world increases, the problem of meeting food

requirements will become increasingly difficult. It may be expected that farming of the sea will become increasingly important. It must also be kept in mind that fission materials may be scattered over thousands of miles of ocean currents. Therefore, the potential contamination of populations of marine animals and organisms may be much greater from a burst near a large body of water, or an underwater burst, than from an air burst over land.

Dr. Donaldson and his group have a background of experience for studying the distribution of fission materials in marine organisms that is not available elsewhere. . . . We would recommend approval of the proposal submitted by Dr. Donaldson except for the study of land flora and fauna. The effect on land animals and flora can be studied equally well if not better in this country.[3]

On April 9, Pearson again wrote Bugher, apparently because a decision on the Eniwetok surveys still had not been made. In this memorandum he summarized information from the Laboratory's report of its 1949 Bikini-Eniwetok-Likiep expedition, concluding:

While I feel that Donaldson's proposal for biological surveys at the next Eniwetok tests is not very detailed, I think that this can be explained in part on the basis that he has no information regarding the nature of the tests, i.e., whether they will be air bursts, surface bursts, tower bursts, or underwater bursts. I believe that if we give Donaldson information on the nature of the forthcoming tests he will present more precise plans. . . .

There is still a question regarding the need for studies of the effects of atomic blasts on marine flora and fauna. . . . I think it would be desirable to reach an early decision . . . so as to allow adequate time for preparations and the background survey which should be made in the area before the tests.[4]

When the decision came, it was related in a circuitous fashion to an interest in the Department of the Interior, which now had assumed administrative responsibility for the Trust Territory, in the possible return to their atoll of the Bikini inhabitants. On May 2, 1952, Bugher addressed a note to Lt. Col. William R. Sturges, of the Division of Military Application, in which he said:

Confirming our telephone conversation, it so happens that the need for a radiological survey of Bikini coincides with our consideration of a plan for a biological survey there by Dr. Donaldson as a part of the long-term study of the distribution of radioactive materials in the marine life. The one survey will be entirely adequate for both purposes. . . .

It will be some months before Dr. Donaldson's team can make this study, and in the meantime we would appreciate any suggestion you may have relative to specific questions needing answer from the point of view of the

Department of the Interior with respect to the possible return of the Bikini inhabitants.[5]

Despite their lack of specific information on the forthcoming tests, Laboratory personnel had no doubt that the 1952 Pacific series would involve either an attempted thermonuclear detonation or experiments preliminary to such a test. Their role, however, would be unchanged. They would make preliminary assessments to determine the levels of predetonation background radioactivity and then move in after the tests to conduct biological sampling. It was expected that a further examination would be made of Bikini. The Laboratory's final draft program was submitted to the Division of Biology and Medicine on July 25, 1952.[6] In this the Laboratory contemplated the use of a team of not more than eight men—six senior scientists, a soils chemist, and a Naval liaison officer—to make preliminary collections at Eniwetok, an intermediate further sampling at Bikini, and a final survey of postshot radioactivity at Eniwetok "as soon as feasible following the detonation." A return to Likiep to obtain additional uncontaminated control material was suggested if this did not disturb the time schedule or burden the support facilities of Task Force 132. The team, as it finally shaped up, included Donaldson, Seymour, Welander, Held, Lowman, Bonham, and Palumbo. Bonham, however, went to the field to take part in the pretest samplings but to return to the laboratory with the samples thus far collected, while Welander, starting later, joined the group for the posttest collections.

The Laboratory group spent the period from October 20 to November 11, 1952, at Eniwetok. Its headquarters was aboard the *Oakhill* (LSD 7), one of the larger World War II landing vessels assigned to the task force fleet. No ashing or counting of samples was planned or attempted at the proving ground, all biological specimens except plankton and rats being packaged in plastic containers, labeled, moved to shipboard deep freeze boxes for preservation, and later shipped by air to the mainland, still frozen, in containers of dry ice.

Seven major stations about the rim of Eniwetok Atoll were selected for pretest and posttest collections. Six of these, on the lagoon sides of Engebi, Aomon-Biijiri, Runit, Japtan, Igurin, and Rigili Islands, were those used in the surveys of 1948 and 1949. The seventh was in the area of Bogombogo and Bogallua Islands,

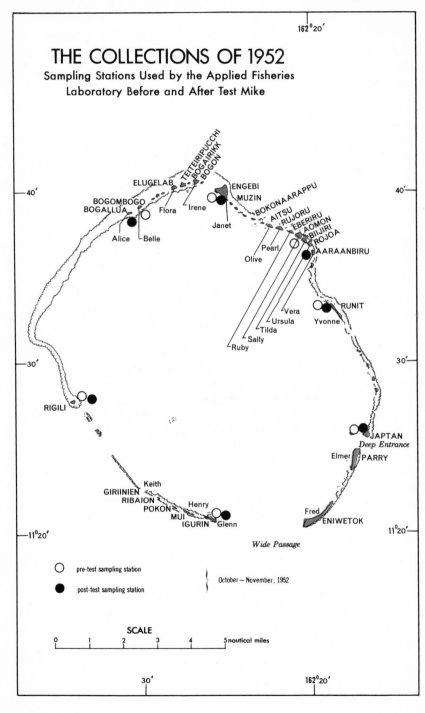

162°20′

THE COLLECTIONS OF 1952
Sampling Stations Used by the Applied Fisheries
Laboratory Before and After Test Mike

TEITEIRIPUCCHI
BOGAIRIKK
BOGON

ELUGELAB

—40′   40′—

BOGOMBOGO   ENGEBI
BOGALLUA   Flora   Irene   MUZIN

BOKONAARAPPU
AITSU
Janet   RUJORU
EBERIRU
Alice   └Belle   AOMON
BIIJIRI
ROJOA
Pearl   AARAANBIRU
Olive

Vera   RUNIT
Ursula   Yvonne
Tilda
Sally
—30′   Ruby   30′—

RIGILI

JAPTAN
Deep Entrance
Elmer PARRY

Keith
GIRIINIEN
RIBAION   Henry
POKON   Fred
MUI   ENIWETOK
IGURIN   Glenn
—11°20′   11°20′—

Wide Passage

○   pre-test sampling station

●   post-test sampling station   } October — November, 1952

SCALE

0   1   2   3   4   5 nautical miles

30′   162°20′

between two and three miles southwest of Elugelab Island, where the Mike shot was to be detonated. Thus most of the collection points were familiar territory although, as members of the team were to discover, the extensive construction program at Eniwetok had altered or eradicated many of the former landmarks and the explosion of the hydrogen device, accompanied by a release of contaminants in unprecedented amounts, would make necessary a drastic revision of their plans for posttest collections. From October 21 until the eve of the Mike shot on November 1 the Laboratory group visited in turn the seven stations to sample fish, invertebrates, and algae—usually "on the lagoon side from the intertidal zone down to a depth of about 12 feet"—and, using task force landing craft, conducted dredging, water sampling, and plankton towing in the lagoon itself, sometimes as far as three miles from the area of reef collections. Each day's operation included a trip to the station island to put out rattraps and to gather, as available, specimens of plants and, occasionally, land vertebrates including birds.

The Pacific Proving Ground, in the days before Test Mike, was a place further changed physically by the nuclear test preparations. By 1952 the joint task force concept, developed in World War II and modified to meet the changing needs of test operations, was firmly established as an organizational pattern. The components—the AEC scientific task group and the groups composed of Army, Navy, and Air Force personnel—were assigned task group numbers as were the units and projects within each. The scientific group was designated Task Group 132.1, and within it were the radiobiologists, members of what was called the Marine Survey Unit, Project 11.5. In the communications code system of the proving ground each island had its simplified un-Marshallese name. Thus Bogallua was Alice, Bogombogo was Belle, Engebi was Janet, Runit was Yvonne, and Japtan, David. In this code, Eniwetok became Fred and Parry Island was Elmer. Elugelab, the site of Test Mike, was designated as Flora.

It was in the area of Elujelab, and on the reefs and islands extending eastward on that north sector of the atoll, that preparations were going forward late in October, 1952. On the island itself had been built a hangar-type structure into which the elements of the hydrogen device were to be placed. This was connected to the small neighboring islands to the east by a causeway over which the device and the associated electronic equipment were to be moved into the shed. For Test Mike, all of Eniwetok was to be evacuated. All members of all task groups and all military and construction and maintenance personnel were to be withdrawn from the atoll aboard Navy and Task Force shipping to witness the explosion from a distance of some thirty miles. On Engebi Island, three miles from point zero, had been erected a huge, four-story, reinforced concrete structure which it was hoped would later provide clues to the character of the destructive forces released by the hydrogen blast.

Mike shot on November 1, 1952, was a detonation whose dimensions exceeded any witnessed on earth to that moment. The fireball which rose from the atoll through the low cloud layer above it was a boiling mass which, through the dark glasses of distant spectators, seemed to be enfolding streaks of black. The great tower of the nuclear cloud had ascended in fifteen minutes to 130,000 feet. Where Elujelab had been was only a crater in the Eniwetok reef, a hole of irregular outline and more than a mile in diameter which, before it was partially refilled by the returning rush of coral sediment and lagoonal sludge, was almost 200 feet deep, virtually as deep as the lagoon bottom itself. Water surging from the point of explosion, it was noted later, had sent a great wave over adjacent islands, including Engebi.

Since Test Mike was to be followed on November 16 by a second and final shot in Test King, the schedule of Applied Fisheries Laboratory post-Mike collections called for completion of sampling at the seven stations by November 8. The schedule was tight, and it assumed that the atoll could be re-entered and collections begun within a reasonable time after detonation. The ships carrying the evacuated task force personnel stood off the southern islands during the day and night of November 1, using only power sufficient to maintain position and headway, but by midmorning of November 2, which was Sunday, teams from the Radiological Safety Section had declared that the south end of the atoll was "clean" and the ships began streaming back into the lagoon. The *Oakhill*, which had carried with her the LCM's assigned to the Laboratory for lagoon work was anchored inside the Deep Entrance by 11:30 A.M. and beginning to unload the small craft and equipment. By afternoon of November 2 the radiobiologists were taking lagoon water samples.

Between November 3 and November 8 the Laboratory team, starting at the southern islands and working north, attempted to cover one by one the seven stations already visited late in October. The proposed trip to Bikini had been canceled out long before, the sampling at Likiep forgotten. The program had reduced itself simply to one of gathering in six days the completest possible collection of specimens from the waters and from the land. And as the trips by LCM were started on the morning of November 3 the routine seemed exceedingly familiar and the effects of Test Mike not immediately apparent. RadSafe readily permitted the radiobiologists, equipped with film badges and protective clothing, to begin their collections at Japtan, where a fine haul of fish specimens was made. Permission also was given for collections at Igurin, Rigili, and Runit during the following three days. The Igurin trip on November 4 also was productive of specimens but without noteworthy developments. But on Rigili on November 5 and on Runit the next day the visible effects of the Mike shot began to be encountered.

Rigili is fourteen miles south-southwestward down the lagoon from the Mike shot crater. Yet there the survey team found that the trees and brush facing the test site had been scorched and wilted by the thermonuclear heat. Many of the terns there were sick, some grounded and reluctant to fly and some with singed feathers, particularly the noddy terns and the sooty terns, whose feathers are dark in color. On Runit Island on November 6 the story was much the same even though Runit, swept so often by atomic blasts and bulldozers, held little more than the straggling scrub that had been noted in earlier surveys.[7] Radiation levels were not dangerously high, but they were high enough to suggest for the first time that the survey program should be completed as rapidly as possible if it were not to be cut short by the approach of the cumulative exposure limits prescribed by RadSafe.

Evidence of the effects of the Mike shot continued to accumulate as the radiobiologists worked northward toward the Mike crater. One of the major stations was on the east reef of Aomon-Biijiri, but on Friday, November 7, the levels of radioactivity still were too high to permit a team to work there for several hours, so on that

Eberiru, Aomon, Biijiri, and Rojoa Islands on Eniwetok's northeast reef, 1959 (Holmes & Narver, Inc.)

The "Henry-Keith Complex"—Mui, Pokon, Ribaion, and Giriinien Islands—southwest rim, Eniwetok, 1959 (Holmes & Narver, Inc.)

day the survey group, accompanied by four members of the task force staff and a RadSafe radiation monitor, took a landing craft to Aaraanbiru Island, five miles north of Runit but two miles below the Aomon-Biijiri station. Before the collecting was started, Lowman and others made a short trip to Rojoa Island, midway between Aoman and Aaraanbiru, to set rattraps and to bring in several short birds for dissection. Radioactivity at Rojoa was at 300 milliroentgens per hour and the visit was no longer than necessary.[8]

After the collections at Aaraanbiru, only one day remained. On that day, November 8, the survey team, proceeding north from Parry in the LCM, would do whatever could be done in the way of getting specimens at the remaining stations in the northerly atoll areas and near the Mike site. The first stop was at Rojoa to pick up the rattraps left there the previous day, but the traps were, disappointingly, entirely empty. At Engebi the group went ashore on an island where the sense of desolation was deepened by the presence of the reinforced concrete building, ruptured and shaken but still standing, on the island flat that had been swept by the blast and by the succeeding surge of water. The body of a bird was seen, but no living animals and only the stumps of vegetation. Held took away a bucket of beach sand for use in later experiments, and some collections of burned vegetation were made, but on the inland areas the survey meters indicated radiation was at 2 to 2.5 roentgens per hour, and the team soon moved off the land into the shallow lagoon waters to spread rotenone for the fish sampling. Among the specimens collected were fish which seemed to have been burned. On each of these fish the skin was missing from one side as if, as field notes said at the time, the animal "had been dropped in a hot pan."[9]

The work at Engebi finished, the party took the LCM westward through the turbid waters of the shot islands and past the Mike crater, which had the appearance of a new deep channel into the lagoon and the depth of which, after the churning of the sludge had subsided, had been estimated at fifteen fathoms. When the LCM, turning southwest, stood off the beach of Bogombogo and Bogallua, three miles from the Mike site, the effect of the energy that had been released a week before was startingly evident. On the survey team's visit to Bogombogo on October 25 the island had been heavily laden by stands of coconut palms and thickly populated by birds. Then it had seemed ideal as a downwind station for sampling after Test Mike, and the group had expected to return there in due time, to make posttest collections. But when members of the team saw Bogombogo again on November 8 the extent of their miscalculation was terribly clear. The island had been stripped of vegetation by the force and heat of the blast. Palm trees had been burned down to the roots. All animal life, so far as members of the team could tell, had been snuffed out. The same was true of Bogallua. The radiobiologists made a collection of fish in the coral shallows on the lagoon side of Bogallua and then, loading their gear aboard the LCM, moved back down the lagoon to the *Oakhill*, which was scheduled to participate the following day in test runs for the King shot evacuation. On Monday, November 10, while members of the group were packing their equipment and specimens for shipment, Lowman and Welander returned to Rojoa to pick up the rattraps left there several days earlier. This time the traps held six specimens.

III

At Runit, at Aomon-Biijiri, at Engebi, at Bogombogo-Bogallua, even at Rigili, it had been apparent that the radiation problem presented by the Mike shot was of an entirely new order of magnitude. This was not to say that it was different radiobiologically. But, as in other years, the radiobiologists had no clues to the total potential contamination to be expected or to the kinds of radioactive materials they might encounter.[9] Their task, even in the face of the new condition created by nuclear fusion, was circumscribed and immediate and consisted only of attempting to discover, after the biotic samples had been returned to the Laboratory, what kinds of radioactivity and in what amounts had been placed by the Mike shot at the threshhold of Eniwetok's biological system. When the counting began, the levels of radioactivity now would be expressed in thousands—frequently in millions—of disintegrations per minute. And, while the higher counts obviously resulted from the fact that collections were made so soon after the theromonuclear blast, it also would become obvious that large amounts of nuclides were involved and that the process of biological absorption already had begun.

The winds of November 1, blowing from the east-northeast, had carried the fallout, as had been anticipated, across the west side of the atoll, and it was there, on the eighteen miles of reef extending from the test site to Rigili that the heaviest contamination probably would be found. This, as it turned out, was true, although not altogether as precisely as the assumption would suggest, for in addition to the very much greater range of effect of the hydrogen bomb there seemed to be other factors, unexplainable but perhaps related to processes of biological uptake, which had altered the local distribution picture even in the week after detonation.

The specimens and samples collected at Eniwetok were frozen and returned by air to Seattle, the pretest batch by Bonham, who flew back to the Laboratory before Mike was detonated. When all the samples had been returned, the counting and analysis proceeded on an around-the-clock schedule—24 hours a day, seven days a week—from November 24 to December 12, 1952. All members of the staff participated in the process. All of the specimens and samples collected after Test Mike were handled in this period, and most of the samples from the pretest collections were counted (because radioactive materials present before Test Mike consisted altogether of long-lived isotopes remaining from the Sandstone and Greenhouse tests) after December 12 but before the end of the month. Because the samples had been gathered in a period of relatively rapid decay of radioactivity, corrections necessarily had to be made for this factor, and the date to which corrections were made was set arbitrarily as December 1, a month after the Mike shot and near the midpoint of the over-all counting period for the Mike samples. The curve from which correction factors were determined was the curve of radiation decay for a sample of sand dredged at a depth of thirty feet from the lagoon near Rojoa and Aaraanbiru on November 7. In general terms, the problem was to determine the degree of long-lived contamination existing in Eniwetok Atoll before Test Mike —the slight but measurable contamination still inhabiting the biological system as a result of earlier tests—and then to measure, for the purpose of assessing probable future biological hazard, the level of contamination present at any manageable point in time, in this case December 1, a month after the thermonuclear shot.

At the base of the contamination puzzle was the water of Eniwetok lagoon. The sampling of water which had been started before Test Mike was resumed on the afternoon of November 3, two days after the Mike shot and immediately after the *Oakhill* returned to her anchorage. The November-December analysis of water showed that samples taken after Test Mike contained radioactivity "several hundred times" greater than the pretest samples, the values rising as the distance from the test site decreased. The counts were not high—the highest 350 disintegrations per minute per milliliter for a sample at Bogombogo—but the pattern was clearly discernible.* For reasons which were not known, the level of radiation even in a pretest water sample was highest off Bogombogo, where the sample depth was forty-five feet.

Radioactivity counted in plankton, algae, and the invertebrates produced a number of interesting questions.

The plankton hauls were made with conical nets a half meter in diameter at the mouth and two meters long. These were towed behind the LCM (usually for a distance of one and one-half miles in an hour) at a predetermined depth in the selected sampling areas. Catches of plankton were small whether the net was fine (173 meshes per inch) or coarse (74 meshes per inch), but the survey team made examinations of the character of the catches—which usually were composed of Foraminifera, snails, copepods, worms, and eggs—to discover if the types of organisms in the nets were determining the variations in counts between hauls and between stations. Frequently there were differences in the catches, but regardless of these there seemed to be a specific relationship between the kinds of organisms present and the amounts of radiation found in the sample. The team made "paired hauls," in which nets of fine and course meshes were towed about the same lagoonal area at the same time. While the composition of the catches thus tended to be similar, the radioactivity often varied in amount. In a posttest paired haul at Bogallua the radioactivity of the sample from the finer net exceeded by seven times—1,160,000 distintegrations per minute per gram compared to 155,000—the

---

*A rainwater sample was collected 33 hours after Test Mike off Eniwetok Island. The 450-cc sample was evaporated and counted on November 4, 87 hours after the shot, using a Victoreen survey meter with a 1-inch end window tube (window thickness 1.8 mg/cm^2). The maximum count was 10,000 per minute.

value of the plankton from the coarser net. Until microscopic examination disclosed no essential differences in the plankton in the two nets, it was presumed that tiny organisms escaping the larger mesh were being caught in the smaller. It was concluded, however, that the finer mesh was capturing inanimate radioactive particles suspended in the lagoonal waters. All of the pre-Mike plankton tows had resulted in hauls containing low but measurable amounts of residual radioactivity still inhabiting the planktonic life zone as a result of Operations Sandstone and Greenhouse, but the post-Mike plankton samples were more radioactive by 200 to 300 times. The postshot samples from the various stations disclosed a pattern of distribution that recalled the unexpected transport of radioactivity about Bikini lagoon, for the fine-mesh sample from Igurin, at the southern tip of the atoll and farthest from the test site, showed a higher count (140,000 dmg) than those at Rigili (71,000 dmg), Aaraanbiru (100,000 dmg), and Runit (48,000 dmg), each of which was much nearer the point of detonation.

Among the algae there proved to be a uniformity of posttest results that was in itself intriguing. The collection included five species of blue-green, fourteen species of green, three species of brown, and seven species of red algae. Before Test Mike, specimens most radioactive were those gathered on or near the islands on which atomic tests already had been held, and the levels of activity were not altogether inconsequential. One specimen found in a stagnant pool on Eberiru Island proved to contain activity counting 54,000 disintegrations per minute per gram (wet weight), and counts in three others from the Runit tide flats averaged 31,000.[10] But in the post-Mike sampling the results seemed to show only that algae samples taken from islands nearer the test site, Aomon, Engebi, Bogallua—those lying, that is, within a radius of nine miles of the shot island—reflected much higher counts but no significant differences in contamination by area or by species. Algae from the more distant and protected areas, such as Japtan (away from the direction of fallout) showed only trace amounts of radioactivity, but the counts of all specimens from Bogallua averaged 5,200,000 per minute (the highest was 14,000,000) while at Engebi the average was 4,000,000, and at Aomon 3,600,000.[11] Of the seven species common to the stations, none showed activity consistently higher than others. The radioactivity of the coralline algae—for example, *Jania*—which contains large amounts of calcareous matter, was not different in the degree of contamination from the succulent forms, such as *Caulerpa,* from the same station. The counts, of course, were gross counts of beta radioactivity, and it developed, both in radiochemical analyses and in examination of autoradiographs, that much of the contamination at that early period following the blast was the result of surface contamination of the "speck" variety—most of it composed of highly insoluble fission products such as cerium, ruthenium, zirconium, and the trivalent rare earths. But, as autoradiographs showed, washing and scrubbing the specimens failed to reduce materially the radioactivity present. A proportion of the contamination was from fission products, not products of the fusion process. The amounts, even when the counts reached levels of millions, were not observably injurious to the vegetable forms (all living algae seemed on inspection to be in normal health and color), but the fission product contamination nevertheless was at a very much higher level than had been noted at Bikini or following the subsequent atomic shots at Eniwetok. The average post-Mike contamination was higher in the algae than in any other group.

The story of the invertebrates did not differ from that of the algae in the distribution of contamination by stations, yet there were vast differences, as it proved, in contamination by species and by the organs and tissues of the specimens. By station, the specific activity of individual samples varied from background levels at Japtan to 15,000,000 disintegrations per minute per gram for the sand from the gut of a sea cucumber picked up at Engebi. One piece of coral (genus *Acropora)* collected at Bogallua on November 8 was discovered, after initial examination by autoradiograph, to contain specific activity of approximately 100,000,000 counts per minute per gram. A peculiarity of this piece of coral was that attached to it were three highly radioactive nodules which seemed of foreign origin. The nodules did not appear to be part of the coral but were so well attached that when one of them was removed for counting it could not be separated from the coral without being broken. The unashed hollow sphere weighed 1 milligram and yielded 100,000 disintegrations per minute. It was considered possible that these bodies were cysts produced by the coral itself to wall off irritating radioactive particles, or that they were rapidly growing neoplastic growths which had concentrated a great amount of radioactivity since the time of the blast.[12]

With such evidence of the ingestion of radioactive materials by organisms at the lower end of the food chains, the question remained of the uptake of radioactivity by the larger animal and vegetable forms—by fish, by birds, by rats, by the vegetation on the islands.

The collections of fish at the seven stations ranged in number from 26 to more than 300 depending on the success of the poisoning and the varieties of species present. Species selected for radio-analysis were those most common to all stations and representative of marine feeding habits and, although most of the fish were the sedentary reef dwellers, a few types which live on the open, sandy lagoon bottom—goatfish, jacks, and flatfish—also were saved for ashing and counting. A total of 237 specimens representing 58 species, 33 genera, and 22 families finally were counted for radioactivity on 768 plates.[13]

In the gross counts of whole-fish radioactivity by station, the higher level of activity was discernible at once. A surgeonfish captured at Engebi before Test Mike had a total count of 30 per minute per gram of wet weight; the surgeon specimen taken from the same area after the Mike shot had a count of 110,000. The preshot blenny from Engebi counted 850, the postshot fish of the same species showed contamination of 340,000 counts per minute per gram. The average of all post-Mike specimens from Engebi was 280,000 counts per minute, the highest average of any station.[14]

An analysis of fish tissues by station disclosed that radioactivity ingested by the animals—and revealed in muscle, bone, skin, and liver—was greatest at Bogallua, downwind, west and south, of the Mike site and in the path of the westward flowing turbidity emanating from the Mike crater where Elujelab formerly had stood. Although Bogallua and Engebi are about the same distance from the shot site, activity in fish tissues at Bogallua was four to eighteen times that of the tissues of specimens from Engebi.[15] The broad circumstance seemed clear, especially in view of earlier experience—the fish living in the waters to the west of the atoll were ingesting, in the first week after Test Mike, radioactive materials carried westward by the cycling waters. In general, the omnivores had taken into themselves by far the heaviest doses of activity—far more, for example, than the carnivores, which seemed to indicate that the greater variety of their diet, which included plant forms already contaminated, multiplied their exposure to radioactivity present in the environment.

When the collecting and the subsequent analyses moved into the domain of the land animals—the rats living in burrows amid atoll vegetation, the terns nesting in the bushes and shrubs, and the shore birds feeding on the beaches—the survey team encountered not only new evidence of the wider impact of the thermonuclear weapon but also, in one instance, the small shadow of what would become a larger question.

The survey group had attempted, not always with success, to gather samples of rats and birds at each major station. The mid-Pacific rat *(Rattus exulans)* is a creature which lives in burrows beneath clumps of grass or under the beach magnolia bushes. From the time of the resurvey at Bikini in 1949 Lowman had experimented with various kinds of traps which could be placed at the entrances of the burrows or along the paths about the small and local feeding grounds. Since the rats live only in vegetated areas and rarely venture far from their underground homes in the shallow coral sands, their place in the contamination spectrum, although uncertain, was presumed to be correlated to that of the plants of their habitat. As for birds, the variety is not large, and the collection of specimens was limited primarily to terns—the white fairy tern *(Gygis alba),* the noddy tern *(Anous stolidus),* species which usually remain close to the nesting ground, and others including the sooty tern *(Sterna fuscata),* the crested tern *(Sterna bergii),* and the arctic tern *(Sterna paradisaea).* Occasionally other specimens would be taken, such as the golden plover *(Pluvialis dominica fulva)* or the turnstone *(Arenaria interpes morinella),* shore birds of migratory habit. The terns live almost altogether on small fish plucked from the water, the shore birds on insects and small crustacea found on the beaches.

The problems of radioanalysis presented by rats and birds were utterly different—different in the availability of specimens, in the variations in diet, and in the degree of certainty with which it was possible to assume some basic relationship between the contamination of the earth and the animal. Yet assays of the organs and tissues of the bird and rat specimens established patterns of similarity and difference that could be explained only in terms of feeding habits.

Before Test Mike, rat specimens had been collected on Engebi, Biijiri, and Rojoa. After the shot, they were found only on Biijiri, and there, nine miles from the shot site, they were ill and lethargic and, unnaturally, sitting or walking on the open sands in broad daylight, so sick that no traps were needed for their capture. No rats at all were found on Engebi, yet it was there, much later, that one of the most interesting problems would arise. The exposure of Engebi to the effects of the Mike shot made it seem impossible that rats had survived. The view was expressed in a subsequent summary by Lowman, who said that there was "little probability" that rats had lived through the heat, the shock wave, the rush of water, and the nuclear radiations that Mike had inflicted on the island. Members of the rat colonies apparently did live through the holocaust, however, and the questions presented by this circumstance would intrigue the investigators for years.

The radioactivity detected in the organs of birds and rats collected before Test Mike was of a very low order, although it was of interest that no activity at all was found in the bones. But after the Mike shot, analysis of the specimens in relation to the islands from which they were taken and to the presence of radioactivity in their tissues disclosed, first, a pattern reflecting the general contamination of the environment—that is, whether the point of collection was near the test site or downwind from it—and, second, and more significantly, degrees of internal contamination indicating the effects of food habits and the ingestion and retention of activity by the animals. A comparative study of the amounts of activity ingested by shore birds and rats, both of which subsist on insects, seeds, and grasses, and of shore birds and terns, whose diets are dissimilar, showed that fission product contamination was present in each of these species—just as it was present in the organisms of the sea—within days, even hours, after the nuclear detonation.

IV

Members of the Laboratory field team had but six days after the Mike shot to make their biological samplings at seven stations about an atoll twenty-two miles in length and eighteen miles across at its widest part. They were more experienced by 1952, and they had gained a familiarity with Eniwetok in two previous surveys there. But in an ocean entity of such dimensions and one shaken and churned by the world's first thermonuclear explosion, the allotment of time was exceedingly small and the collection of specimens, even though it numbered hundreds, scarcely was more than the merest beginning of a task of observation whose ramifications were becoming ever more complicated. Even so, the program of radioassay which began in November of that year, including the making of hundreds of autoradiographs and of radiochemical analyses, was quite as much as the Laboratory's small staff could handle. The report of the Mike shot results was completed and forwarded to the scientific director on June 10, 1953.[16]

The questions surrounding the position of the radiobiological programs in the Pacific still were not reconciled within the Division of Biology and Medicine in 1953. Operation Ivy had demonstrated the potential dimensions of the need. The Applied Fisheries Laboratory, as Pearson had pointed out in 1952, had unique experience at the test atolls. Yet the programs in the Pacific, as they had evolved, seemed incompletely developed. The Laboratory held the view that, even though it existed outside the mainstream of Pacific testing activity, it had done everything possible to draw to the attention of the Division the necessity for continuous and detailed studies. On its part, the Division, as would be revealed shortly, believed that the concepts and the delineation of program requirements had to flow from the Laboratory, which had the depth of experience. In the annals of the proving ground, as in those of the Laboratory, the discussions and decisions of 1952 and 1953 would assume a new significance when the tests of 1954 placed the proving ground, for the first time, into the realm of international relations.

The appointment of Bugher as head of the Division of Biology and Medicine had occurred during the final months of preparation for Operation Ivy. In the process of familiarizing himself with Division operations, he had attended a Bio-Medical Program directors' meeting at Hanford and later had observed at Eniwetok, before and after the Mike test, the radiobiological operations that were within the realm of his responsibility. There was no reason or need for Bugher to visit the Laboratory in Seattle, and it was

Eniwetok Marine Biological Laboratory (EMBL) on Parry Island, Eniwetok Atoll, in 1959 *(Holmes & Narver, Inc.)*

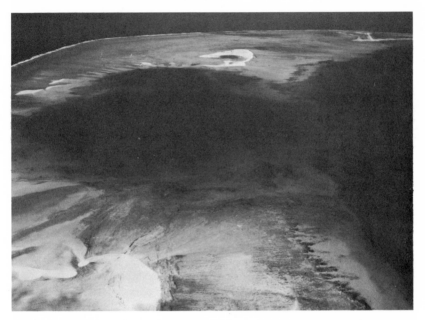

The "Gene complex" on Eniwetok's north rim showing Test Mike crater in 1959 *(Holmes & Narver, Inc.)*

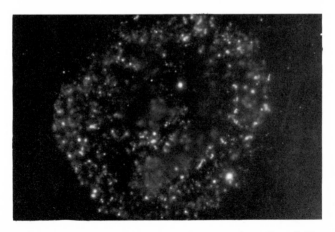

Autoradiograph of Eniwetok plankton sample, collected November 8, 1952, and exposed eight days (November 20–28) *(Laboratory of Radiation Biology)*

not for a year that he did so, using the occasion to urge a more aggressive programing. But Bugher's sense of the longer meanings of the biological studies was reflected almost at once in an augmentation of facilities at the proving ground. In December, 1952, while members of the staff still were involved with processing the Mike shot materials, the Applied Fisheries Laboratory was visited by Joseph S. Butts, biochemist of the Biology Branch, who discussed with Donaldson, as he had discussed with the heads of other agencies, the Division's idea for establishing a permanent biological station at Eniwetok. Three months later, in a letter from Karl M. Wilbur, physiologist of the Biology Branch, the Laboratory was informed that plans for the Eniwetok biology station were ready to go ahead. Wilbur had visited Eniwetok with representatives of the Pacific Science Board and of the Biology Advisory Panel of the Office of Naval Research. "As a result of this visit," Wilbur wrote Donaldson, "the Division of Biology and Medicine is now ready to take steps to institute a small, modest laboratory on Parry."[17] The Laboratory, Wilbur indicated, would be available for use in any kind of Pacific biology investigation, whether or not related specifically to nuclear testing:

> Plans are still in the initial stages. However, we feel that it is an appropriate time to ask interested individuals to give an indication of the probability that they might wish to carry out studies there. If as many as four persons would wish to go during the first year, even though on problems only indirectly related to the responsibilities of the AEC, the Division will consider that this warrants going ahead with the project.
>
> . . . We shall look forward to any suggestions which you may have concerning the utilization of a permanent laboratory at Parry in the furtherance of your studies.

On behalf of the Laboratory, Donaldson replied that laboratory-office space for six to eight scientists would be sufficient. An air-conditioned instrument room might make possible, he said, preliminary counting of radioactivity. The eventual result of these conversations and letters was the creation in 1953, six years after the original establishment of the proving ground site, of the Eniwetok Marine Biological Laboratory—the "EMBL"—on Parry Island. The laboratory was shared, as the programs developed, by a number of agencies interested in radiation problems, including the Commission's New York Operations Office. In the new facility the biologists had, for the first time, a laboratory on land and, more important, a permanent headquarters in the field and a sense of continuity of program.

There were other evidences in 1953 of the changes wrought by Test Mike. Programing was going forward for the new test series in 1954, and the Los Alamos scientific laboratory was expecting that extensive radiobiological surveys would be required. The Applied Fisheries Laboratory, among others, had been informed in general terms of these preparations. Before the year was out, on November 1, 1953, Bugher went to Seattle for a review of the Applied Fisheries Laboratory program, and the results left no doubt that the Division of Biology and Medicine now wanted, and expected to get, very much more—and more detailed—information on radiation contamination in the Pacific.*

The Applied Fisheries Laboratory notes on the November 1 conference with Bugher undoubtedly made liberal use of paraphrase in recording the development of the conversations, yet the notes reflect quite clearly the emphasis then being placed by the Division on acquiring information on radiation contamination on a very much more comprehensive level than had been considered possible or necessary in other years. There had not been, Bugher felt, either a proper appreciation of the importance of marine biology studies or, on the other hand, a sufficiently substantial pressure from any direction, including the direction of the Laboratory, for a wider approach. Donaldson had described the Laboratory's program as being outside the main line of proving ground interest and therefore necessarily operating on an occasional service basis. Of this, Bugher said:

> There has not been on our staff an understanding of the marine biology field. I wanted to do something about that. We begin more and more to realize that we are dealing with the small end of a large subject. This is particularly true of atomic weapons. Somewhere in the use of our large-scale weapons is a tolerance dose for humans. To pay attention only to the small fraction of the earth that is dry is an error. There has been a certain lack of request due to lack of comprehension of what needed to be done. We have a situation where the expert knowledge is here in your laboratory.
>
> I asked Karl Wilbur to really take some time and thought and out of

*The U.S.S.R. had detonated at least two more atomic test shots in August, 1953, one of them, on August 12, a thermonuclear device. Great Britain, whose successful shot had been exploded in the Monte Bello Islands off Australia, in October, 1952, had followed this with two more shots at Woomera, Australia, in October, 1953.

that arose the biology station at Eniwetok. . . . That move is in the
scientific interest. You will certainly make use of it for whatever time
you feel you can give. We, in turn, must be guided by whatever suggestions
come from you.[18]

A little later, Bugher linked the problems of the Pacific with
those of more distant implication:

> Regarding the atmospheric problem: As you realize, when we were
> dealing with bombs of the past it was with yields of 100 kilotons. We had
> the distribution of contaminal materials at the more turbulent areas of
> atmosphere. For the Mike shot last fall we had for the first time the
> ejection into the stratosphere of man-made materials. . . . We are very
> much interested in sampling the fallout distribution in the sea as well as
> on land, particularly of strontium-90. We will have quite an extended
> strontium sampling from now on, and this should tie in with your work.
>
> We have certain questions we must answer. To what extent have we
> modified an atoll environment so that it is no longer suitable for human
> habitation? To what extent have we modified the environment for eco-
> nomic trade? Suppose we have an attack on the West Coast. What are
> the possibilities of recovery from it? These are the questions the answers
> to which would add to our substantial knowledge of the biological reactions
> themselves. . . .[19]

Bugher elaborated during the talk on the importance of the
strontium-90 question.* Throughout the meeting with the members of the Laboratory staff, which lasted for several hours, there
was the unmistakable suggestion that the studies of Pacific radiobiology were regarded as fundamental to understanding of the
larger problems introduced by Operation Ivy. The "small end of
a large subject" went far beyond, but certainly also included, the
laborious sampling of plankton, algae, fish, plants, and birds by
which the radiobiologists had attempted to trace the paths of
fallout radiation in the atoll.

---

*Bugher undoubtedly was referring to the organization in the autumn of 1953
of "Project Sunshine," a broad program of studies of the behavior and distribution
of strontium 90.

As the Commission later reported, monitoring stations were beginning in 1953
to record the first detectable deposits of strontium 90 "and the sampling and
chemical assay procedures of researchers were beginning to detect its distribution
in the atmosphere, on the surface of the earth, in food materials, and in the skeletons
of animals and humans." (USAEC, January, 1957)

Original participants in Project Sunshine were the Enrico Fermi Institute for
Nuclear Studies, University of Chicago; Lamont Geological Observatory, Columbia
University; the U.S. Department of Agriculture, the U.S. Weather Bureau, and the
AEC Health and Safety Laboratory. Planning activities had been sponsored in the
summer of 1953 by The Rand Corp., Santa Monica, California.

Chapter Seven

1954: CASTLE

I

THE DECISION TO remove Bikini from its provisional status and to bring it into the proving ground was made by the Commission in September, 1952. Not since 1946 had Bikini been used in connection with a testing program except, incidentally, as a support area and as a base for meteorological and observations stations. Now it was to experience again participation in nuclear testing activities, this time as a site of additional thermonuclear detonations, one of which would have repercussions of world-wide significance, would alter the character and intensity of studies of the biological distribution of nuclear materials, and would spread from one side of the Pacific to the other the search for radioactive contamination in the ocean.

In June, 1952, Holmes & Narver had been authorized to make at Bikini a preliminary reconnaissance of the kind made earlier at Eniwetok, but with a view toward determining the feasibility of using Bikini as "an auxiliary proving ground." Holmes & Narver teams visited Bikini in the summer of 1952, surveying the terrain and noting in the tangles of growth the few remaining evidences of Crossroads. The Holmes & Narver report, submitted in August, found auxiliary operations feasible and presented estimates of cost of site development and support services. Bikini would be supported from Eniwetok, and plans then contemplated construction on Bikini Island of a port-of-entry base camp accommodating 250 men, camps for 500 men on each of the projected test islands, an airstrip at the base camp and liaison airstrips at each test site, beaching and docking facilities for landing craft, scientific stations like those being constructed for Operation Ivy, and facilities for radio communication with Eniwetok. A joint survey of Bikini by contractor, task force, and Commission representatives in mid-September, 1952, determined that the base camp should be shifted to the five southern islands, Airukiiji to Eninman (now Oboe to Tare in the proving ground code), west of Enyu Channel, islands that would be joined as necessary to accommodate operational facilities. "Beachhead" construction operations were authorized to begin on October 1, 1952.

Public announcement of the Bikini decision was made by the Commission on April 2, 1953. In its announcement the Commission said:

> To accommodate the rapidly expanding program of developing and testing new and improved nuclear weapons the United States Atomic Energy Commission is enlarging the Pacific Proving Ground in the Marshall Islands to include Bikini as well as Eniwetok Atoll. . . .
>
> Use of Bikini is necessary because of the limited size of Eniwetok, where tests were conducted last November. Eniwetok will be the headquarters and main operating base for the Proving Ground. Bikini and Eniwetok will remain under the civil jurisdiction of the Department of the Interior. AEC uses the area under agreement with Interior.
>
> Bikini was last used in 1946 for testing military effects of conventional atomic bombs. At that time its inhabitants were evacuated from the Atoll. After study of suitable alternative sites and consultations with the people, they were relocated on the island of Kili in the southern Marshall Islands. Since the 1946 tests, the Nevada Proving Ground of the Atomic Energy Commission has been established and is continuing in use for frequent tests, one series of which is now underway.
>
> The United Nations is being notified by the Department of State that Bikini Atoll and its territorial waters have been declared closed for security reasons in accordance with the provisions of the Trusteeship Agreement between the United States and the Security Council of the United Nations.[1]

The Nevada series then in progress was Operation Upshot-Knothole, which had been opened on March 17 and would con-

Campsite on Bikini Island, the east reef beyond *(Holmes & Narver, Inc.)*

Station on Enyu Island, Bikini Atoll, during Operation Redwing, 1956 *(Holmes & Narver, Inc.)*

tinue until June. The enlargement of Pacific facilities was occasioned by the advent of the thermonuclear bomb. It had become impossible to detonate at the single Eniwetok site the devices then being programed for experimentation, and plans for a 1954 series involving Bikini already were maturing. By January, 1953, the base camp on Eninman (now Tare) was about half complete, and in the months that followed, as the scope of the test requirements became clearer, the Eninman camp and others at Bikini were expanded to house almost 2,000 engineering-construction personnel. An Operation Ivy camp on Rojoa (Ursula), Eniwetok, was reactivated, and additional facilities were provided on Eniwetok and Parry Islands. The Airukiiji-Eninman complex became virtually a single island as bulldozers pushed sand and coral on the connecting spits and reefs and prepared the area for support operations. A 4,500-foot airstrip was constructed to accommodate four-engine (C-54) aircraft. Five test detonations were to be conducted at Bikini and a sixth on Eberiru Island, Eniwetok, north of Aomon-Biijiri.[2]

The new task force was Joint Task Force Seven. It carried the same numerical designation as the earlier force that had conducted Operation Sandstone in 1948, but the present organization was of a far more permanent nature, created as a continuing entity to conduct the test program of 1954 and also the programs that would be held thereafter in the Pacific on alternate years. Within the task force framework were five task groups, the first of which was Task Group 7.1 incorporating scientific and technical personnel. Others were Task Groups 7.2, 7.3, and 7.4, including the Army, Navy, and Air Force components, and Task Group 7.5, to which were assigned all contractor (Holmes & Narver) and Department of Defense personnel. The scientific group, Task Group 7.1, was headed in 1954 by William E. Ogle, who had served as assistant leader of the Test Division in Operation Greenhouse, and whose deputies were Duane Sewell, of the University of California Radiation Laboratory, and Captain Duncan Curry, Jr., U.S.N. (Ret.), in charge of task group administration. An advisory group included representatives of the Radiation Safety Section, the Health and Safety Sections, the Test Division of the Los Alamos Scientific Laboratory, and the University of California's Livermore Laboratory. The administrative units included, much as in the typical military organization, those devoted to personnel and administration, plans and operations, logistics, and test facilities. Within the complex of Task Group 7.1 operating units, the Applied Fisheries Laboratory's radiobiological survey program was designated as Program 19, Project 19.1, Marine Survey.

The Laboratory had been aware that tests were scheduled for Eniwetok and Bikini in 1954 because of the expectation at Los Alamos that marine surveys would be included in test plans. On August 14, 1953, more than two months before Bugher's visit to the Laboratory, Donaldson had been informed of the Laboratory's program number and had been urged to begin immediately to outline the Laboratory's 1954 survey requirements for submission "within a week or so."[3] On August 25, Donaldson had carried to Los Alamos a hastily drawn document titled "Preliminary Statement of the Proposed Program for Marine Survey Unit, Section 19." In this it was proposed that the Laboratory "attempt to carry out a biological succession survey of one or more sites near the test area before the test, immediately following the detonation, and somewhat continuously during the biotic recovery phases after the test." The draft suggested that, depending on the character and probable area of destruction of the test shot, the task group reserve on an appropriate island "a strip 1,000 feet wide, from the outer reef across the island and extending out into the lagoon to deep water" for use in a study more detailed than any visualized before. To provide continuity of observation, without which the Pacific surveys were pointless, it also was proposed that after the initial postshot survey, field teams of two men each, rotated at two-month intervals, continue to observe the processes of biological change or recovery for a period of six to eight months.[4]

At Los Alamos, the Laboratory's plan was discussed in meetings conducted by Captain Curry and including Ogle, Thomas L. Shipman, head of the Health Section, Major John D. Servis, head of Radiological Safety, and others. It was determined, as a basis for further planning, that the survey should be related to the single shot scheduled at Eniwetok—a test then carrying the code name Jughead—because "the number of relatively large shots at Bikini Atoll would cause a serious overlapping of contamination effects, thus introducing undesirable variables."[5] It is clear from the text of the draft proposal that Donaldson and his staff had been thinking of Eniwetok, drawing the plans in relation to the experience during Operation Ivy, and that until the conversations at Los Alamos Donaldson had no firm knowledge of what was planned at Bikini. When the meeting of August 25 was continued in Captain Curry's office the following day it was decided, among other things, according to the conference notes, that:

> b. A survey party of one or two men from Project 19.1 will visit Eniwetok the first two weeks of January 1954 to select control stations. A helicopter and LCM will be required part time. Six Project personnel will arrive at Parry about three weeks before JUGHEAD and will remain until JUGHEAD, two to four weeks. Thereafter two men will remain at Parry for about one year, the personnel being rotated every two months. Quarters and messing will be required on Parry. Building 218, now on the drawing board, will be constructed for the project, and will include the necessary counting and dissecting spaces and facilities. . . . A helicopter will be required as soon after JUGHEAD as radiological conditions permit to recover samples, and thereafter part time use of an LCM. . . . Telephone or radio communications will be required at the stations selected.[6]

Building 218, then "on the drawing board," was the Eniwetok Marine Biological Laboratory.

From August, 1953, until early in 1954, while work at Bikini went forward and plans for the spring series were maturing at Los Alamos, the Applied Fisheries Laboratory evolved a more detailed plan for radiobiological operations at Eniwetok during and after Operation Castle. In October, 1953, the Laboratory was notified that the Jughead shot originally scheduled at Eniwetok now would become one of the six shots being programed at Bikini and that a lower-yield shot, Ramrod, was projected for Eberiru Island. Donaldson replied that the change made no essential difference in the Laboratory's proposed studies but that "to continue our operational plans we need to have the expected date of RAMROD."[7] The date then anticipated, the Laboratory was told, was March 29. The Eberiru shot was now referred to as Echo. Finally, on February 15, 1954, the Laboratory forwarded to Task Group 7.1 its "Operations Outline for Program 19, Marine Survey Unit."[8]

In this final and more thoroughly developed plan the Laboratory proposed that it make a series of studies before and after Test Echo, that these studies be continued uninterruptedly for one year, and that during the year it also make "spot checks" at Bikini, on a quarterly schedule, of the levels and distribution of radioactivity resulting from the succession of shots to be detonated there. The plan followed but greatly modified the concepts of the previous August. The visit of Bugher had had effects on the thinking of the Laboratory staff and, presumably, on the planning of Task Group 7.1 for the marine surveys. Because the distribution of fallout could not be determined until after the shot, the Laboratory could only assume the feasibility of using Aaraabiru and Aitsu Islands as focal points for the postshot surveys. These, however, were tentatively chosen, and Mui Island, on Eniwetok's southwest reef, was selected as the control island. Instead of examining a 1,000-foot-wide strip from the outer reef to the deep waters of the lagoon, it now was proposed to make minute studies of a series of small, 3-foot-square areas lying at intervals of 50 to 200 feet along two transects of the islands, one at right angles to the reef and the other parallel to it.

Final placement of the transects would await further study (including study of aerial photographs) of the islands in relation to the circle of probable destruction of the test shot, but the hope, at least, was to make as thorough an examination as possible of island and reef flora and fauna. The sizes of the study areas would have to be adjusted to accommodate sampling, but for the first time there would be, instead of the random collection of specimens necessarily employed in other years, a carefully calculated and predetermined program of observations laid out with some prior knowledge of the test situation. Rough calculations of the amounts of radioactivity that might be encountered had been made. Sampling would be of the same groups of organisms used in other surveys—fish, invertebrates, algae, plankton, and the land animals and plants—and sampling by species would be limited in numbers and to those whose places in the atoll ecology were firmly established. New attention would be given to the plant-soil relationships in the check points along the transects. As for Bikini, it was proposed that exploratory observations be made there late in March, 1954, followed by full-scale studies in July, September, and December and by additional short collection trips in March, 1955.[9]

The 1954 plan laid emphasis on control—on careful delineation of the paths of action and on the transfer to the field, so far as was possible in so open and wave-swept a place as an atoll reef, of the

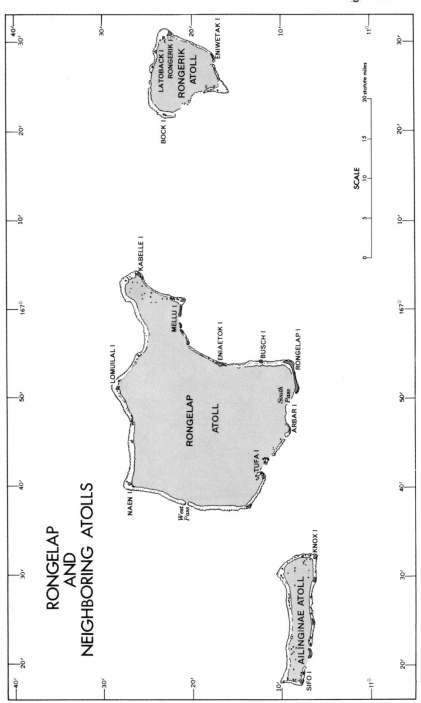

RONGELAP
AND
NEIGHBORING ATOLLS

RONGERIK ATOLL
LATOBACK I
RONGERIK I
ENIWETAK I
BOCK I

KABELLE I
MELLU I
LOMUILAL I
ENIAETOK I
BUSCH I
RONGELAP I
RONGELAP ATOLL
South Pass
ARBAR I
TUFA I
NAEN I
West Pass

AILINGINAE ATOLL
KNOX I
SIFO I

SCALE

0   5   10   15   20 statute miles

experimental procedures that would have been used in a laboratory. The plan suggested that field work begin at Eniwetok about
March 1.

II

The Operation Castle test series was opened at Bikini on March
1, 1954. The first detonation in the proving ground was Bravo.
Its yield in energy release was placed at about fifteen megatons.[10]
At such a level the device was 750 times more powerful than the
nominal atomic bombs used at Crossroads eight years before and
very much more powerful than the Mike shot of 1952.

Bravo was a surface shot, detonated at 6:45 A.M. The test may
have been of greater yield than had been calculated, but the effect
would have been only the production of an explosion proportion-
ately greater than that of Test Mike, either in immediate physical
terms or in the release of radiation products, except that the shot
took place at a moment at which circumstances were combining
to produce mishap and human suffering, the first such results
attributable to a test program. Because Bravo was detonated on a
coral island, its energy and heat carried upward—its cloud reached
an altitude of 100,000 feet—a great volume of radioactive particles
which would fall down rather quickly to the earth's surface when
the turmoil of the nuclear fire had been dissipated. And on that
morning there was blowing across the Pacific an upper wind which
would carry the Bravo fallout not to the north, as had been expected, but eastward toward the inhabited atolls of Rongelap,
Ailinginae, and Rongerik, the last the atoll on which the Bikini
people had spent a brief and difficult interlude. In the area of
the eastward fallout, some eighty miles from Bikini, there also was
a Japanese long-line fishing vessel, the small (100-ton) *Fukuryu
Maru* No. 5.

Bikini, like Eniwetok at Test Mike, had been evacuated before
shot time. Ships carrying task force personnel were arrayed thirty
miles eastward in the area normally upwind. But Radiological
Safety Section staff members became aware soon after the cloud
had reached its maximum height that its behavior was erratic, and
Geiger counters on some of the naval vessels began to record, an
hour after shot time, an increase in radioactivity, so that personnel
were ordered below decks and the ships made secure. Within a

few hours RadSafe aircraft and communications networks had determined the direction and extent of the fallout and the general levels of radioactivity laid across the ocean from Bikini and, as it proved, over the neighboring atolls. The presence of the *Fukuryu Maru* was not suspected.

During Operation Crossroads and subsequently, Bikini had been the center of a relatively small restricted zone which unauthorized ships were forbidden to enter.* With the establishment of the proving ground at Eniwetok, the area about that atoll too was placed under restriction, but the prohibited zone consisted only of the atoll itself and of waters three miles to seaward. For Operation Ivy there was laid about Eniwetok a much greater "Danger Area" which extended approximately ninety nautical miles to the east and west (to the east, about half the distance to Bikini), and sixty miles to the north and south of the atoll. When Bikini was incorporated into the proving ground, this "Danger Area" had been enlarged so that it encompassed both atolls and thus placed in the northern Marshalls a restricted zone extending approximately 335 miles from east to west and 150 miles from north to south. Although fallout from the tests normally was expected to be carried west, the eastern edge of this zone had been placed as far east of Bikini as possible without encroachment on Ailinginae Atoll of the neighboring Ailinginae-Rongelap-Rongerik group. The Commission later noted that a Notice to Mariners dated May 23, 1953, had been issued to foreign nations through the Navy Hydrographic Office that a danger area had been established in the Marshall Islands with boundaries at 10° 15′ N. and 12° 45′ N. and at 160° 35′ E. and 166° 16′ E.[11] This was an area of just over 50,000 square miles.

The Bravo fallout reached beyond the margin of the danger area then prescribed. The plume of Bikini particles, carried aloft in the twenty-mile-high cloud, fell across the ocean and atolls in a long ovule pattern reaching more than 200 miles, its southern fringe touching Rongelap and Rongerik, a streak of heavy contamination virtually bisecting Rongelap, and extending out into the ocean toward Utirik. If the Bravo shot had been detonated at Eniwetok, the fallout would perhaps only have brushed Bikini,

*Hydrographic charts (Oct., 1952) described this zone as bounded by parallels of 11° 28′ N. and 11° 43′ N. and by meridians of 165° 10′ E. and 165° 35′ E.

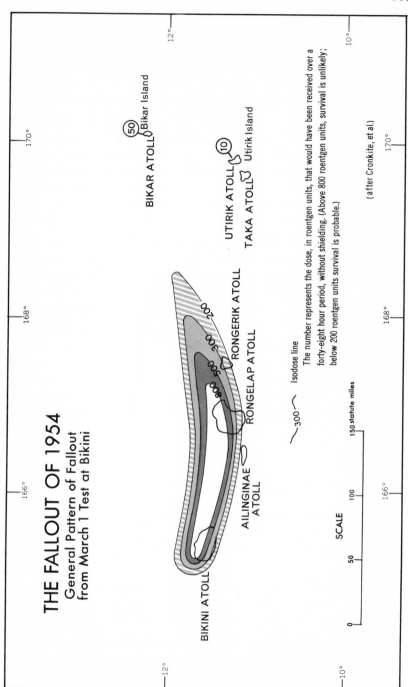

THE FALLOUT OF 1954
General Pattern of Fallout
from March 1 Test at Bikini

SCALE

150 statute miles

BIKINI ATOLL

AILINGINAE
ATOLL

RONGELAP ATOLL

RONGERIK ATOLL

BIKAR ATOLL○Bikar Island

UTIRIK ATOLL○10
TAKA ATOLL○ Utirik Island

~300~ Isodose line

The number represents the dose, in roentgen units, that would have been received over a forty-eight hour period, without shielding. (Above 800 roentgen units, survival is unlikely; below 200 roentgen units survival is probable.)

(after Cronkite, et al.)

which could have been evacuated. But it may be assumed that Bikini was the site of Bravo for the very reason that the fallout, predictably heavy, was expected to behave in a predictable fashion.

The public announcement immediately following the March 1 shot was characteristically cryptic. On that date, a Commission news release attributed to Admiral Strauss, the chairman, a statement that "Joint Task Force SEVEN has detonated an atomic device at the AEC's Proving Ground in the Marshall Islands. This detonation was the first in a series of tests.[12] Even as the announcement was being made in Washington the task force was receiving reports of the harm the fallout had wrought. More than 200 Marshallese on Rongelap, Ailinginae, and Utirik, and twenty-eight American military personnel stationed on Rongerik had been exposed to doses of radiation, and all of these people had to be evacuated, the Marshallese to Kwajalein and the military personnel to naval hospital facilities afloat or ashore. The evacuation was carried out by naval aircraft and surface vessels in the two days following the arrival of the fallout, which at Rongelap was described as "snowlike" and at Ailinginae and Rongerik as a "mist."[13] While there was not as yet any information on the relative severity of the dosage nor, as it developed, on the exact time the fallout arrived at Rongelap, where exposure seemed to have been heaviest, the task force asked the Commission and the Department of Defense to organize a medical team to care for the exposed persons and, in the meantime, emergency decontamination and medical procedures were organized by the Medical Department of the U.S. Naval Station at Kwajalein.

By March 9, eight days after the Bravo shot, the AEC-Department of Defense special medical team had been organized and airlifted to Kwajalein. Its staff included personnel from the Naval Medical Research Institute, the U.S. Navy Radiological Defense Laboratory, the Armed Forces Special Weapons Project, and the Commission's Division of Biology and Medicine. Within this period it had been established by examination of all individuals that, as was later reported, "a significant amount of penetrating radiation to the entire body had been received and that extensive contamination of the skin and possible internal deposition of radioactive materials had occurred."[14] No individual in the exposed group was believed to have received a lethal dose. On the other hand, never before had there occurred a situation in which it was necessary to study so large a group of human beings so soon after radiation exposure. Members of the medical team were joined by special consultants from the Pacific Fleet, the Commission, the Armed Forces Special Weapons Project, and other agencies, including the Trust Territory. Bugher returned to the Pacific to observe and assist the studies of radiation injury, and the Division of Biology and Medicine dispatched two physicians, LeRoy, as special representative of the director, and Charles L. Dunham, then chief of the Medical Branch.[15]

There seems to have been no doubt from the time of the evacuation that the care and observation of the exposed persons would involve procedures carried out for a long period of time. The question of when the atolls again would be habitable obviously was open. No one yet knew that the *Fukuryu Maru,* whose crew of twenty-three Japanese fishermen had been exposed to the same "snowlike" substance that had fallen on the Rongelapese, was making its way back across the Pacific to its home port of Yaizu City, where its arrival and the subsequent disclosure of the condition of its crew would create fear and panic in Japan. On March 11, the Commission offices in Washington, apparently hoping to be reassuring, made the first public statement about the Bikini accident. The Commission's announcement said:

> During the course of a routine atomic test in the Marshall Islands, 28 United States personnel and 236 residents were transported from neighboring atolls to Kwajalein Island according to plan as a precautionary measure. These individuals were unexpectedly exposed to some radioactivity. There were no burns. All were reported well. After the completion of the atomic tests, the natives will be returned to their homes.[16]

III

The story of the exposure of the Japanese fishermen was published in Japan by the *Yomiuri,* one of Tokyo's three largest newspapers, on the morning of March 16, two days after the *Fukuryu Maru* had put into Yaizu. While the people of the atolls and the military personnel on Rongerik had been under the care, and also under the control, of the task force organization and its parent agencies, neither care nor control had been possible in the case of the Japanese who, having lived for two weeks in a contaminated vessel at sea, had ended their cruise disturbed and frightened by their condition—which in the severest cases included darkening of the skin, burns on various parts of the body, and loss of hair— but apparently only dimly suspecting the nature and possible extent of the illnesses that had overtaken them. Press association reports brought news of the *Fukuryu Maru* incident to the United States on March 15, although the first reports were scant. By the day following publication of the *Yomiuri* story, however, Japan was feeling the first stirrings of a panic which would continue for many weeks.

What had happened to the *Fukuryu Maru* was related by her master, Hisakichi Tsutsui and members of the crew as Japanese reporters, doctors, and scientists began to piece together the scraps of information immediately available. The vessel, owned by Kakuichi Nishikawa, had departed Yaizu City on January 22, 1954, to fish for tuna in the area of Midway, north of the Marshalls and more than 2,000 miles from Japan. Weeks later the ship, having had only indifferent success in the Midway fishing grounds, had worked its way slowly southward toward the Marshalls and, on the early morning of March 1, was drifting silently on the Pacific swells, her lines out, at a point north of Rongelap. Captain Tsutsui and members of the crew knew of the presence of the American proving ground in the Marshalls, but no test had been held at Bikini since 1946 and the most recent explosions had been detonated two years before at Eniwetok, more than 200 miles from the waters in which they were fishing. They were not aware, they said later, of any warning of renewed tests. When the thermo-nuclear Bravo device was detonated at 6:45 A.M., one member of the *Fukuryu Maru* crew, Shinzo Suzuki, standing alone on the deck in the early morning light, saw the western horizon filled by a yellow glow and ran into the cabin to awaken his shipmates, who emerged from their bunks to watch in amazement the changing light which resembled a sunrise. "Seven minutes later," as Captain Tsutsui recalled it, "we heard a deafening explosion and then saw in the next instant a huge mushroom form shooting up in the distant sky. About ninety minutes after the blast, snow-white ashes began falling all around the ship."[17] The ashes appeared in a gradually thickening cloud as if a high mist had changed to snow, and they fell on the deck and fishing gear and on the clothes of the puzzled crewmen. The particles of snow were gritty. Some of the crew members tasted them in efforts to determine their origin. To some of the Japanese, the light in the west had suggested that perhaps the Americans were engaged in new tests, but none apparently was able to connect the light with the snowlike phenomenon manifesting itself an hour and a half later. They were perplexed and half-fearful. In any event, the *Fukuryu Maru,* after a month and a half at sea, was low on fuel and nearing the end of her cruise. Captain Tsutsui headed his ship north toward Wake Island and began the long run home. By the end of the third day one after the other of the crew members would experience nausea, itching, burning about the eyes or mouth, or other effects of the exposure to which they still were being subjected because they had taken only the most superficial measures to cleanse themselves or their vessel of the white dust.

Even ill as the crewmen were, and conscious of and alarmed by their symptoms and the alterations on their coloring, they were timidly reluctant to seek medical attention. The owner of the *Fukuryu Maru,* Nishikawa, realized when he met the vessel at the Yaizu dock that some of the crewmen were suffering some unknown affliction and, with Hoshio Misaki, the fishing master, he attempted to telephone the Yaizu Cooperative Hospital. Since the *Fukuryu Maru* had arrived on Sunday morning, however, the callers were put off, and it was not until that afternoon that the cases were brought to the attention of the physician in charge, Dr. Shunsuke Oh-i, who referred them the following day to the Attached Hospital of the University of Tokyo.[18]

Publication of the story by the *Yomiuri* produced in Japan immediate reactions of shock and indignation. Debates in the Diet turned at once to the Bikini case, and Premier Shigeru Yoshida's government was questioned concerning United States jurisdiction in the Marshalls. On March 16 Foreign Minister Katsuo Okazaki said that the United States might be asked to pay compensation to members of the Japanese crew, and reported to the Diet that the government was instituting an investigation of the "exact area" in which the *Fukuryu Maru* had been fishing.[19] On March 17 United States Ambassador John Allison proposed a joint Japanese-American investigation of the incident and said that the injured fishermen would be attended by a team of three

Japanese and three American physicians drawn from the staff of the Atomic Bomb Casualty Commission, which continued to be engaged in its long-term study of Hiroshima-Nagasaki victims. On the following day Allison visited Vice Foreign Minister Katsuzo Okumura to express official United States concern over the accident and to pledge full efforts to assist the injured. By this time two of the men were reported seriously ill at the Tokyo University Hospital while the others were under observation and treatment at Yaizu. Soon seven were hospitalized at the University and the remaining sixteen at the National Tokyo First Hospital. One of the seriously ill was Aikichi Kuboyama, radio operator of the *Fukuryu Maru*, who, after a period of what appeared to be slow recuperation, would die on September 23 of a liver disorder complicated by the development of jaundice and pneumonia.[20]

Reaction to the shock of the announcement of the *Fukuryu Maru's* encounter with the Bikini ashes was followed by a panic which the Japanese could compare only to the cholera panic of 1935. There is little doubt that the occasion was seized by left-wing groups to stir resentment against the government of occupied Japan and against the United States, but the scope and depth of the reaction indicate that the incident had touched emotional and economic nerves of great sensitivity. More than a year later, Yoshio Hiyama, Secretary and Acting Chairman of the Japanese Science Council's Special Committee on the Effects of Radioactivity, wrote a small paper, an *Annex* to the voluminous reports of research inspired in Japan by the Bikini mishap, and in his introduction he suggested in the most modest language the mood of March, 1954:

> This so-called "Bikini Incident," which reportedly caused a considerable amount of damage to the natives and the Americans as well, probably due to some miscalculation of the effect of the bomb or incompleteness of guarding, aroused a great worry among the Japanese public who were not yet free from the horror of Hiroshima and Nagasaki.[21]

The Bikini case also touched a vulnerable spot in Japan's economy. Japan lives by the sea, and her fishing industry is basic to both her economy and her diet. In 1952, Japan's consumption of marine products had been 4,285,000 tons, of which 93 per cent was used directly as food for her people.[22] The industry employed more than 330,000 workers whose meager income was not being improved by a slow shift to expanded fishing operations under government assistance. To these thousands of workers and members of their families, sympathy for the twenty-three stricken crewmen was sympathy for the worker and particularly for the worker on the small, independent vessel. Beyond this was the fear of radioactivity, of the unknown and the unseeable. When it was learned that the *Fukuryu Maru's* catch had been sold into the markets there began a frantic search for these fish. Immediately the Japanese people, so dependent on fish products for so large a proportion of their food, refused to buy tuna, or, at length, fish products of any kind.* Most of the *Fukuryu Maru's* fish soon were discovered and buried, but nothing now could allay public concern. Fish dealers found themselves unable to sell tunas, shark fins, *sushi* (vinegared rice with fish), *kamaboko* (fish meal), or other foods, so that they dumped tons of unsold and unsalable supplies. Within days, the price of tuna had fallen 50 per cent. The operations of the fishing fleets—hundreds of boats still were at sea—were thrown into confusion. Fish markets began to close temporarily, at Yaizu on March 17 and in Tokyo and Misaki on March 19. Fourteen dealers in Yaizu and ten in Masaki were reported in bankruptcy. For three days after March 22 about 1,000 retail dealers in Yokohama closed their shops. In some markets dealers posted signs with announcements such as "EAT MISAKI TUNA AND KEEP AWAY FROM RADIATION DANGER." By April 2 the dealers of Tokyo had organized a mass meeting to protest further nuclear testing, and there the banner said, "IT DOESN'T TAKE A BULLET TO KILL A FISH SELLER. A BIT OF BIKINI ASH WILL DO THE JOB." Japanese economists, confessing the hopelessness of attempting to make comprehensive estimates of the total economic losses sustained, nevertheless estimated that losses to dealers in Misaki alone by March 26 totaled 45,000,000 yen ($125,000) and that losses in Yaizu markets between March and September amounted to 240,000,000 yen.[23]

In this atmosphere of rising apprehension the Japanese government took measures that were direct but, in the circumstances, restrained. The Ministry of Health and Welfare issued on March 18 an instruction that all fishing boats which worked in or passed

---

*In Yokohama, on March 18, thirty-six persons stricken by food poisoning were believed at first to have eaten fish from the *Fukuryu Maru.* Government health authorities traced their sickness to another source.

The *Fukuryu Maru* No. 5 during her period of quarantine *(Kyodo Photo Service)*

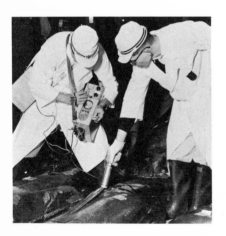

(Above and right) Radiation survey of tuna conducted by Tokyo metropolitan health authorities at the Tokyo Central Fish Market, 1954 *(Sanitary Examination Laboratory, Tokyo)*

through the area of the Northern Marshalls should enter only at any of five ports—Tokyo, Shogama, Misaki, Shimizu, or Yaizu City—where preparations had been made to check each hull and each catch for radioactivity.* The temporary "urgent" standard of permissible radioactivity was fixed at 100 counts per minute on a beta ray Geiger-Muller counter applied at ten centimers from the body of the fish. The long-line boats customarily operated in the prime tuna grounds of the Central Pacific (Japanese reported that approximately 19 per cent of the total tuna catch came from the area restricted by Japanese authorities, a volume exceeded only by hauls from south of the Equator and the Indian Ocean), and thus most of the long-line boats were affected by the Ministry order and were intercepted for testing at the control ports. Ultimately, over a period of several months, approximately 1,000,000 pounds of fish from almost 1,000 boats—between 4 and 5 per cent of the fish tested—were buried or thrown into the sea.[24]

The "great worry" of the Japanese was fed daily by reports and editorials in the press, which demanded compensation by the United States for the victims of the "Bikini ashes."† As the general apprehension rose it came to encompass not only the fish brought home from the Pacific by the Japanese fleet but the westward drifting waters of the Pacific itself. Parents hesitated to let their children visit the beaches, and in Japanese classrooms the discussions sometimes included such topics as "We may not be able to swim this summer."[25] With increasing frequency town assemblies began to protest the H-bomb. In these was expressed the distress of people directly affected by the disruption of the fishing industry, the tens of thousands of fishermen and members

*The area extended approximately from the easternmost Marshalls to Truk, in the Carolines, and from a line just north of the Equator to the vicinity of Wake Island.

†Neither the depth of the Japanese feeling nor the scope of the developments following the incident ever was fully reflected in reports reaching the American press. It was not until details of the incident began to trickle in from Tokyo, however, that the American public received any intimation of the character of the March 1 test and, as a result, news reports from Japan appeared to be regarded as important because they contained clues to the power of the nuclear weapons. Frequently the Tokyo dispatches appeared side by side with stories quoting American public officials on progress in weapons development. On March 16 strong press coverage was given a television interview of Representative W. Sterling Cole (New York), then chairman of the Joint Congressional Committee on Atomic Energy, in which Cole confirmed that the United States had a hydrogen bomb that could be delivered anywhere in the world "if we have bases close enough to the target."

of their families whose incomes, low enough even in prosperous times, now was sharply reduced or cut off entirely. Back of all the other fears generated by the Bikini incident was the generalized fear that the United States was thrusting into the atmosphere and dumping into the ocean incalculable quantities of radioactive materials which, insidiously and cumulatively, presented a great danger.

The concern that was evident in the many communities and at all of the social and intellectual levels of Japan would not be eased merely by assurances from the United States that the condition was not as severe as it seemed. But in actual fact, no one could give such assurance.

On March 17, the Department of State issued a statement saying:

> The United States Government is gravely concerned over reports that some Japanese fishermen have suffered injury during the course of atomic tests in the Marshall Islands. The United States Government is conducting an investigation in cooperation with Japanese authorities on all the facts in this case in order to determine how this regrettable accident occurred despite the careful precautions taken and including warnings issued over a wide area.

Within the week, Merril Eisenbud, the head of the Health and Safety Laboratory of the Commission's New York Operations office, had been sent by air to Japan to check for himself the circumstances of the case, to inspect the *Fukuryu Maru* lying in quarantine in Yaizu, and to offer the services of his office and staff in any measures that seemed indicated. John Morton, Director of the Atomic Bomb Casualty Commission, already had responded to a request from the University of Tokyo to visit the two Japanese fishermen then under care at the university hospital and to discuss their cases with the attending physicians. As a result of the contacts established by the United States Embassy with the Ministry of Foreign Affairs, and in accord with the suggestion of Ambassador Allison, a joint conference of Japanese and American scientists was held on March 24 in the Ministry of Foreign Affairs Building in Tokyo. Eisenbud represented the United States at this meeting, at which the fallout problem was discussed at great length. A product of the discussions was the establishment of an arrangement by which the Health and Safety Laboratory would make for the Japanese radiochemical analyses of urine specimens collected from the *Fukuryu Maru* patients in an effort to determine the amounts and character of internal radiation contamination.[26]

Assistance of this kind, which would continue for months, obviously was not enough in a situation that already involved widening public alarm. Eisenbud attempted to be both helpful and reassuring. As director of the Commission laboratory specifically concerned with the measurement of atomic fallout, he spoke with considerable authority. He was, however, discussing the present matter as the spokesman for the nation whose tests had caused the difficulty. Moreover, the Japanese must certainly have felt under the circumstances that the reassurance, if not the safety, of their nation depended upon their own efforts to uncover the truth about the case. The imponderables of radiation contamination, ranging from the unknown levels of radioactivity in the "Bikini ashes," which still had not been analyzed, to the possibility of radiation absorption by organisms in the distant Central Pacific placed before Japanese scientists problems with which they were ill-prepared to cope. Japan's interest in atomic energy development had been low because there had been no anticipation of the use of such energy for either power or weapons. Japan's fisheries people and biologists had had no preparation for the role in which the circumstances had thrust them. Nevertheless, in a time of such internal stress, only assurance from the most believable sources would suffice. The Japanese felt that they must determine for themselves the level of hazard presented by the American tests.

While Eisenbud was in Tokyo, Ambassador Allison handed to the Japanese Foreign Office a statement prepared by the Commission. A transcript was made available simultaneously on March 24 in the United States. The statement said in part:

Test Organization has restudied the entire test situation in light of recent experience and on its recommendation the danger area has been expanded and new limits notified to mariners and airmen in navigational publications disseminated 22 March 1954. Test Organization has greatly increased scope and intensity of its elaborate and continuous survey of the danger area by air to make sure that all craft approaching or inadvertently entering area are immediately warned. . . .

Opinion Atomic Energy Commission scientific staff based on long-term studies of fish in presence of radioactivity is that there is negligible hazard, if any, in consumption of fish caught in Pacific Ocean outside immediate test areas subsequent to tests. Some hazard from consumption of fish caught

178   *Proving Ground*

in immediate test area short time subsequent to tests. Extent of this latter
type of hazard can be determined and guard set against it by monitoring
radioactivity in fish catch from affected areas during period of test and short
time thereafter. United States Government establishing such monitoring
Pacific ports; understand Japanese Government doing same. To gather
further scientific knowledge on subject, United States Government making
scientific analysis of any data gathered by its own Pacific port checks and
will assist Japanese Government and universities in making similar scientific analysis of data resulting from Japanese port monitoring.

As to ocean currents, the warm currents which flow from the Marshall
Islands area . . . move slowly (less than a mile an hour). Any radioactivity
collected in test area would become harmless within a few miles . . . and
completely undetectable within 500 miles or less.[27]

The assertion concerning the undetectability of radioactive
materials 500 miles at sea would have been difficult to corroborate.
Eisenbud, with the encouragement of Bugher, however, seems
to have made arrangements with CINPAC for Health and Safety
Laboratory monitoring outside the immediate test area during the
1954 series even though the task force had felt this unnecessary.
Apart from any data thus assembled, the only information available to the Commission was that accumulated by the Applied
Fisheries Laboratory in earlier studies of contamination within or
adjacent to the test atolls.

Meanwhile, the Japanese scientific community, with the support
of government agencies, was preparing to initiate its own studies
of the distribution and ocean transport of radioactive materials
deposited in the Pacific.

IV

The developments of March, 1954, were setting the stage for an
intensification on an international scale of medical and biological
investigations related to the problem of nuclear fallout. For the
moment, however, these developments were emergency in character and focused in the Tokyo hospitals, where the burned fishermen were being examined and treated, and at Kwajalein, where
the Marshallese and the American military personnel were under-
going care.

In the region of the proving ground, the relatively early realization of the hazard presented by the Bikini fallout had permitted
the organization of remedial procedures long before the *Fukuryu*

Maru reached her home port and the world learned of the further mishap. The survey of the Marshallese and American evacuees had revealed immediately that there was extensive contamination of skin, hair, and clothing, particularly among the Marshallese, and decontamination measures had been instituted as soon as possible both aboard the evacuation ships and in the base facilities at Kwajalein through which the victims were processed. The natives of Rongelap, sixty-four men, women, and children, had received the highest calculated dose of radiation, later estimated at 175 roentgen units of gamma radiation in fifty-one hours from the time of the Bravo shot until they were taken off the atoll.[28] The twenty-eight Americans on Rongerik had received the second highest exposure, but these men had been aware of the potential hazard and had instituted their own protective measures, putting on additional protective clothing and, so far as possible, remaining inside the aluminum buildings in which they were housed. Once the collective machinery of the Navy and the task force had swung into action, medical care was available at all times. Complete medical histories were sought. Each person was examined on arrival at the Kwajalein dispensary and subsequently as developments suggested. Routine "sick calls" were held twice each day, and the skin of each individual was examined at frequent intervals. Since internal deposition of radiation materials undoubtedly had occurred in some instances, evaluation of internal contamination, by systematic study of excretions, was instituted. The hospital beds on Kwajalein were used for all persons whose condition required that they be given hospital care. For the others, emergency housing accommodations were established.[29]

None of these activities or conditions was generally known or reported outside the proving ground. The evacuation had been accomplished with such speed that Rongelap, Allinginae, and Utirik became, for the moment, museum exhibits of Marshallese life, the huts furnished but empty, the native outriggers standing where they had been drawn up on the lagoon beaches, and the stone-bordered streets and walks of the communities bearing only the footprints of persons now gone. Only the animals and fowls of the community had been left behind, and these, which would be removed before March ended, would contribute to the accumulating appreciation of the level of exposure to which the human beings had been subjected. While the immediate problem existed, the care of the victims demanded the full attention of the hastily mobilized medical staffs, although some further monitoring was conducted on the islands by Radiological Safety teams to assist medical evaluation of the problem. But before March was out the first steps were taken in what would become a long and continuous radiobiological examination of Rongelap, where the most serious contamination existed.

In accordance with plans approved weeks before, Held and Palumbo, as an advance team from the Applied Fisheries Laboratory, had started to the proving ground on February 28 to open the new Eniwetok Marine Biological Laboratory and to prepare for the surveys before the Nectar shot at the end of March. Donaldson and Olson, leaving later, had arrived at Eniwetok on March 18 accompanied by Major Charles Barnes, U.S.A.F., on temporary assignment to the Applied Fisheries Laboratory from the Air Force Veterinary Corps and added to the staff to provide additional assistance in studies of vertebrates. Shortly thereafter, on March 21, by which time Bugher had arrived at Eniwetok from Kwajalein, the Laboratory received an inquiry from Pearson, through Ogle, of Task Group 7.1, concerning the feasibility of making a preliminary radiobiological sampling on the contaminated islands. On March 24, the five Laboratory staff members then in the proving ground area were transported to Bikini by air to go aboard the *Nicholas* (DDE 449) for a survey of Rongelap. With members of the Laboratory group were Shipman, of Los Alamos, Thomas N. White, P. R. Schivone, of RadSafe, and W. W. Robbins, a task force photographer.[30]

The *Nicholas,* which had been standing by to carry the small expedition to Rongelap, was held at Bikini for an additional twenty-four hours while arrangements were made by Task Group 7.1 to fly a group of Marshallese, accompanied by Trust Territory representatives, from Kwajalein to Rongelap to capture some of the pigs and other domestic creatures that had been abandoned on Rongelap during the evacuation. The *Nicholas,* departing Bikini on the evening of March 25, entered Rongelap lagoon at daybreak and, while Shipman and others made radiation surveys of the southerly islands, the Laboratory group went in the DDE's motor whaleboat toward the islands of the north.

Rongelap, largest of the group of three atolls which also includes Ailinginae and Rongerik, is an atoll of irregular outline, its southeast reef pressed inward so that the lagoon, which is some twenty-five miles long, curves from the protected South Pass toward a long projection to the northeast on which the anchor island is Kabelle. South of Kabelle and above the southeasterly curve is Labaredj, and it was on these islands that the Laboratory team made its first examinations.

There had been no time, between March 21 and 25, to develop a detailed survey plan, and the Laboratory was, in any event, still responsible for advancing the carefully worked out program at Eniwetok. At Rongelap, the Laboratory could make only a quick sampling of biological materials with emphasis on the gathering of specimens of animals and plants—fish, clams, crabs, coconuts, papaya, arrowroot, and pandanus—used by the natives for food. The biological collections were made in a single day, first at Labaredj and then at northerly Kabelle, but at each island the group also made a series of readings on the field survey meters (Juno No. 89). On Labaredj the beta radiation readings on counters held one inch above the ground ranged up to 1.5 roentgens per hour and on Kabelle to 2.8 roentgens, in each instance the higher readings being obtained within the island vegetation or on the windward edges of the stands of trees. At such levels, extended exposure of personnel would have been unwise even if a more comprehensive biological program had been possible. Never before had members of the Laboratory staff encountered radiation at such levels so long after the initial contamination. After almost four weeks, and despite an intervening tropical storm which could only have had the effect of rinsing off superficial deposits of radioactive particles, the vegetation on Rongelap's northerly reefs still retained substantial amounts of surface contamination. The extent to which this residual radiation was invading the biological system and being distributed about the atoll could only be determined by analysis of March 26 specimens and, as it proved, by specimens collected in a series of subsequent samplings. The usual samples of water, algae, and invertebrates were added to the collection of fish and plant specimens so that the complete biological spectrum could be brought to view. The March 26 collection was swift and cursory, but it was the first of a series of observations that would be continued for many years.*

In the days following March 1, the task force, whose work scarcely was begun, had been preparing to resume test operations. The restricted zone about the proving ground had been enlarged (a move that had been immediately demanded by the Japanese press after the *Fukuryu Maru* returned home) so that it now encompassed a sector of ocean of some 375,000 square miles in area, approximately eight times larger than the zone prescribed before March 1. The second shot at Bikini was detonated on a barge in Bikini lagoon on the morning of March 27, and this test was witnessed by Admiral Strauss, chairman of the Commission, who returned to Washington to submit to President Eisenhower on March 30 a report of his visit to the proving ground and who released on the following day a 2,500-word statement—by far the most comprehensive yet released—describing the background and circumstances of the test programs and the efforts being made to cooperate with the Japanese.[31]

The additional Bikini tests were followed by a single detonation at Eniwetok before the operation was closed in May. Members of Program 19.1, whose preshot surveys had been started at Eniwetok late in February, continued their preliminary work in the field until the Eniwetok test was accomplished, and then they set in motion the postshot "succession studies"—the controlled field surveys—that had been proposed to the Division of Biology and

---

*The first survey of Rongelap was ended in an incident that came dangerously close to tragedy. While the survey team worked ashore on the northern islands, the *Nicholas* had received radio orders to return to Bikini by the following morning to take up an assigned position in the fleet then moving outside the atoll to observe the second of the Operation Castle tests. By nightfall the northern shore party had not returned to the vessel and the *Nicholas* thus faced the alternatives of waiting in the lagoon, and subsequently risking a night passage through a difficult and unmarked channel to the sea, or moving out into the open water to be ready to leave for Bikini the moment the survey whaleboat could be taken aboard. The *Nicholas* chose the sea. Not until midnight, while the vessel rode the swells off Rongelap Island, did the people on board sight a flare from the whaleboat, which was drifting without power in the darkness toward the breakers at the island's seaward edge. The survey group had returned to the whaleboat at dusk and had set out down the lagoon to find the *Nicholas*. When it was discovered that the vessel had moved outside the lagoon, members of the party attempted to find the channel in the darkness by listening for the sound of the breakers. Just as they reached the open water the whaleboat's engine stopped and they were carried back toward the jagged coral of the outer reef. The *Nicholas* lowered a second boat and ultimately pulled the disabled craft out of danger. It was nearly dawn before the *Nicholas* got boats and personnel aboard and started the run for Bikini.

Medicine. By May, however, the work at the proving ground was cast against a far larger backdrop of public awareness and concern. The successive disclosures at Rongelap and Yaizu City were preparing the stage for operations that would span the Pacific. The carefully plotted transects on Aaraanbiru and Biikiri had not lost their importance, but the puzzle of oceanic radio-biology now also held the attention of the Japanese.

The final test of Operation Castle, the Nectar shot, successor to the Jughead, Ramrod, and Echo proposals of the preliminary Los Alamos planning, was detonated from a barge in Eniwetok lagoon at 6:20 A.M. on May 14 (Eniwetok time). On the following day a Japanese research vessel, cheered from Tokyo dock by crowds of spectators, sailed eastward on what would be the first of the long-range surveys of fallout radiation in the open ocean. This vessel, the *Shunkotsu Maru,* meant to cruise directly through the waters of the United States Proving Ground.

V

In March, 1954, the only organization in Japan capable of approaching the problems presented by the *Fukuryu Maru* case was the Atomic Bomb Effect Research Commission, which was under the chairmanship of Rokuzo Kobayashi, head of the National Institute of Health of the Ministry of Health and Welfare.[32] The care of the twenty-three fishermen immediately occupied the attention of the medical staffs of the Tokyo hospitals, but the examination of the *Fukuryu Maru* and its contaminated gear swiftly drew into the case additional specialists from a number of laboratories. With the establishment of the system for monitoring catches of fish returned through the five Japanese ports, more than a dozen laboratories, including the National Hygienic Laboratory and the National Institute of Health, undertook analyses of fish on which contamination was discovered. But the ramifications of the case, and the clear need of the government and the scientific community to respond in some comprehensive way to the rising public feeling, suggested at once that enlargement and coordination of research efforts were necessary. On March 25, eleven days after the return of the *Fukuryu Maru* and the day following the joint conference with Eisenbud, the Atomic Bomb Effect Research Commission, which now found itself the primary advisory agency on the Bikini incident, was enlarged by the addition of new members and by the appointment of special committees on clinical research, environmental hygiene, and food sanitation. Throughout the month of April, while Japan's anxiety continued to rise, the preliminary research efforts were conducted within this modified Commission program.[33]

By the end of April, increasing numbers of Japanese scientists had dropped whatever work engaged them to join the Bikini research. Studies were proposed of the possible contamination of food crops, livestock, and drinking water. The Ministries of Agriculture and Forestry, of Education, and of International Trade and Industry were increasingly concerned with problems cutting across jurisdictional lines. On May 1, accordingly, the Science Council of Japan, acting as a coordinating agency for the government, established a special committee to design a further and more comprehensive organization, and by May 10 there had been set up a Special Committee on the Effects of Radioactivity which had as its purpose the coordination and direction of research. Head of the Committee was Seiji Kaya, President of the Science Council, and with him were four leading scientists who served as executive secretaries. The Committee itself included about one hundred scientists, most of whom were members of subcommittees or sections to conduct and direct research in physics and chemistry, medicine, biology, fisheries, geophysics, and (later) agriculture. Little more than a month later, on June 14, the Japanese cabinet authorized the Ministry of Health and Welfare to set up another organization to meet the government's need for coordination of scientific activities within the ministries, and this new body proved to be the Council for the Coordination of Researches for Measures Against Atomic Bomb Injuries.[34] Its first meeting was not held until later in the year, but its members would take part in the joint Japanese-American scientific conferences which would result, in the end, in exchanges of information and the resolution of many of the frictions which marked the earlier relationships.

The mood of Japan in March and April, 1954, was not one, however, in which her scientists could be content merely to search out and assess the bits of contamination brought to the homeland in the holds of the fishing boats or by the ocean and its atmosphere.

The determination of the scientists to discover the extent of the presumed hazard was given force and focus by the development of a plan to send an ocean research vessel directly into the Bikini area to sample the waters and ocean organisms in the vicinity of the Operation Castle tests. Bikini was the source of the problems, and the initial levels of contamination, the Japanese felt, could only be discovered there. Plans for the research expedition were discussed late in March and matured during the month of April while the Operation Castle tests still were in progress. Determinations concerning the scope and character of the surveys were made by a committee of five sections—Biology, Air and Sea Water, Meteorology, Oceanography, and Environmental and Food Hygiene—in which important roles were played by Yoshio Hiyama and Motosaku Fujinaga, chairman of the Research Department of the Fisheries Agency. Although the Japanese scientists were themselves apparently divided on the degree of the danger or on the methods whereby it might be assessed, certain of the key figures, these certainly including Hiyama, were men representing moderate and stabilizing elements in a situation of great tension.*

The vessel prepared for the cruise was the *Shunkotsu Maru,* a research and training ship of 580 tons operated by the Fisheries Training Institute. Her selection was made by the Japanese Fisheries Agency, which was the official sponsor of the expedition in cooperation with a number of other offices including the Central Meteorological Observatory, the Meteorological Research Institute of the Tokai District Observatory, the Tokyo Fisheries College, the National Hygienic Laboratory, the Department of Fisheries of the University of Tokyo and the Hydrographical Division of the Maritime Safety Agency. The expedition leader was Hiroshi Yabe, head of the Resources Department of the Nankai District Fisheries Research Institute, and the group aboard included twenty-two scientists forming a unit called the Bikini Waters

*Members of the planning group were: *Biology:* Hiyama, Yasuo Suehiro, University of Tokyo; Keishi Amano, Tokai Regional Fisheries Laboratory; Tadayoshi Sasaki, Tokyo College of Fisheries; and Hiroshi Nakamura, Nankai Regional Fisheries Laboratory; *Air and Sea Water:* Yasuo Miyake, Meteorological Institute; Eizo Tajima, St. Paul University; and Fumio Yamazaki, Scientific Research Institute; *Meteorology:* Miyake; *Oceanography:* Michitaka Uda, Tokyo Fisheries College; Kanji Suda, Hydrographic Office; Yoshiyuki Matsue, University of Tokyo; Miyake and Sasaki; *Environmental and Food Hygiene:* Kakuma Nagasawa, National Hygiene Experimental Station; and Yuzo Toyama, National Institute for Preventive Medicine.

Investigation Team. Nine reporters from Japanese newspapers and news agencies were aboard the vessel and these, with members of the crew, brought the personnel of the expedition to seventy-two.[35]

The cruise of the *Shunkotsu Maru* represented an entirely new approach to the study of residual radioactivity in the waters of the Pacific, an approach not only new but far more sweeping than anything yet attempted by the United States for the simple reason that the Japanese, having no access to the information from which calculations of contamination might have been drawn, were forced to seek for themselves whatever information or understanding might be extracted from study of the waters in the near vicinity of the nuclear tests. The Japanese were late-comers to such aquatic radiation research because they had had no atomic tests and because their sole experience had been related to the Hiroshima-Nagasaki condition. They were familiar with the techniques of ocean sampling as normally practiced by the fisheries, oceanographic, and hydrographic agencies, but in the realm of ocean radiobiology they had at their disposal only information published in earlier years by the Applied Fisheries Laboratory and the few other laboratories that had been involved in the early work at Bikini. Nevertheless, the *Shunkotsu Maru* expedition was planned to permit the Japanese to conduct across thousands of miles of the Western Pacific the same kinds of sampling that the American scientists, primarily the Applied Fisheries Laboratory staff members, had conducted until that time in the waters and on reefs of the test atolls. When the *Shunkotsu Maru* sailed from Tokyo Bay and headed southeastward toward the Marshalls a new phase of the Pacific search was begun.

The beginning, however, was a product of the tangled scientific-social complex that gripped the port cities, the government, and large segments of the Japanese people. The crowds of well-wishers that cheered the *Shunkotsu Maru* on her way, and the presence of the reporters aboard the vessel, attested to the importance attached by the Japanese to this venture into the waters of the American proving ground. Yet one part, at least, of the scientific community had anticipated that the cruise would involve representation by the United States so that it would become, in effect, a joint Japanese-American exploration of the questions presented by fallout radioactivity in the sea. The initial conference in Tokyo on March 24 had achieved only limited results, but in April the United States was invited by Japan to send experienced scientists to join the projected survey. There was an interest in having aboard the *Shunkotsu Maru* American scientists who were familiar with the problems of aquatic biology that would be encountered, and particularly, if possible, representatives of research in fisheries, the field in which Japan's "great worry" then was centralized. The invitation for United States participation, transmitted through the American Embassy to the State Department, led to consultations with the Atomic Energy Commission and the appointment, late in April, of two United States representatives to Japan's scientific mobilization.

One of the two delegates was Donaldson, in whom were combined the background of fisheries research and the experience at the test atolls in the problems of aquatic radiobiology that now occupied the Japanese. The other was W. R. Boss, then on a two-year leave from Syracuse University to serve as a physiologist with the Biology Branch of the Division of Biology and Medicine. Donaldson and Boss were sent to Japan explicitly to accompany the *Shunkotsu Maru*. Their arrival by air at the Tokyo airport on May 24 had been coordinated with the anticipated date of departure of the research ship. But by May 24, when they disembarked at Tokyo, the *Shunkotsu Maru* already was nine days at sea, making her way from Marcus Island to Wake on the second leg of her long journey. For whatever reasons (the urgent interest of the Japanese newspapers, whose reporters aboard the vessel subsequently would file periodic radio reports on the progress of the expedition, may have been a factor) the *Shunkotsu Maru* had not waited for the Americans.

The members of the two-man team were faced with interesting and perplexing alternatives. It still would have been possible for the Americans to join the vessel at Wake Island or elsewhere, perhaps, provided proper arrangements could be made by the Japanese. On the other hand, there was apparently a feeling, in the membership of the Japanese planning group as in the American Embassy, that more would be accomplished by consultations with Japanese scientists and with representatives of the Japanese tuna industry. Such conferences, of course, could only be arranged on invitation, and it was an open question whether it would be more helpful to seek a comprehensive scientific meeting on the entire problem or attempt a series of conferences more limited in scope. The alternatives were discussed in meetings at the Embassy on May 25 and 26, where Boss and Donaldson, while indicating their willingness to take part in any activity that would help ease Japanese tensions, pointed out that they were not in fact equipped to discuss with the Japanese the whole range of problem areas.[36] More than a month would pass before a conference was arranged.

The two delegates, as representatives of the United States in a situation both complex and delicate, were inexperienced in diplomacy but well equipped by temperament and interest to work with Japanese scientists and fisheries research and management personnel. As products of teaching and research activities in American universities, they could approach the Japanese people with a sympathetic appreciation of their views, respecting Japanese anxiety while conveying, in their behavior, assurance that the problems would yield to understanding and that they themselves were quite willing to give any help possible in the effort to bring the contamination difficulty into perspective. Lacking in their first days in Japan a specific opportunity to confer on a formal basis, the Americans visited research installations and fisheries operations in the Tokyo area—the Fisheries Agency, the Hydrographic Office, the Tokyo fish markets (which they found to be closed), the fishing ports of Urayasu and Funabashi on Tokyo Bay, the Tokai Regional Fisheries Laboratory, and other points—and everywhere they consumed fish dishes in the Japanese restaurants.[37] Their host and guide on many of the trips was Professor Hiyama, the secretary of the Special Commission on the Effects of Radioactivity, with whom Donaldson had become acquainted some years before. Frequently with them, too—he had, in fact, been at the Embassy to meet them—was Tetsuo Tomiyama, of Kyushu University, a member of the Fisheries Section of the Special Committee, who had been a student at the University of Washington before World War II and who, in the post-Bikini research, was conducting experiments in the assimilation by aquatic organisms of strontium 90 and other radionuclides.*

*In 1956 Tomiyama returned to the University of Washington to spend a year participating in the work of the Applied Fisheries Laboratory.

On June 11, 1954, almost three weeks after the arrival of the American representatives, the Japanese Foreign Office transmitted to the United States Embassy an invitation to a joint Japanese-American scientific conference.[38] The invitation listed the names of the Japanese scientific and ministerial representatives designated to take part, among them Hiyama. There followed a period of diplomatic communication, so that it was not until June 30 that the conference actually was held. The meeting was convened at 2:30 P.M. at Kasumi Kaikan, a conference building maintained by the Japanese Foreign Office. The Japanese delegates included K. Tsurumi, chief of a division of the Asian Affairs Bureau of the Foreign Office; Isamu Nagai, a bacteriologist of the National Institute of Health; Miyake, of the Meteorological Research Institute; Fujinaga, of the Fisheries Agency; Masayasu Kusumoto, of the Environmental Sanitation Bureau of the Ministry of Welfare; Keishi Amano, of the Tokai Regional Fisheries Laboratory; and Hirotake Kahehi of the Department of Radiology of the Tokyo University Hospital.[39] The American delegation included Boss, Donaldson, and Cabot Sedgwick, of the United States Embassy.

The conference was informal in composition and procedure. The principal Japanese spokesman was Tsurumi, who welcomed the group on behalf of the Bureau of Asian Affairs. Donaldson outlined general concepts of radiation tolerances and the problems associated with determining effects of internal and external exposure. Boss explained for the group the then recently established maximum permissible levels of exposure accepted by the Atomic Energy Commission and United States Food and Drug Administration and discussed the procedures used in calculating the levels.[40] Discussion was somewhat impeded by language difficulties, but there were many questions from the Japanese. After a dinner served in the conference quarters, the talk proceeded until late in the evening. The atmosphere had been cordial throughout.

The American visitors finally had met the Japanese under conditions which permitted them to describe—informally, frankly, but in precise terms—what they knew of the radiobiological phenomena that now held attention in Japan. After the conference, on July 1, Boss and Donaldson left Tokyo for Guam, Kwajalein, and Eniwetok, where Laboratory work was proceeding on the post-Castle survey at the atoll. Three days later on July 4, the *Shun-*

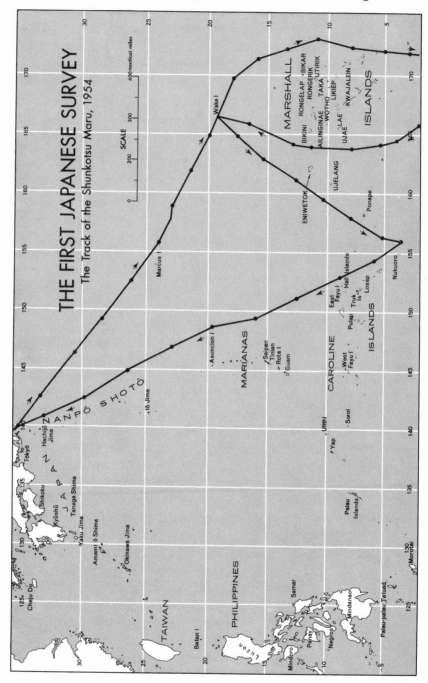

THE FIRST JAPANESE SURVEY

The Track of the Shunkotsu Maru, 1954

kotsu Maru sailed into Tokyo Bay to end a cruise of 8,800 miles. She was cheered into her berth at Shibaura by crowds of Japanese.[41]

VI

Yabe and his associates in the Bikini Waters Investigation Team had been at sea for approximately seven weeks. Their cruise, begun on May 15, the day following (although this was not known to the Japanese) the last of the Operation Castle tests, had taken them southeast past Marcus Island and on to Wake Island, which they reached on May 25, after pausing three times for preliminary samplings and "general observation." The vessel remained at Wake until May 28, when it set out again on a curving southerly course which took it some 500 miles east of Bikini and to a point just south of the Equator and in the vicinity of Ocean Island, a course which was marked by five stops for "general observation" and three for long-line fishing operations of the kind conducted by the *Fukuryu Maru*. From this point in the South Pacific, which was reached on June 6, the *Shunkotsu Maru* turned north and proceeded back to Wake Island on a course that took the vessel between Eniwetok and Bikini and through the heart of the proving ground. On this run the *Shunkotsu Maru* again used her long-line gear in the hunt for tuna and other pelagic specimens, one of the stops being made at the very mid-point of what had been the proving ground's restricted area. The Japanese were back at Wake by June 15, but two days later they set out again to make traverses of the waters west of Eniwetok. By June 24 they had run across the western edge of the restricted area and southwest of Ponape in the Caroline Islands, and from there they set a final course toward home, their last observations being made June 28 and 29 in the vicinity of the Marianas.[42] Between May 15 and July 4 the Bikini Waters Team had taken ocean samples at twenty-nine stations scattered about the American test atolls and over an area of more than 900,000 square statute miles.

The materials brought back by the Japanese team included, according to their summary reports, 500 liters of sea water from the Bikini area "containing strong radioactivity," 400 additional samples of sea water collected at other points along the route, 1,000 samples of water taken by the oceanographers in connection with studies of ocean currents, 3,000 samples of fish viscera, and

100 samples of other materials of radiobiological interest.[43] Their logs were filled with the data gathered in the course of the observations en route.

The Bikini Waters Investigation Team had conducted its ocean program under the general guidance of an Advisory Group which included members from the primary fields of interest. On July 6, after the *Shunkotsu Maru* had returned to Tokyo, the team was dissolved and in its place was created the Bikini Investigation Commission composed of the scientists of the planning group and those who had participated in the cruise. The reports resulting from the studies conducted by members of the Commission ultimately occupied thousands of pages in the Japanese literature. The assessments of the Pacific materials disclosed that, weeks after the close of Operation Castle, clearly identifiable "streaks" of contamination could be detected flowing westward from the Eniwetok-Bikini area in the waters of the ocean. The oceanographers found contaminated surface water (450 counts per minute per liter) moving east-northeast of Bikini, in a direction opposite to that of the main-flowing North Equatorial Current, which led them to suspect the presence of a hitherto unknown countercurrent.[44] The maximum activity in the sea water was noted in a sample taken on June 21, 1954, at a station 312 miles west of Bikini, where the radiation level was 91,000 disintegrations per minute per liter of water.[45] (The calculations were expressed in disintegrations per minute above the normal level of 600-700 disintegrations in naturally occurring potassium, a radioisotope common in the sea.) Water samples taken in depth indicated that in some locations residual radioactivity was present several hundred meters below the surface. While the Japanese reported that contamination of air and rainwater was of "no significance," they said that contaminants were distributed in the sea "from 10° N. to 18° N. and 150° E. to 175° E. . . . ." or from the northern Marshalls westward almost to the Marianas.[46]

As for the biota, from the plankton up to the tuna and shark and other fish so important to Japan's diet and economy, the Japanese not only found the radiation levels impressive but noted that the planktonic forms seemed to be concentrating radioactivity—in some cases, apparently, selectively—and thus playing significant roles in the movement of materials in the sea and in the transfer of contaminants up to the oceanic food chains. "With regard to tuna fishing grounds," a Japanese summary said,

the big-eyed tuna grounds in the North Equatorial Current are most contaminated, followed by the Equatorial Countercurrent area, where are located important fishing grounds for yellow-fin tuna and black marlin. The South Equatorial Current area, important for yellow-fin, is uncontaminated.[47]

Observations of the kind made by the Japanese had been made long before in proving-ground surveys by United States radiobiologists. This did not, however, diminish the importance of the *Shunkotsu Maru* findings in the open ocean in 1954, for no such survey ever had been attempted in connection with the United States nuclear tests. The Japanese reports reflected an understandable feeling that the conclusions not only were new—which, in the open water sense, they were—but that they indicated what small consideration had been given by the United States to the possibility of a persistent and far-ranging distribution of ocean contamination following nuclear detonations at the test atolls. An analysis of the radiological contamination of fish was made by Toshiharu Kawabata, of the Food Control Department of the National Institute of Health, a study which examined particularly the role of plankton in the radiobiological cycle. Kawabata noted:

According to the investigation by AEC around Bikini, Eniwetok and other atolls, the highest radioactivity was detected in herbivorous and omnivorous fishes, and it was in plankton-feeders. On the contrary, our investigations, so far as measured on the open sea, detected the highest activity in plankton-feeders. The discrepancy may be attributable to the difference between the pelagic and the coral fishes and to that between the explosion power of the atomic bomb used at that time and the hydrogen bomb tested at this time, although these remain problems to be solved later.

On May 31, 1954, Strauss, the Chairman of the U.S. Atomic Energy Commission, made a statement in his explanation against the problem of radiological contamination of tunas, "We have no evidence of extensive contamination in tunas or other fishes by the nuclear tests at Bikini Atoll." Nevertheless, our expedition has found high contamination in planktons and small-sized fishes inhabiting the open sea and even in large-sized migrating fishes. . . .

From the findings above described, it may be concluded that the contamination of large-sized fishes came chiefly from their baits [food], and the route of contamination may be: sea water—plankton—small-sized fish—large-sized fish. But the feeding habits differ from one to another. . . .

Therefore, the difference in the extent of contamination of large-sized fishes may be related to their food habits, or the food chain.

. . . .

The mechanism of transference of radioisotopes into fish bodies remained unsolved, as does the metabolic function of the fishes. The species of fishes, environmental conditions of laboratory experiments, the kind of radioisotopes, the form of radioisotopes in water or food, their absorption rate and their concentration are those [problems] to be further investigated.[48]

In his reference to the Atomic Energy Commission investigation of contamination at the atolls, Kawabata was citing the report of Applied Fisheries Laboratory on its survey of Bikini, Eniwetok, and Likiep in 1949. As Kawabata recognized, there was no thermonuclear device in 1949. He and his associates nevertheless had enlarged the realm of information about test-related contamination while delineating, from an entirely different point of view, the same problems that had engrossed the United States radiobiologists ever since Crossroads.

Through the summer and early fall of 1954 the members of the Bikini Investigation Commission continued their studies. The death of Kuboyama, the radio operator of the *Fukuryu Maru*, occurred on September 23, and this opened a new period of widespread mourning throughout Japan and on the thousands of fishing boats working in the Pacific and Indian oceans, which received the news by radio. In the Japanese markets the prices of tuna continued to be erratic, while the tonnages of fish condemned and discarded actually, for a time, increased. Discoveries of tuna catches which failed to pass the government-prescribed standard reached an all-time high in September and October, 1954, six months after the completion of the Castle tests.[49] Between May and November voluntary radiation inspection procedures were conducted at thirteen ports in addition to the five designated by government order, and through these thirteen ports passed the vessels whose operations were generally in the coastal waters. Thus, while the numbers of discarded fish decreased at the five government-designated ports, which handled boats from the distant fishing grounds, the numbers increased heavily at the thirteen ports processing boats from the coastal areas. It was not until January, 1955, that the monitoring of commercial catches was terminated.

The cruise of the *Shunkotsu Maru* was followed by two other Japanese expeditions from which came data on the distribution of Bikini radioactivity. The *Keiten Maru*, the 265-ton training ship of the Faculty of Fisheries of Kagoshima University, sampled water and marine organisms on a cruise to the Coral Sea between October 28, 1954, and January 28, 1955, although she found only trace amounts of radioactivity in the equatorial waters. The *Daifuji Maru*, an experimental fishing vessel owned by the Shizuoka Prefecture, took aboard three representatives of the Nankai Regional Fisheries Research Laboratory who made radiological samplings during a cruise to the Fiji Island fishing areas between November 30, 1954, and February 19, 1955. On her return the *Daifuji Maru* cruised just west of the Marshalls, nearer Bikini than on her outward course, where the amounts of radioactivity encountered in sea water and plankton, although lower in value than those encountered earlier, still were measurable.[50]

Chapter Eight

1955-1956: SURVEYS OF THE SEA

I

BY 1954 the initial evolution of United States nuclear weapons had entered what would come to seem in perspective a climactic phase. The March 1 test at Bikini probably represented, without reference to the tragic results flowing from it, an exploration into levels of energy release from which, now that they had been approached, a withdrawal should be made. The effort which necessitated the tests in the Pacific and in Nevada was but a part, although a large and costly part, of a nuclear program which was becoming wider and more diverse and thus tending at last to balance the original, historic emphasis on experiment with nuclear explosion. Long before the Castle tests there had appeared an interest in the development of atomic energy for peaceful purposes. In his address before the United Nations General Assembly on December 8, 1953, President Eisenhower had pledged the United States to a program in which it would "devote its entire heart and mind to find the way by which the miraculous inventiveness of man shall not be dedicated to his death but consecrated to his life," and with this the United States had undertaken to initiate an Atoms-for-Peace program which would become the conscience, if not at once the

196

principal instrument, of national policy in the nuclear field. With the passage of the Atomic Energy Act of 1954 there came into existence authority for actions in the international field which had not been possible under the act of 1946. These developments were products of the processes of maturity, implicit in the times and in the urgency of the need to refine national policy in a scientific area of revolutionary social significance. Rongelap and Japan documented the urgency. The Marshallese evacuated to Kwajalein and the Japanese fishermen being treated in Tokyo hospitals were witnesses to the immediacy of the problems of human welfare that could be inadvertently created by the slightest miscalculation of the conditions surrounding nuclear detonation. The hysteria in Japan was evidence of how poorly prepared were great populations of the world to cope with the suggestion of real or imagined danger. The halting diplomatic and scientific communications during the "Bikini Incident" revealed the extent of the need for communicable fact. The cruise of the *Shunkotsu Maru* showed how little was known about the disposition or effect of large amounts of fallout radioactivity in the sea.

The initial visit of the Applied Fisheries Laboratory group to Rongelap on March 26, 1954, had permitted only a brief and preliminary assessment of the condition of the abandoned atoll. The examination of the northern islands and the analysis of the biological samples had demonstrated, however, that reoccupation would not be possible for a considerable time. On April 13, Stanton Cohn and Lieutenant R. S. Farr led a small party to Rongelap for a further survey by the U.S. Naval Radiological Defense Laboratory and the Naval Medical Research Institute.[1] Two months later, the Marshallese who inhabited Ailinginae and Utirik were returned to their home atolls, which had been declared safe, but the Rongelapese were transferred from Kwajalein to a new community area that had been prepared for them at Ejit Island, Majuro Atoll. In July, Donaldson, Welander, and Lowman, who were continuing the post-Nectar collections at Eniwetok, were flown by Navy aircraft to Rongelap to make additional collections there. At the end of the year two more such brief visits would be made.

Faced with the necessity of maintaining contact with a situation almost 8,000 miles from its offices, and in a period when the proving ground would have been returned to an inactive status, the Division of Biology and Medicine could only seek information that would permit it to keep in touch with developments. In October, Pearson sent to Donaldson in Seattle a file of atoll contamination data and a suggestion that further surveys be incorporated in the Laboratory's current planning. Pearson wrote:

> While considerable material has been collected from several of the atolls in the line of fallout from the 1954 Pacific Weapons Tests, there has not been a definitive plan for survey of the area. The requirements outlined here have been planned with the objective of providing information on which a decision can be made relevant to the return of the natives from the Majuro Atoll to Rongelap. In view of this the major biological collections should be made around Rongelap Atoll. Since information is not available in the Washington Office regarding the flora of the individual islands or the extent to which food plants are gathered from these islands, it is recognized that the plan [should] allow for some flexibility and that individuals making the collections exercise their judgment.
>
> In addition to providing information relevant to returning the natives to Rongelap, there is the unusual opportunity of obtaining information on the movement of fallout material in the food chain of fauna and flora of the atolls of the Mid-Pacific.[2]

The statement stipulated that samples should be taken of soils, food plants, algae, fish, invertebrates, birds, and water, both fresh and salt. Also transmitted were tables of radioactivity levels as recorded early in March in Rongelap Village and in other locations in the atolls by Radiological Safety representatives and members of evacuation teams. On December 8, Held and Olson, who already were in the field, were accompanied to Rongelap by Walter D. Claus, chief of the Biophysics Branch of the Division of Biology and Medicine, and two Radiological Safety officers, and on December 18, Donaldson, Held, and Olson returned for further collections of biological specimens. With them was Jared Davis, of the Aquatic Biology Group of the Hanford plant at Richland, Washington, and two representatives of the Naval Radiological Defense Laboratory. The processing of the biotic materials and the analyses of the data emanating from these trips were accomplished at the Applied Fisheries Laboratory and in the NRDL.

By December, 1954, nine months after the initial contamination, Rongelap obviously was not yet safely habitable by its Marshallese owners, but while these events were proceeding in the northern Marshalls, Japanese and American scientists finally were being brought together for the first time in a formal conference on the effects of radioactivity. The contacts of Boss and Donaldson in May and June had been tentative, improvised, and conducted in the period of alarm, but from the informal meeting of June 30 the Japanese had gained, at least, as Hiyama later reported, the realization that "the American scholars were willing to offer their utmost cooperation wherever the mitigation by science of the injuries and damage by the Bikini Incident was possible."[3] Accordingly, there was held in Tokyo from November 15 to 19, 1954, a closed joint conference of Japanese and American representatives in which members of the United States delegation attempted to describe and delineate for the Japanese their procedures and interests in current studies of radiation effect.

Boss and Eisenbud were among the United States delegates, as were Pearson and Claus, of the Division of Biology and Medicine. With them were John H. Harley, chief of the Analytical Branch of the Health and Safety Laboratory of the New York Operations Office; Sterling B. Hendricks, head chemist of the Soil and Water Conservation Branch of the U.S. Department of Agriculture; and Morse Salisbury, the Commission's Director of Information Services. The Japanese group included fifteen of the scientists who had been most closely identified with the work of the Committee on the Effects of Radioactivity and the Bikini Investigation Commission, among them Hiyama and Miyake, Kenjiro Kimura, dean of the Faculty of Science of the University of Tokyo; Masanori Nakaizumi, chief of the Department of Radiology of the University of Tokyo and a member of the Panel on Radioisotopes of the Prime Minister's Scientific and Technical Administration Commission; and Fumio Yamasaki, chief of the Applied Nuclear Physics Laboratory of the Scientific Research Institute.[4]

No part of the five-day meeting was devoted specifically to the Bikini question. The agenda directed discussion to such matters as instrumentation systems, the use of radioisotopes in agricultural and biological research, laboratory techniques for measuring radioactivity in foods, soil, water, and air, decontamination procedures, and determination of maximum permissible doses. The Bikini question necessarily hovered about the meeting—the Japanese still were monitoring the catches of fish returned to their ports—but the specific situation that had occasioned the conference now had become simply a point of departure for discussions which ranged over areas of research method and concept, particularly in relation to medicine, agriculture, and biology.* But from this meeting came, as an unanticipated by-product, plans for the first of the United States surveys of radioactivity in the ocean.

II

Yasuo Miyake, the geochemist among the members of the Japanese delegation, had not been aboard the *Shunkotsu Maru*, but as an important member of Japan's standing committee he had met with Boss and Donaldson in June and he had directed, as head of the Department of Geochemistry of the Meteorological Institute, a share of the work on the materials brought back by the Bikini Waters Investigation Team. He was familiar with the Japanese data on the levels and distribution of radioisotopes found in the Pacific after Operation Castle, and during the course of the joint conference he discussed the findings in general terms with Eisenbud and other American representatives. It occurred to Eisenbud that, even after making allowance for decay and dilution, measurable quantities of activity still might be present in the waters of the Western Pacific and that, whether or not this proved to be true, an investigation would be valuable, providing new data at a later point in time or establishing with some finality, at last, the terminal point of the condition that had haunted Japan.[5]

On the return of the American delegation, Eisenbud sought from Allyn C. Vine, of the Woods Hole Oceanographic Laboratory, an opinion on the probable movement and dispersion, by the early months of 1955, of the water mass in which the Japanese had found contamination. In Vine's judgment the Bikini waters of mid-1954 soon would be reaching the coasts of Japan. Pursuing his idea, Eisenbud suggested to the Division of Biology and Medicine the possible usefulness of a further Pacific survey, and the proposal was discussed at an *ad hoc* meeting in Washington on January 12, 1955, at which Eisenbud and Vine were joined by

*Also hovering about the meeting were Japanese newspaper reporters, for whom press statements were prepared jointly by Salisbury and Hiyama. At the conclusion of the closed conference, the Japanese held a meeting on November 29 at which the contents of the joint session were reported to members of the Council for Research on Measures Against Atomic Bomb Injuries and of the Special Committee on the Effects of Radioactivity.

representatives of the Scripps Institution of Oceanography and the Office of Naval Research. Vine and John D. Isaacs, of Scripps, urged the project on the grounds that there was a considerable probability, as the report of the survey later stated, "that the radioactive water still was contained in the currents and, although reduced in intensity, might well be on the way to Japan."[6] They suggested that such an investigation might disclose the extent to which radioisotopes had been concentrated by plankton, in the intervening periods of months, or by the tuna feeding on the plankton in the westerly currents.

The program that resulted from this meeting was called Operation Troll. It was the first of the United States efforts to sample the distribution in the ocean of the radioactive products of nuclear tests, and its importance in an ethical sense was quite as great as its significance as a scientific operation. The Japanese aboard the *Shunkotsu Maru* had put to sea in an atmosphere of urgency. Operation Troll was conducted under no such pressure. But the expeditions were separate parts of a single investigation, both valid. Operation Troll sought to complete the record begun by the *Shunkotsu Maru*.

Planning for the survey was conducted by Eisenbud, Boss, and Harley, who was designated to lead the cruise; Warren S. Wooster, Scripps; James W. Smith and John J. Kane, of the Office of Naval Research; and Howard Brown, of the Division of Biology and Medicine. To Operation Troll was assigned the Coast Guard cutter *Roger B. Taney*, Commander Albert J. Carpenter, U.S.C.G. Harley's survey team included two senior scientists, Seymour, representing the Applied Fisheries Laboratory, the marine biologist, and Wooster, of Scripps, the oceanographer. Other members were Robert W. Gilkey, of Scripps, senior marine technician; and Robert S. Morse and Rudolf Anker, of the Health and Safety Laboratory. Harley, in addition to directing the work at sea, was in charge of the radiochemical analysis of samples and of the experimental operation of a new device designed in the New York Operations office to obtain continuous readings of radioactivity in the ocean.

The *Taney* departed San Francisco on February 25, 1955, to conduct ocean sampling from the Marshall Islands to Guam and on through the western Pacific from Morotai, in the Moluccas, to

Okinawa and Japan. The techniques and equipment employed by the *Taney* were to be, with the single exception of the operation of the experimental radiation measuring device, those used in oceanographic observation. Water samples were collected at predetermined depths in Nansen bottles, bronze tubes clamped at intervals on a steel cable and closed automatically in sequence when weights descending the cable released tripping mechanisms at their ends. The collection of plankton was accomplished with standard oblique tows of 1-meter plankton nets retaining organisms larger than 0.5 millimeter in diameter and, at each hydrographic station west of the Marshalls, a short vertical tow for microplankton with a 17-centimeter No. 20 net. A radiochemical laboratory was installed in the weather balloon shelter on the observation deck of the *Taney* and counting equipment in the adjacent weather office.[7]

The *Taney* began its collections on March 9, 1955, at a point several hundred miles east of Rongelap and of the area where the *Fukuryu Maru* had encountered the snowlike particles from Bikini almost exactly a year before. The vessel was refueled at Kwajalein on March 13, and then began a run through the Bikini-Eniwetok waters, obtaining in the area of the proving ground its first samples of flying fish. Moving west, the *Taney* paused off Truk, in the Caroline Islands, so that a small boat could be put off to collect samples of reef fish and coral from an island at the north rim of the atoll, and by March 22 the expedition had reached Guam, where more reef collections were made and a preliminary report of the early phase of the survey was sent to the New York Operations Office. Beyond Guam, the *Taney* moved for five days through the waters patrolled by the Japanese fishing fleets until on March 27 the vessel reached Douglas Reef, in the Philippines, where a further halt was made to permit collections of reef fish and invertebrates before the ship turned south toward Morotai. On April 9 the *Taney* laid a course for Japan, and on April 14 members of the group went ashore at Yokosuka, on Tokyo Bay. There they met informally with Japanese scientists to give them a summary of the preliminary data.[8]

The *Taney* returned to San Francisco on May 3. The cruise had covered 17,419 miles. In some seven weeks the survey had made collections at 46 principal ocean stations and 40 intermediate points spread over the western Pacific at intervals of 180 miles.

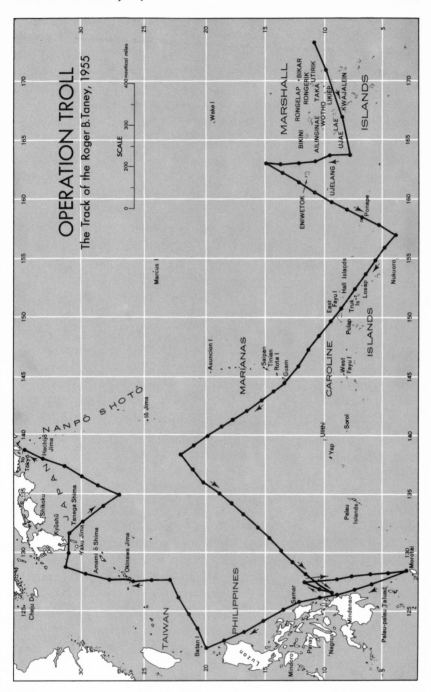

OPERATION TROLL
The Track of the Roger B. Taney, 1955

Samples of plankton had been taken at 85 stations in oblique tows at 200 meters of depth, and 889 samples of water had been taken to depths of hundreds, and occasionally to depths of thousands, of feet. After leaving Kwajalein, the *Taney* regularly was taking samples at depths to 600 meters with bottles at 10 intermediate levels (10, 25, 50, 75, 100, 150, 200, 300, 400, and 500 meters). In addition, four-bottle casts to a depth of 400 meters were made at each of the supplementary stations, and late in the survey, at stations 42 and 45, additional collections were made to depths of 800, 1,000, and 1,200 meters.

The *Taney's* unique equipment was its experimental device for measuring ocean radioactivity. The device was a scintillation probe designed and constructed at the Health and Safety Laboratory under the direction of Harris D. LeVine, chief of the Instruments Branch, to conduct continuous monitoring of radioactivity in sea water. The probe was a counter whose sensing element and associated batteries and circuits were housed in a stainless steel tube seven feet long that could be lowered overboard by winch and cable so that, when the *Taney* was under way, the instrument was towed through the water some 200 meters astern (and 5 to 10 feet below the surface at the ship's cruising speed of 17 knots), sending signals to a continuous recorder installed in the shipboard laboratory.[9]

The probe represented an effort to devise, even before the United States ocean survey had begun, a new method of achieving a continuous and comprehensive plot of whatever activity might be encountered at the ocean's surface. The probe proved of limited value in the *Taney* survey because of operational difficulties and because the activity generally was below the level of sensitivity of the instrument. Despite the difficulties, members of the *Taney* team thought that the probe had possibilities. Their judgment was that the probe "would be of considerable value in assessing sea water activity shortly after a detonation,"[10] and this was the use to which a subsequent probe would be put.

The *Taney* team found that the levels of radioactivity in the Pacific, a year after Operation Castle, were exceedingly low. There was nothing surprising in this, but it was noteworthy that the activity was detectable and that its distribution and behavior were in accord with the earlier interpretations of the Japanese. The levels still were sufficiently high to permit the preparation of long-distance plots from both the oceanographic and biological points of view. The average surface activity along the *Taney's* track was 93 disintegrations per minute (above the 600-700 level of natural isotopes) per liter of water.[11] The maximum readings were at a level of about 500 disintegrations per minute. The examination of radioisotopes at the lower depths presented questions of greater complexity, for in the lower waters the scientists were dealing with distribution factors about which little was known. At depths of 200 meters or more, for example, the water samples were being taken from below the stirred layer of the ocean's surface and below the level of the thermocline, the depth at which there is a rapid decrease in temperature and an increase in the density of the water. The stirred layer is of varying thickness, but in it there is a relatively rapid movement of water both horizontally, with the currents, and vertically in response to the forces of wind and temperature. The *Taney* scientists believed that the zooplankton, the small animal organisms swimming in the water, were function-ing in the radiobiological machinery of the ocean in the way that had been only dimly suspected at Bikini in 1946—concentrating selected isotopes within themselves, holding activity within the upper waters in which they live, and circulating the activity vertically within the stirred layer as they moved up and down in the waters in response to light. Highest counts of activity in the stirred layer were found off the coast of the Philippines, but there was a marked decrease of activity in the waters immediately off the coast of Japan, suggesting that movements of the North Equatorial Current had brought contamination to Japan's doorstep, but that there it was being swept away by the waters of the Kurishio Current. The report of the survey ultimately stated that water and plankton samples confirmed the existence, a year after the Opera-tion Castle tests, of "widespread low-level activity in the Pacific Ocean," and that the measurement of plankton offered "a sensitive indication of activity in the ocean."[12] In none of the fish samples did the *Taney* team find meaningful concentrations of activity. As the Troll report said, "None of the edible portions of fish collected on Operation Troll showed activity levels that would be of con-cern. In addition, the activity levels were so low that radiochemical analyses were not possible."[13] Activity, by 1955, was below the levels at which chemical techniques could distinguish between whatever radioisotopes were present.

The *Taney* cruise finished the investigations begun by the Japanese, confirming the Japanese data, but at the new point in time, and adding significant points on the flattening curve of decay and dispersion of ocean contamination from nuclear tests. The *Taney* gathered evidence which supported the Japanese thesis that activity from Operation Castle was being captured by ocean organisms and transported westward by the North Equatorial Current. Yet the highest concentration of contamination in the main current had been found on April 1, 1955, off the coast of Luzon, where the average was 190 disintegrations per minute per liter of water down to a depth of 600 meters.[14] The levels of activity were so low that they could not possibly cause concern as health hazards. But the *Taney* team said that similar attempts should be made to assess radioactivity in the ocean resulting from any future tests. That was the field problem toward which the *Shunkotsu Maru* and the *Taney* had pointed.

III

While the widening search was drawing attention more frequently to matters beyond the test atolls, Applied Fisheries staff members were maintaining their continuous round of observations at Eniwetok. There, by 1955, a question had arisen which, although it remained to the end without answer, seemed to be related directly to the ability of a race of warm-blooded animals to exist, in health and without observable genetic change, in an area that had been subjected repeatedly to the multiple effects of nuclear detonations.

The question concerned the colonies of rats on Engebi Island. Periodic sampling and observation of the Engebi colonies had been conducted, by 1955, for more than six years, a period in which Engebi had been the site of two atomic shots, within the radius of destruction of two thermonuclear detonations, and the scene of repeated and extensive engineering operations incidental to testing. The twelve months of continuous work in the Pacific after Operation Castle had provided, however, the first opportunity for consistent and detailed observations of the rats as residents of Engebi. In view of the known experience of Engebi Island as a nuclear test platform, the question now arose insistently as to how the rats had been able to survive repeated nuclear blasts and to continue to rebuild their numbers in a radically altered and frequently highly irradiated environment.

Few spots on earth had been exposed to more prolonged periods of violence than Engebi. In the years between 1944, when the island had been subjected to preinvasion bombardment, and 1954, when it felt for the fourth time the impact of nuclear detonation, Engebi's 250-acre triangle had become a barren, sandy plot from which the coconut palms and other trees had long since disappeared and on which the most significant features were man-made structures, including the great reinforced concrete building that had survived the pressures from the Mike shot on Elugelab in 1952. From 1948 to 1952, Engebi had been a principal collecting area for rat specimens, even though the island had been the site of the early atomic detonations in 1948 and 1951. After the Mike shot, the search for rats had extended over Engebi, Biijiri, and Rojoa Islands, but only on Biijiri, nine miles from the point of explosion, had specimens, weak and ill, been found. Engebi was much nearer than Biijiri to the Mike site (the center of the island was 3.2 miles from ground zero), and the low terrain had been exposed to a sequence of forces which included thermal radiation, initial nuclear radiation, shock, water waves, and residual nuclear radiation. Members of the Laboratory group, inspecting Engebi briefly a week after Test Mike, had seen the effects of these forces and had encountered beta-gamma radioactivity at a level of 11 roentgens an hour. No living animals except the transient birds could be found, and thus they had reported that there was "little probability that any rats survived on Engebi." But while it may have been unreasonable to expect that rats had survived, some had done so. Furthermore, rats survived the Nectar test of 1954, when a device detonated in the Mike crater had sent another surge of contaminated water over Engebi. By 1955, grass and scrub vegetation was sprouting on the island again, and in this new cover colonies of rats were establishing new runs and burrows. The colonies were being rebuilt even though the population had been subjected not only to physical shocks of unprecedented force but to amounts of radioactivity sufficiently high to cause the early deaths of individual survivors and genetic changes in offspring.

Treeless plain of Engebi Island in 1955 in area occupied by rat colonies *(Laboratory of Radiation Biology)*

A rat burrow built in the mildly irradiated soil of Engebi Island *(Applied Fisheries Laboratory)*

Specimens of mullet collected by Applied Fisheries Laboratory in reef pools, in 1954 with growths of green algae in what was believed to be scar tissue from thermal burns *(Laboratory of Radiation Biology)*

The rats of Engebi, as members of the *Rattus exulans* species, are animals whose relatives are found in many parts of the Pacific from the Hawaiian Islands to the Malay Peninsula. They are representatives of a group which has been split, however, into many local races in adaptation to island or atoll environments and in which marked differences exist between the races as to the size of individual members and as to choice of habitat. In general, members of the species are herbivorous, although insects form a portion of their diet, and at Engebi, while the rats are typically nocturnal, they frequently are found abroad in daytime because there are no predators or competitors to concern them. Their nests, composed of loosely matted grass stems, usually are built in burrows six to twelve inches below the surface of the ground, but occasionally the tunnels extend to eighteen to twenty-four inches below the surface, or nests are found immediately beneath boards, slabs of concrete, or protective rubble. Areas between the openings of the burrows are crossed by well-marked runs weaving between bunches of grass and leaves.

In 1955 the rats of Engebi were living on a treeless plain on which the man-made structures were the test buildings, underground bunkers, floors or concrete foundations of temporary buildings, a steel tower, trenches, roads, and an airplane landing strip. The distribution of the rat colonies seemed to be governed, however, by the arrangement of the plant communities—grasslands, areas of matted plants, and areas of bushes. Since the rats were most numerous in the grasslands, where they fed on the seeds of *Lepturus, Thuarea,* and *Fimbristylis* and on the leaves of *Triumfetta* and *Sida,* all common grass plants, the availability of food undoubtedly determined the distribution of the colonies. In the areas of densest colonization, observers from the Laboratory frequently saw rats scurrying along the runs and across open areas in the early morning and late afternoon, and many were seen at midday. It was possible only to guess at the size of the rat population, yet observations during selected hours produced figures on which it was possible to base rough estimates of the size of the major grasslands colony. From one vantage point Lowman counted the numbers of rats abroad at various times of the day in an area 100 feet square, and in that area of 10,000 square feet the numbers of rats ranged from 15 to 60. Assuming an even distribution of animals throughout the inhabited grasslands—an area of 660,000 square feet, or about 15 acres—some 1,000 to 4,000 rats would have been aboveground during any daylight hour. Without doubt the population was several times larger.[15]

The presence of rats in such numbers after four nuclear test series became the more remarkable as members of the Laboratory staff considered in detail the circumstances under which the colonies had re-established themselves. Broadly, three sets of effects entered their considerations—the effects of the preliminary construction associated with weapons tests, the effects of the tests themselves, and the effects of the construction in modifying the effects of the weapons. The pretest construction, which had involved the grading of large areas, had encouraged the formation of grasslands in which the rats lived, but it also had altered the locations of rat burrows, had forced the animals into new nesting areas, and had divided and isolated groups of rats from the main colony. Before each nuclear test, and particularly before the tests of 1952 and 1954, the grassy areas in which the rats lived had been cleared by bulldozers and reworked for the installation of dikes, bunkers, cables, and buildings, so that weeks before the actual shot the rats were living in much-changed surroundings. At the time of the detonation, thermal radiation and residual nuclear radiation unquestionably exerted the greatest possible effect on the new, separated, and rearranged colonies.

In the cases of the Sandstone and Greenhouse detonations, the effects of initial nuclear radioactivity must have been devastating. Lowman calculated that the Easy shot, during Operation Greenhouse, resulted in an initial gamma dose of from 6,400 to 10,000 roentgens in the center of the colony.[16] Rats aboveground at the time of detonation had little chance to gain cover in time to escape, although those six to twenty-four inches below ground, Lowman believed, probably were exposed to less than 10 roentgens of gamma radiation. Neutron radiation in the center of the colony from Test Easy was calculated at one and one-half to four times the lethal dose, and within the burrows it probably was reduced by only one-tenth to one-half its open-air level. It was unlikely that any rats in burrows near the center of the colony survived.

Residual nuclear radiation levels following the Mike shot were very high. Animals aboveground would have received 2,800 to

6,700 roentgens during the first hour and those in the burrows 112 to 1,120 roentgens. During the first nine days following detonation, rats in burrows received 250 to 2,500 roentgens of total integrated dose.[17] Cumulative levels probably were higher as a result of radioactive materials being washed into the burrows by the surge of water from the Mike crater, and the percentage of rat survival probably was extremely low. Because the Nectar device of 1954 was detonated over the Mike crater, water was lifted into the column and both thermal and residual nuclear radiations were of lesser effect. The total integrated residual nuclear radiation dose for the center of the colony a week after the Nectar detonation was 65 roentgens of gamma and 290 roentgens of beta-gamma activity. Animals in the burrows, it was calculated, would have received a maximum of 55 to 80 roentgens of beta-gamma if they stayed in the burrows for most of the week. Several animals collected nine days after Nectar had beta burns as well as thermal burns, however, and even during later visits to the island it was not uncommon for members of the Laboratory staff to collect living rats on which losses of patches of fur and searing of the flesh testified to their exposure to sources of residual beta radioactivity.[18]

The questions posed by the examination of the rat population were the more intriguing because, so far as could be determined by the most careful investigation of the evidence, the rats of Engebi were completely isolated, there had been no opportunity for immigration of animals from other sites, and the apparently thriving colonies of 1955 represented the natural rebuilding of populations that had been reduced four times by nuclear detonations. It was a possibility that new blood had been injected into the Engebi colonies by the arrival of rats on vessels bringing equipment and supplies to the island, yet the Eniwetok variety of *Rattus exulans* is a field rat and the probability of specimens being transported in supply crates was extremely small. It also was possible that rats of Old World species might reach the island by vessel, yet such rats differ markedly from Eniwetok rats in color and appearance and individual specimens almost certainly would have been picked up or their progeny would have been apparent as the products of mixed bloodlines. Invasion by new animals by more direct means seemed, on the other hand, even less likely. The Eniwetok islet nearest Engebi is Muzin, only 1,300 feet to the southeast, yet between that islet and Engebi there is a continuous flow of reef water which, according to tidal conditions, varies in velocity from one to two and one-half feet per second and in depth from six inches to ten feet. The neighboring island to the northwest is approximately 6,000 feet away and no rats ever had been observed there. Furthermore, no rats ever have been found swimming in the water off any of the islands at Eniwetok. Members of the Laboratory staff could not escape the conclusion that the Engebi rat colonies were wholly self-contained and that the circumstances of the rats' survival deserved specific investigation.

Studies of the effects of internal exposure of the rats were conducted by Lowman at the EMBL and, later, at the University laboratories. Radioactive materials had entered the bodies of specimens, he found, by inhalation, by ingestion of contaminants in water and food and on the fur, and through open wounds. Iodine 131 appeared to be the principal isotope gaining entry by inhalation.[19] After the Nectar detonation concentrations in the thyroid were at levels considered excessive, but specific radioactivity in organs and tissues changed with time and within nine weeks activity in the thyroid was so low that measurement was difficult. The day following detonation of the Nectar shot, specific activity of the skin was just below that of the thyroid, with activity still lower in the gut, bone, lung, kidney, muscle, and liver. Within five weeks, however, specific activity was greatest in the bone of random specimens and continued to be so for the remainder of the year. Chemical separations, decay curves, and absorption curves indicated that most of the radioactivity in muscle was due to the presence of cesium 137, and no strontium 89-90 was found in that tissue. In bone, however, isotopes included rare earths (approximately 20 per cent), small amounts of zirconium and niobium, and strontium 89-90 at a level of about 10 per cent of the total activity present. In January, 1955, the bones of rats contained strontium 89-90 in amounts approximating the maximum permissible dose, but no bone tumors had been discovered and none was found in specimens collected later. In general, the deposition of radioactivity within the bodies of the rats followed familiar patterns. In a report in May, 1955, Lowman said:

> In view of the fact that this population had been subjected to high levels
> of radiation capable of producing genetic effects in the survivors as well as

early deaths of others, observable effects upon the present inhabitants should have occurred. However, the pregnancy rate and the average number of embryos per litter do not vary significantly. . . . The sex ratio does not vary from a 50-50 ratio. Except for those taken shortly after detonation, almost all individuals examined during the last year appear to be in good physical condition. . . . In addition, the main colony is expanding both in numbers and in occupied area.[20]

Within the Division of Biology and Medicine, Lowman's preliminary description of the problems led to suggestions that a plan of operations be prepared. A draft proposal was submitted to the Division on June 3, 1955.[21] In the meantime, the pressure of events in Japan and at Rongelap was directing attention toward the problems of ocean fallout. With so many questions needing answers, and with experienced personnel in such short supply, the rats of Engebi had to wait.

It had been Lowman's belief, as he indicated in his informal reports, that the survival of a basic stock of rats had been assured, even after four nuclear detonations, by two factors—the presence of groups of rats separated from the main colony by engineering construction and beyond the lethal range of the neutron flux, and the use as "burrows" by unknown numbers of rats of the deep bunkers and cable tunnels on Engebi, where they were protected from all of the effects of nuclear blast except the residual contaminations. If either or both of these factors preserved a small number of healthy animals, the rebuilding of the colonies might proceed until the delayed effects of low-level irradiation began to become apparent. Lowman was certain that in three of the four detonations only animals heavily shielded by coral or concrete could have survived—but such survival of a population was, under the circumstances, a fact of considerable significance.

IV

During the early months of 1955, while the *Taney* was at sea, a new series of tests had been conducted at the Nevada Proving Ground in what was called Operation Teapot, a series that included at least fourteen detonations and represented the most extensive program conducted to that time at either of the two test sites. On May 17, in a separate Pacific program called Wigwam, a single underwater device was exploded at a depth of 2,000 feet off the west coast of the United States, and this was the first underwater explosion since Test Baker in 1946.* While none of these activities involved the Applied Fisheries Laboratory, there was the expectation that the Laboratory would be used in connection with the 1956 Pacific tests in a new program whose objectives could not yet be described, but throughout 1955 and into the winter of 1955-56 the Applied Fisheries Laboratory was occupied by the many new questions flowing from the events of 1954.

By April, 1955, the Laboratory had been engaged continuously for thirteen months in the Eniwetok work. The new field schedule was one in which two- and three-man teams were rotated to the proving ground for periods averaging one month. Between February, 1954, and March, 1955, the eight senior members of the Laboratory staff had spent 1,082 man-days in the Pacific area. The Rongelap and Japanese situations had modified considerably the Laboratory's responsibilities. The effects were more significant than the temporary involvement of Donaldson in the Japanese discussions or of Seymour in the *Taney* investigation. The nuclear test program had been moved further into the field of international relations. Lingering residues of Japanese feeling, while never obvious, nevertheless were detectable in some sectors of the Japanese scientific community, although these always were overlaid by a genuine and substantial interest in the scientific problems themselves. In the United States there was a rising concern with the question of strontium 90, an enlargement into the area of public discussion of the interest mentioned by Bugher in 1953, and the Atomic Energy Commission's concern was expressed in research approaches suggested by Commissioner Willard F. Libby. These developments gave new pertinence to information bearing on the matter of possible contamination in the Pacific.

Uppermost among the problems was Rongelap. The care and observation of the Rongelap people was proceeding under the joint auspices of the Navy and the Trust Territory. As in the

*The United States had not escaped the tuna scare of 1954. West Coast tuna canners had experienced a depressed market which forced out of business several smaller operators. To anticipate public reaction, at the time of Test Wigwam, the Commission asked the Division of Biology and Medicine to set up a fish monitoring program. Automatic radiation counting systems were installed at major West Coast canneries and military personnel were trained to hand-monitor fish brought to the smaller canneries. The Food and Drug Administration, which conducted the program, was able to assure the public that no contamination existed.

(Top) Abandoned buildings, Rongelap, May, 1957 *(Holmes & Narver, Inc.*
(Center) Beach at abandoned Rongelap village, 1956 *(Holmes & Narver, Inc.)*
(Bottom) Native well on Rongelap, 1956 *(Holmes & Narver, Inc.)*

case of Bikini eight years before, the question of Rongelap's future habitation depended on assessment of the extent to which there had been an uptake of radioisotopes by fish and plants and other atoll products used by the Marshallese for food. The preliminary spot checks that had been made at Rongelap before the end of 1954 were followed by three additional visits early and late in 1955, one a joint expedition between January 25, and January 30, 1955, by the Naval Radiological Defense Laboratory and the Applied Fisheries Laboratory, and two more by Applied Fisheries staff members—Seymour, Held, Lowman, and Bonham—from October 21 to October 23 and on November 7, 1955. Each visit produced land survey data and additional soil and biological samples. Soil samples were sent to the New York Operations Office for radioanalysis. Biological materials selected for preliminary evaluation were analyzed at the Eniwetok laboratory, but most of them were processed at the Applied Fisheries Laboratory, from which data were forwarded to the Division of Biology and Medicine.

In February, 1955, the results of the Atomic Energy Commission's investigation of the 1954 fallout were incorporated in summary in a detailed public report attempting to cover the whole range of known effects of nuclear explosion. In this report the levels of the initial contamination were disclosed for the first time. Of the fallout laid across the Pacific from Bikini the statement said:

> 20. . . . Inside Bikini Atoll at a point 10 miles downwind from the explosion it is estimated that the radiation dosage was about 5,000 roentgens for the first 36-hour period after the fallout. The highest radiation measurement outside of Bikini Atoll indicated a dosage of 2,300 roentgens for the same period. This was in the northwestern part of Rongelap Atoll, about 100 miles from the point of detonation. Additional measurements in Rongelap Atoll indicated dosages, for the first 36-hour period, of 2,000 roentgens at 110 miles, 1,000 roentgens at 125 miles, and, farther south, only 150 roentgens at 115 miles from Bikini.
>
> 21. Some distance farther south from the point of detonation, at about 160 miles downwind and along the axis of the ellipse, the amount of radioactivity would have seriously threatened the lives of about one-half of the persons in the area who *failed to take protective measures*.* It is estimated

*Original emphasis.

that the radiation dosage at that point was about 500 roentgens for the first 36-hour period.

22. Near the outer edge of the cigar-shaped area, or approximately 190 miles downwind, it is estimated that the level of radioactivity would have been sufficient to have seriously threatened the lives of 5 to 10 per cent of any persons who might have remained exposed out-of-doors for the first 36 hours. In this area the radiation dosage is estimated at about 300 roentgens for the first 36-hour period.

23. Thus, about 7,000 square miles of territory downwind from the point of burst was so contaminated that survival *might* have depended upon prompt evacuation of the area or upon taking shelter and other protective measures.[22]

The Biology Branch, as custodian of the radiobiological information on which decisions on the Rongelap matter would be based, was pressed repeatedly for current and refined data from the contaminated atolls and this pressure was reflected in the work of the Applied Fisheries field teams. On April 1, 1955, Donaldson, on returning from a brief visit to the proving ground, reported in a letter to Pearson that during the preceding thirteen months the Laboratory had processed 12,378 biological and other samples, adding that "the problem now is how to evaluate this mass of data" and put it into usable form. By August, 1955, the Laboratory had forwarded to the Commission a report of its analysis of 1,499 biological and soil and water specimens collected at Rongelap in 1954 and on January 25 to 30, 1955.[23] The report gave particular attention to atoll products used by the natives for food and, although the data reflected an expectable decline in radioactivity levels during the period of almost eleven months since the initial contamination, the results showed that biological uptake and cycling of radioisotopes were proceeding actively. Samples of coconut meat collected on March 26, 1954, averaged 1.16 microcuries of total beta activity per kilogram of wet tissue while by January 30, 1955, the level had declined to .036. Fish muscle on March 26 averaged 2.74 microcuries but fish liver averaged 204.0. Ten months later the values of fish muscle and liver had dropped to .10 and 3.52 microcuries. Similar declines were found in clam muscle, crab muscle, the liver and muscle of birds, and in squash, papaya, arrowroot, and pandanus.[24] The processes of concentration and redistribution of activity were observable. In both edible and inedible plants the specific activity was higher in the leaves than in the fruit, but the later collections showed that leaf buds formed after the initial fallout contained as much activity as the older leaves. The values for arrowroot collected in January, 1955, on Rongelap Island, which was outside the zone of primary contamination, were similar to the activity values found in arrowroot from the heavily contaminated northern islands. This also was true of algae collected at depths of 10 to 25 fathoms of lagoonal water off southerly Rongelap Island and northern Kabelle. "It appears likely then," the Laboratory said, "that although maximum fallout occurred at the north end of the atoll, the radioactive material is being redistributed throughout the atoll, at least in the deeper waters."[25] A similar anomoly was discovered in the study of birds.

Analysis of the 1954-55 samples disclosed that terns captured on the southern islands contained more than six times as much activity in the bone and intestinal tracts as terns from the contaminated northern islands, and more than five times as much in the muscle and liver.[26] Terns are not migratory in habit and they subsist on the small fish which swim in schools in the atoll lagoons, but the differences in the levels of contamination made it seem possible that the birds from the southern Rongelap islands somehow had access to food supplies containing greater amounts of radioactive materials and that these supplies, if they were not at Rongelap, might be at Ailinginae, which lies seven and a half nautical miles to the southwest. Such a conjecture might have been significant only as a commentary on the ramifications of atoll contamination except that it had, in this instance, a more direct connection with the Rongelap case. The Rongelap people, who used nearby Rongerik to raise supplementary food crops, also were known to hunt birds on Ailinginae to further augment their food supplies. The birds formed a part of the food chain important to man, and thus in this new instance a small but peculiar deviation in the expectable pattern of radiation behavior opened up a new area of consideration.

Plans for the October-November resurvey of Rongelap were initiated in September, 1955. The request that the evaluations be brought up to date was transmitted by Dunham, who had become director of the Division of Biology and Medicine. The field team sent from Seattle on October 12 was joined at the proving ground by Robert Taft, Radiological Safety officer of the Commission's Resident Engineer staff, and the group was taken to Rongelap aboard a Navy LST. This time the survey included Ailinginae, although the major effort was directed at Rongelap and to the collection of soil and biological samples from which might be determined the absolute values of contamination and the rate of its decline. The activity of most samples collected on the northern islands of Kabelle and Labaredj still was higher than that of similar samples taken from the south, including Rongelap Island, and the levels of activity in soils and land plants at Enibuk Island, Ailinginae, were only a third as high as those at Rongelap. The lone exception to the October generalizations was the tern, for the October examination of the bird specimens confirmed the January observation.[27] The bone and tissue of Ailinginae terns contained on the average twice as much radioactivity as those of terns captured at Kabelle and other islands more directly in the line of fallout. The reason still was obscure and seemingly bound into the complex of numberless small mysteries contained in the contamination problem. The amounts of activity were low, but their presence underlined the prevalence of low-level activity in the atoll almost twenty months after the March 1, 1954, detonation at Bikini.

The October work at Rongelap included extensive sampling of soils, particularly in the sands at the low tide lines and at the lagoon bottom. On the bottom off Kabelle activity of the samples occasionally equaled that of the island sands, but ranged down to one-third of its value. The land surveys of October 21 to 23 included readings taken at intervals across Kabelle, Labaredj, and Rongelap Islands with the meter (Beckman MX-5) held one inch above the soil. After the survey team had concluded its sampling and had returned to Eniwetok, a message from the Division of Biology and Medicine requested a "complete survey of the islands" with the meter held at the three-foot level. The survey of November 7 was in response to that request. On that day Seymour and Held were returned by air to Rongelap to go over the ground even more intensively. By evening they had covered Rongelap and Larabedj Islands, making readings at both the three-foot and one-inch levels. In all, they covered some seventeen locations on Larabedj and twenty-three on Rongelap, traversing the village from the lagoon landing area and making readings in the huts and the community buildings, including the school.[28]

The Division's request almost certainly was related to discussions then under way concerning the future of Rongelap, discussions which now touched more frequently the question of strontium 90. The need often produced requests for data directly from the field, and the Laboratory was forwarding to Dunham or to Boss copies of its daily logs in which reports of readings and analyses were contained. On November 7, after Seymour and Held had completed their new land survey, Boss sent a letter to Donaldson in Seattle in which he said:

> The information included in the daily log of the Marshall Islands field team has been very helpful. Dr. Gordon Dunning is primarily interested in strontium-90 activity data, and he has raised the following questions:
> 1. What is the strontium-90 activity per wet gram of weight in plants and (in) liver, meat, etc., of marine animals? In other words, what percentage of the total activity is represented by the strontium-90?
> 2. What is the gamma dose at Rongelap?
> 3. In soils, what is the strontium-90 activity per square foot?
> 4. What are the readings at the 3-foot level at your different collecting stations on the two islands (Kabelle and Labaredj)?[29]

The three-foot readings had been obtained before Boss wrote. The strontium 90 matters were covered in the Laboratory report filed on December 30, 1955. The analyses showed that for all food plants except coconuts the strontium 90 value approximated 4 per cent of the total activity present in the samples. For coconuts, the percentage was 1 per cent. No strontium 90 was found in the soft tissues of pelagic or reef fish or clams. The bone sample of a single fish, a bonito, yielded a maximum strontium-90 activity of 8 per cent. Neither the muscle or bone of the terns contained strontium 90, but the coconut crab, which feeds principally on land plants, had strontium-90 levels of 3 per cent in the muscle and 12 per cent in the liver (hepato-pancreas), where calcium salts are stored. The radioisotopes in salts leached from the carapace of the crab were found to consist entirely of strontium 90 and yttrium 90.[30] In the lagoon bottom samples collected in October, 1955, 0.7 per cent of the activity was strontium 90. Of the total radiostrontium activity of the Rongelap lagoon bottom the Laboratory said:

The sand profile in 49 feet of water off Rongelap Island had the lowest level of radioactivity of the lagoon bottom profiles taken in October, 1955. The average radioactivity level for the top eight inches of sand in this sample was 0.19 uc/kg. Using this value for the average of the radioactive contamination on the bottom of Rongelap lagoon and a strontium 90 content of 0.7 per cent, a total of 380 curies of strontium 90 for the top eight inches of the lagoon bottom is obtained. This is probably a minimum value.[31]

While Rongelap continued to be a focal point, the continuous round of sampling proceeded at Eniwetok and the search for information widened to include other atolls, notably Ujelang, in the Marshalls, and Ponape, in the eastern Carolines, the nearest points in the path of the west-southwest currents at which repeated checks could be made of the possible presence of ocean-borne contamination. Visits also were made to Likiep and Wotho, and to Tarawa, in the Gilberts. These trips usually were brief, one- or two-day expeditions by Navy amphibian aircraft. Each produced new biological samples for radioanalysis.*

V

The 1956 test series at the Pacific Proving Ground was Operation Redwing. The program was to be opened in May and shots would be scheduled through June and into July at both Bikini and Eniwetok. The devices would be of lower yield and greater variety than those tested in 1954 and the series would include the first airdrop of a thermonuclear bomb.

The planning for the radiobiological work in 1956 was conditioned by all that had happened in the Pacific since Operation Castle. The Applied Fisheries Laboratory still was concerned with the Rongelap case, as was the Naval Radiological Defense Laboratory, but at the same time it had before it half a dozen lines of possible action stemming from the prolonged observation at Eniwetok in 1954 and 1955. The concentrated experience after the Castle tests had confirmed that the patterns of distribution of released radioactivity in biological organisms were, within rough limits, predictable. But the knowledge by no means extended to the metabolic processes involved or to the parts played by certain less complex organisms in the selection and retention in the environment of certain long-lived isotopes. In looking forward to

*For a summary record of the decline of radioactivity at Eniwetok following Test Nectar (1954), see Appendix 1.

1956, the Laboratory saw its own program as one in which it might pursue, in even more detailed fashion, the questions that had been lost or ignored in the period of special demands following the Bikini incident.

In the exoskeletons of the land crabs, for example, strontium 90 had been found to constitute 50 per cent of the accumulated radioactivity. There was the matter of the red alga, *Asparagopsis,* which in 1954 had been observed to concentrate iodine 131 in amounts up to 18,000 times greater than those present in surrounding waters while other algae showed no such disposition. And there was, further, the absorbing puzzle of the rat colonies on Engebi Island. These and other facets of the Pacific work were yet to be approached in consistent fashion. But behind all of the alternatives was the opportunity to conduct surveys of the ocean during a test operation.

An ocean survey in connection with Operation Redwing was considered a possibility long before the character of the operation itself had taken shape. While Redwing would include no detonation as large as Bravo, it was inconceivable that a new test program would be planned without appropriate attention to the possible westward drift of fallout contamination. The matter continued to be of vital concern to the Japanese, who by the early months of 1956 were planning a new and more extensive marine expedition in one phase of which the *Shunkotsu Maru* would be dispatched on a second cruise through waters west of the proving ground during the test series.* In January, 1956, there had been no decision on whether a United States survey would be conducted during Redwing or, if one were to be held, by what organization and with what objectives. Whatever the elements entering into the question of objective, the matter of what organization was to perform the survey probably was a critical one. The Applied Fisheries Laboratory was not an oceanographic research unit and its Pacific experience, extensive at it was, had been almost wholly in the field of island and reef ecology. Yet the proposed ocean survey was an extension of the earlier work and a development

*The Japanese in 1956 organized an international survey, EQUAPAC, involving France and Peru and which they hoped the United States would join. In this operation studies were conducted across the full width of the equatorial Pacific and included observations near the proving ground for which the *Shunkotsu Maru* again was employed.

proceeding from the same point of origin. Furthermore, the Laboratory had a plan. On March 15, 1955, while the *Taney* still was at sea, the Laboratory's annual report had discussed the general conditions suggesting further ocean exploration.[32] More specific recommendations were included, at the suggestion of the Division of Biology and Medicine, in the outline of its 1956 program as submitted by the Laboratory on February 7, 1956.[33] In this the Laboratory proposed that three cruises be made in July and August, one during the nuclear test series "to outline roughly the area of contamination by sampling rapidly and at great intervals, beginning in the area of predicted fallout"; the second to measure the distribution across the ocean; and the third "to make reef collections at islands in the pattern of the contaminated water."[34] The character and extent of the 1956 survey probably was determined in part by these proposals, but the ultimate decision was to make two surveys, rather than three, the first to measure marine contamination during the test series and the second to attempt to trace the farthest drift of fallout after it had been dispersed and diluted in the ocean.

On March 28, 1956, Dunham described in a letter of authority to Donaldson the terms under which the marine operations would be conducted. He said that the Division of Biology and Medicine had assigned to the Applied Fisheries Laboratory the task of conducting "two marine biological open sea surveys beginning June 10 and September 1," and that:

> The primary mission of these two surveys is to ascertain (a) the levels of introduced radioactivity resulting from the tests in the water, plankton, and fish, and (b) how far the activity extends westward in the North Equatorial Current. It has been recommended to the Task Force:
> (a) That the ship should operate from the area of highest average fallout to the westward fringe of the detectable introduced radioactivity in the water, and
> (b) That you or Allyn Seymour and the ship's captain be briefed as to the location where fallout from each shot fell into the sea prior to each survey.[35]

Dunham also said that continuous water monitoring would be conducted during the cruises with "necessary instrumentation" provided by the New York Operations Office—which meant that a new model of the probe would be used, as Harley and the mem-

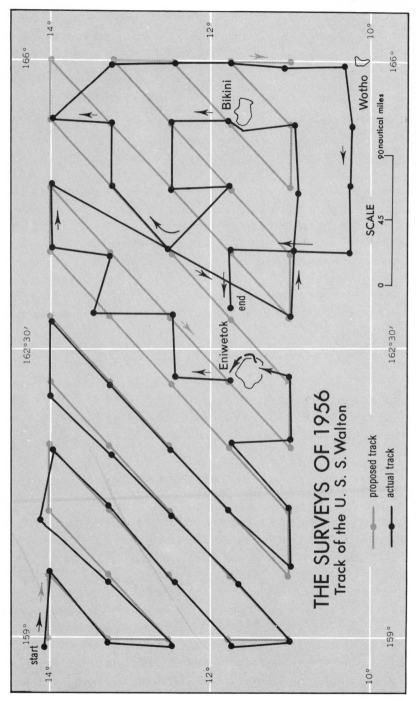

THE SURVEYS OF 1956
Track of the U. S. S. Walton

proposed track

actual track

bers of the Operation Troll team had suggested. Water samples would be obtained from the surface and at 25, 50, 75, and 100 meters at appropriate stations, plankton tows would be made "in areas of both high and low activity," and fish would be collected for radioanalysis wherever possible.

The ship assigned to the June survey—the survey to be conducted while Operation Redwing was in progress—was the U.S.S. *Walton* (DE 361), Commander Arthur T. Emerson Jr., a destroyer escort detached from the fleet in the Far East and ordered to report to Eniwetok on June 5 to receive research equipment and to enable Commander Emerson to join Donaldson and Seymour at the precruise briefings. The Redwing test series was in progress when the *Walton* reported at Eniwetok to submit to her conversion and to meet the survey team which included Donaldson, Welander, Seymour, Lowman, and Olson. The series had been opened with a detonation on Runit Island of a relatively small atomic device, but on May 21 a B-52 had climbed to 50,000 feet above Bikini to make the first United States airdrop of a thermonuclear bomb over a target on Namu Island, at the northwest corner of the atoll. Other test shots of various types were scheduled during the ensuing weeks.

The conversion of the *Walton* included installation on her afterdeck of a power winch and A-frame to handle the steel sampling cable and an outboard platform for work with plankton nets and water-sampling bottles. Radiation counters and laboratory tables were placed in quarters below. On the afterdeck was mounted a shipboard model of the New York Operations Office scintillation probe, constructed so that sea water would be brought to it by the ship's pumps for continuous monitoring, the water entering the tank and flowing about the sensing element before being discharged over the side of the vessel.

The initial survey problem was the design of a cruise pattern that would permit the taking of a maximum number of samples at the prescribed depths and over a sufficiently large area to make certain that ocean contamination was being assessed at its maximum. The survey also had to be compressed into the shortest possible time. The course as it was projected involved moving the *Walton* on a series of northeast-southwest traverses of the ocean within an area some 400 miles in length and 200 miles in width.

The cruise would begin about 180 miles west of Eniwetok—as far west as the farthest point of possible drift of waterborne contamination—and would move eastward on angled track lines to a line thirty miles east of Bikini, covering in ten days fifty collection stations spread across a grid of more than 70,000 square miles.[36] It would be necessary for the *Walton* to make a fuel stop at Eniwetok at the mid-point of the survey.

The *Walton* departed Eniwetok on June 11, reached its first station at 8:00 A.M. on June 12, and continued for five days and nights the first half of the ocean-sampling program, re-entering Eniwetok lagoon on the morning of June 16 with water and plankton samples from twenty-four stations. The probe, mounted on the deck, had functioned without difficulty, but operation through contaminated waters had led to contamination of the instrument itself. This factor later was adjusted by plotting a "normal" curve of the ten-day cruise with the background readings of the waters of Eniwetok at the start, mid-point, and end of the sampling. These "normal" levels were two microroentgens on June 11, nine microroentgens on June 16—the mid-point—and 125 microroentgens on June 21, when the survey was concluded.[37]

Departing Eniwetok again on June 16, after a six-hour pause for refueling and for making an operational report to the joint task force, the *Walton* continued the survey to its end. The pattern, however, was interrupted on June 17 by orders to the *Walton* to move out of the area during a new test explosion, with the result that the vessel was forced to proceed to an area south of Eniwetok until she was cleared to continue. The remaining stations were visited on a zigzag course ending in a series of east-west, north-south runs about Bikini. In all, the *Walton* had touched fifty-three rather than fifty stations by the time she returned to Eniwetok.

Analysis of the *Walton*'s samples disclosed that radioactive contamination was present in relatively heavy concentrations in identifiable locations within the survey area, which finally covered 78,000 square miles. Radioactivity diminished in value around the edges of the sampling area, indicating that the survey had, in fact, encompassed the waters in which the heaviest contamination would be found. Counts of activity in the surface waters were considerably higher than those down to 100 meters, for the fallout deposited

Laboratory group boarding U.S.S. *Walton:* Welander (left), Held, Donaldson, Lowman, Capt. Emerson, Seymour, Hines *(Holmes & Narver, Inc.)*

Net used for plankton sampling, U.S.S. *Walton (Holmes & Narver, Inc.)*

(Left) Welander conducting water sampling, U.S.S. *Walton Holmes & Narver, Inc.)*

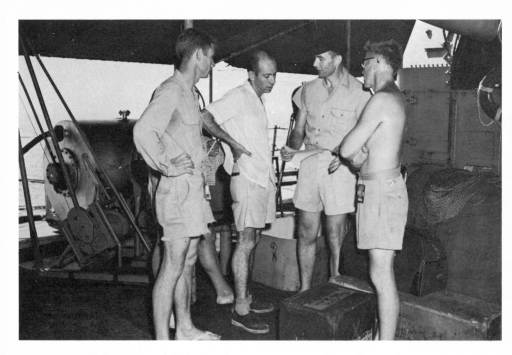

Lowman, Held, Seymour, and Welander aboard the U.S.S. *Walton*, 1956 *(Holmes & Narver, Inc.)*

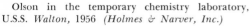

Olson in the temporary chemistry laboratory, U.S.S. *Walton*, 1956 *(Holmes & Narver, Inc.)*

(Upper right) Palumbo recording dry weights of algae samples in EMBL, 1957 *(Laboratory of Radiation Biology)*

(Lower right) Lowman (left) and Held at shipboard probe, U.S.S. *Walton*, 1956 *(Holmes & Narver, Inc.)*

on the surface during the tests had not yet penetrated the stirred layer. The surface water samples had an average value, for the 3,300-mile run, of 10,000 disintegrations per minute per liter of total beta radioactivity, whereas water sampled from the 100-meter depth had the lowest average content, about 3,900 disintegrations per minute.[38] It was noted that, while measurable amounts of activity were found in the waters of each station sampled, the lowest values were found in the northwest part of the survey area, in that part where the survey had started, while the highest readings were found immediately north and west of Bikini, where maximum readings of 120,000 disintegrations per minute were recorded.

The pattern of plankton contamination was a magnification, many times over, of the contamination in the water. The average value of radioactivity in plankton was 71,000 disintegrations of total beta activity per minute per gram, the highest value, found in a sample taken north of Bikini, being 1,200,000 disintegrations per minute. On a weight-for-weight basis, the average value of plankton radiation was 7,000 times that of the surface water. The minimum level, of 1,300 disintegrations per minute, was almost as high as the maximum level recorded by the *Taney* survey of 1955, so that it was assumed that the entire area covered by the *Walton* was contaminated to some extent. The levels of plankton contamination, highest north of Bikini, diminished rapidly to the south and trailed off gradually to the northwest, except that there was a long stream of plankton contamination extending from Eniwetok to Bikini and on to the southwest corner of the survey area, a stream identifiable for more than 300 miles. Examination of the measurements by the probe showed that the curves checked closely with those produced by the surface water samplings on most of the fifty-three stations.[39]

VI

As the cruise of the *Taney* was a sequel to the cruise of the *Shunkotsu Maru*, so the survey conducted by the U.S.S. *Marsh* (DE 699), Commander Wilfred G. Chartier, was a sequel to that of the *Walton*. This time, however, the missions were related in purpose and schedule. The *Walton* had sampled and outlined the radiation-tagged water mass while it was forming during Operation

Redwing. The *Marsh* attempted to follow the Redwing contamination across 1,000 miles of ocean between the proving ground and Guam.

The *Marsh* expedition, as had been anticipated in the original instruction to Donaldson, departed Eniwetok on September 1, 1956, on an operation that made two zigzag sweeps, one east to west, one west to east, from Eniwetok to Guam and return, taking samples in twenty days from seventy-four ocean stations. On September 1, when the *Marsh* left Eniwetok for its first station, Operation Redwing had been over for six weeks and the major elements of the task force had been sent home. Seymour, who had been with both the *Taney* and the *Walton*, was in charge of the survey team that included Lowman, Held, and John Donaldson, now a biologist with the Washington State Department of Game. The equipment used aboard the *Marsh*, except for a few refinements, was that used on the *Walton*. The probe, overhauled for the new assignment, was used for continuous monitoring along a track 7,500 miles in length. The water collections were slightly deeper than those of the *Walton*, sampling being made this time at the surface and at depths of 25, 50, 100, and 150 meters, but the plankton tows again were from a depth of 200 meters, well below the bottom of the stirred layer. Of the seventy-four stations visited by the *Marsh*, thirty were between Eniwetok and Guam, covering the waters between 9 and 12 degrees north of the Equator; thirty-four more on a track from Rota and Saipan, in the Marianas, to Wotho Atoll, in the Marshalls, sampling waters between 12 and 15 degrees north; and ten were spaced along a final swing north of Wotho, past Rongelap and Bikini, and back across the proving ground to Eniwetok.

The *Marsh* brought back the answer to the question of how far and at what levels of activity contamination had moved westward. At Guam, samples of water showed very low levels of radioactivity, yet the values at the surface were four to twenty times the lowest values (48 counts per minute per liter of gross beta) found northeast of Bikini, where test contamination was virtually absent.[40] Thus it appeared that the westward fringe of the drift had reached, in September, the vicinity of Guam, but at levels so low that they were significant only for the purposes of identification. Furthermore, the maximum value for water, regardless of place or depth

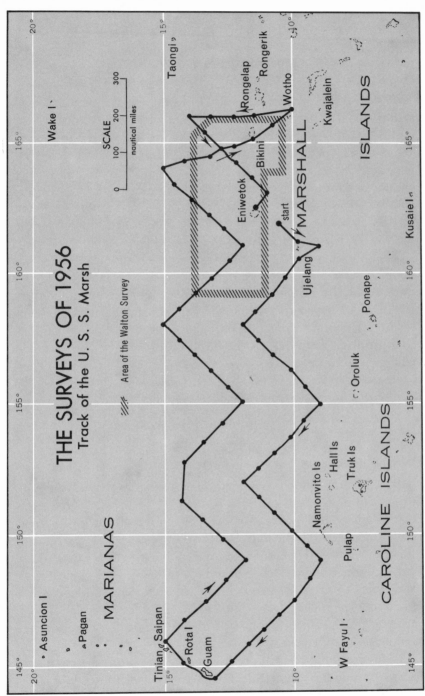

THE SURVEYS OF 1956
Track of the U. S. S. Marsh

SCALE

0   100   200   300

nautical miles

////// Area of the Walton Survey

MARIANAS

Asuncion I

Pagan

Tinian Saipan
Rota
Guam

W Fayu I.

Pulap

Namonvito Is

Hall Is

Truk Is

Oroluk

CAROLINE ISLANDS

Ponape

Kusaie I.

Wake I.

Taongi

Rongelap   Rongerik

Rongelap   Wotho

Kwajalein

Bikini

Eniwetok

start

Ujelang

MARSHALL   ISLANDS

of the sample, was 19,000 disintegrations per minute of total beta, and this single sample was taken from the surface at Station 2, southwest of Eniwetok toward Ujelang Atoll, as the cruise began. Levels of radioactivity diminished sharply thereafter, trailing off to the lower values, while the samplings down to 150 meters were variable in content and seemed, as the report later stated, to fall into regional patterns. As all of the earlier surveys had discovered, the *Marsh* also found that plankton were the most sensitive indicators of the presence of radioactivity. The highest value of total beta activity in plankton, 21,000 disintegrations per minute per gram, was found in samples taken eighty miles north of Eniwetok, and the lowest, 27, near Guam. The average of ratios of plankton activity to sea water activity was 2,500 to 1, much lower than the ratio of 7,000 to 1 reported by the *Walton* three months earlier.[41]

The *Marsh* survey between September 1 and 20, 1956, completed the second phase of a two-stage study of a radiation-tagged water mass. It had found radioactivity from Redwing at lower levels, as had been expected. It also confirmed the general accuracy of the Japanese in their original analysis of the ocean contamination problem, even though the levels again were below those that could cause concern.

In one of his reports of work with plankton collected by the *Shunkotsu Maru,* Kawabata had said,

> Although the mechanisms of the accumulation of radioisotopes in planktons and their action in the organisms are still vague, it is, by all means, of importance that certain planktons selectively accumulate specific radioactive elements of minute amount in the sea water in their bodies.[42]

In a slightly different way, the *Marsh* samples showed the same thing. The plankton collected by the *Marsh* revealed differences of contamination by area—by the parts of the ocean from which they were taken. Radioactive elements found in plankton collected ninety miles north of Eniwetok differed from those encountered in plankton collected some hundreds of miles west of Eniwetok, and this apparently was because the predominant species of plankton differed by area. The Laboratory recommended further study of this problem because of its bearing on the disposition of fallout contamination in the ocean.

A further difference appeared in radiochemical analysis of the *Marsh* samples. Although fission products had been presumed to present the principal problems associated with nuclear detonation, a considerable proportion of the total radioactivity found in plankton, and in the few fish samples, was radioactivity induced in such common elements as zinc and iron. The significant contaminants, including strontium 90, were in many instances either totally absent or present in only faintly perceptible amounts.[43] The residues of fallout radioactivity in the ocean were of a different character than those found on land. In the initial radiochemistry in studies of the *Marsh* samples, comparisons were made of groups of stations along the *Marsh* track. In a report of this work published in February, 1958, Lowman pointed out that radioactive zinc, cobalt, and iron—nonfission products—actually contributed an average of 71 per cent of the radioactivity in the *Marsh* plankton samples.[44] Work with the samples seemed to show, he said, that fallout in the ocean was being handled by a mechanism which tended to scour out and eliminate the fission products while it selected and concentrated the nonfission products. He suggested that such fission products as strontium and cesium were being carried to the bottom of the ocean by the coral dust of nuclear fallout, leaving nonfission elements to be absorbed and concentrated by the living organisms of the upper sea.

The *Marsh* results were summarized and reported in the autumn of 1956 while Seymour was beginning a two-year appointment as a marine biologist in the Environmental Sciences Branch of the Division of Biology and Medicine.

Chapter Nine

1957-1959: RONGELAP

I

BY THE SPRING of 1957 Rongelap Atoll had been without human inhabitants for three years. The thatched huts of the village were sagging or collapsing, and grass sprouted in the packed sand of the streets. The church, ignited in some unknown fashion, had been burned to its bare poles. By that spring ten surveys and radiobiological samplings had been made at Rongelap, seven of them by the Applied Fisheries Laboratory and three by the U.S. Naval Radiological Defense Laboratory (NRDL). The most recent visit had been made by Donaldson, Welander, and Olson on July 23 and 24, 1956, immediately following the close of the Redwing test series and the cruise of the *Walton*. Rongelap's radioactivity still was at levels at which permanent residence would have been of doubtful wisdom. By that time it nevertheless was certain that repatriation was possible in the foreseeable future and that preparation should be made for restoring the Rongelapese to normal living at their home atoll. As early as June 16, 1956, a month before the post-Redwing surveys, Holmes & Narver had been authorized to prepare plans for rebuilding the native village, and two days later the District Administrator of the Trust Territory

234

at Majuro submitted a report, apparently prepared somewhat earlier, on the housing and other community needs of the Rongelap people on their return. On July 9, a survey party of fifteen Holmes & Narver personnel went by ship from Parry Island to Rongelap, and there they were joined on July 11 by representatives of the Trust Territory and by five members of the native council who were flown from Majuro by seaplane to consult on the sites of the new living areas and on plans for dwellings and community facilities, including a new chapel to replace the church destroyed by fire.[1]

There was a general impression in this period that repatriation might be authorized by November, 1956. From July to November, while the Applied Fisheries Laboratory survey was made and the results compiled, planning for repatriation proceeded. On July 26, Holmes & Narver forwarded to the AEC representative at Eniwetok four sets of plans for the proposed construction of new village units on Eniaetok and Rongelap islands, and these were sent on August 8 to the Commissioner of the Trust Territory, Delmas H. Nucker. Through August and September the plans were reviewed by all agencies and certain modifications or additions suggested, as in the suggestion of the Trust Territory that Rongelap be given a two-way radio communication facility. By October 1, 1956, most of the plans, costs, and time requirements for the Rongelap repatriation had been worked out and the new villages platted. The time required was placed at 160 days from the date repatriation was approved—50 days for shipment of materials from the West Coast, 20 days for fabrication of major housing units at Parry Island, and 90 days for clearing and construction at Rongelap. Additional arrangements for easing the transfer of the native group also had been agreed upon. The Joint Task Force was to furnish approximately $1,300 per month for six months for the support of the natives during the initial period of readjustment and lesser amounts for the balance of the first year. A native labor force of twenty-four men was to work with Holmes & Narver crews during construction to provide both assistance and interpretation of native habits and needs. The Trust Territory was to provide pens and cages for the shipment of fowl and livestock by LST from Majuro to Rongelap, and two thirty-foot boats were to be sent along for native use.[2] All elements—the Rongelapese, the

Trust Territory, the Joint Task Force, the Atomic Energy Commission, and Holmes & Narver—awaited the moment when a decision could be made on the date of the natives' return.

By November 1, 1956, the Commission still was considering the results of the post-Redwing resurveys of Rongelap biology. In anticipation of an early decision, the Eniwetok office made arrangements with the Military Sea Transport Service for assignment of an LST to carry construction materials from the United States and to support the Rongelap work by furnishing quarters and subsistence for labor crews. Late in December word was received at the proving ground that no decision on the return of the natives could be expected before January, 1957, but it was not until February 26 and 27 that orders were received. The Commission's message to the Commander of the Pacific Fleet said that

> as a result of the evaluation of recent radiobiological resurveys of RONGELAP and adjacent islands it was determined that the RONGELAP people could be returned to their home atoll; the High Commissioner of the Trust Territory had concurred in this decision; and CINPACFLT was requested to implement previously approved plans.[3]

Thereafter Rongelap was made ready for the repatriation. Materials shipped from the Zone of the Interior were fabricated and loaded at Parry Island, and on May 1 four members of the Rongelap Council were flown to the atoll to remain ashore during construction of the new village. On May 25 the construction force boarded the loaded LST 618 at Enyu Island, Bikini, and proceeded to Rongelap and Eniaetok islets to unload materials and heavy equipment for the building program. The work proceeded into June. All but one of the former native houses were removed and new houses, raised on pilings in the traditional Marshallese manner, were erected in the village plats. The fresh-water facilities, including fifteen concrete and seven aluminum cisterns, were improved and enlarged. Bathhouses, latrines, storage sheds, cookhouses, eating houses, and boat sheds were provided. The council house and the chapel were raised, and more than eight miles of road were bulldozed through the vegetation of the principal islets, 64 acres of coconut groves were thinned for renewed cultivation, and almost 7,000 square yards of land cleared for recreational use. The radio shack was equipped and made ready for operation.

On June 21, 1957, the LST 618 departed Parry Island to pick up

Rongelap Council on return to atoll, May 1, 1957 *(Holmes & Narver, Inc.)*

Rongelap families coming ashore from LST 618, June 29, 1957 *(Holmes & Narver, Inc.)*

First flag raising in new Rongelap village, June 29, 1957 *(Holmes & Narver, Inc.)*

the members of the Rongelap community and their personal property at Ejit Island, Majuro. The number of the Rongelapese now had been increased to 250 by marriages and births and by the return of persons who had been away from the atoll at the time of the 1954 fallout. The vessel arrived at Ejit at 8:00 A.M. on June 25 and began the loading shortly thereafter. The loading was finished by the evening of June 26. The LST left Majuro for Kwajalein early on the morning of June 27, and by afternoon the vessel had cleared Kwajalein and was en route to Rongelap. The Holmes & Narver staff report later described the scene:

> On board the LST 618 for the return to their homeland were 250 natives with their personal belongings carried in every conceivable kind of container from woven mats to galvanized wash tubs to new airplane luggage. Also on board were five coffins bearing the remains of Rongelapese who had died during the intervening 39 months since their forced evacuation in 1954. Returned with the natives were 30 pigs, 60 chickens, six dogs, one cat, one duck, one pet pigeon, and 12 outrigger canoes.
>
> For this journey, special arrangements had been effected in the LST 618 for the safety and comfort of the passengers. Wire screening was placed at the ship's rail, at hatches, and at ventilators to protect children playing on deck. On the troop deck were located bunks with mattresses, one for each person, made up with clean bed linen. During the daylight hours of the return voyage, all the Rongelapese remained on the upper deck beneath a large canvas awning. In spite of close confinement, the people appeared contented; they were going home. The trip was pleasant and uneventful, and the vessel arrived at Rongelap on the morning of 29 June 1957. Before debarking, all the Rongelapese gathered beneath the deck awning. There they offered prayers and hymns of thanksgiving to God for their safe return to their native land.
>
> The ship beached at 0900 hours that date. First object to be seen upon debarking was a huge canvas sign strung up between palm trees. In Marshallese it proclaimed, "GREETINGS, RONGELAP PEOPLE. WE HOPE THAT YOUR RETURN TO YOUR ATOLL IS A THING OF JOY AND YOUR HEARTS ARE HAPPY." By evening, the natives, their livestock, and other personal possessions had been set ashore. . . .[4]

II

In other times it might have been presumed that the Rongelap story, except for precautionary periodic observations of native health, was at an end. Yet questions of significance still were unanswered. Medically, further observation of the Rongelapese was indicated, and the circumstances of the case invited further investigation of possible long-term radiation effect. Never before in history had an isolated human population been subjected to high but sublethal amounts of radioactivity without the physical and psychological complexities associated with nuclear explosion. The Japanese populations of Hiroshima and Nagasaki were other large groups that had been exposed to heavy doses of ionizing radiation, but in these cases the conditions were complicated not only because little was known about the level of original contamination or about the individual dosage, but also because the victims usually had suffered trauma, psychic disturbance, thermal burns, or other ills resulting from atomic blast. At Rongelap, on the other hand, the original radiation dosage was established with reasonable accuracy, the immediate evacuation of the people had permitted examination of all individuals during the early stages, and the subsequent histories of the cases were well documented. There was, in addition, the circumstance that the group of about one hundred Rongelapese who had been absent from the atoll in March, 1954, comprised an ideal control group or comparison population.[5] These members of the community were relatives of the exposed people and thus of the same genetic stock, and they matched the exposed group reasonably well in age, sex, and numbers. Thus, when the Rongelapese were once again on their native atoll, there existed both the impulse and optimum conditions for continuing the medical studies. The Bikini accident of 1954 not only had created the most powerful obligation to do whatever had to be done to heal and care for the innocent Rongelap victims but also had provided in its circumstances an unparalleled opportunity to continue the studies that might help avoid tragedy in the future. The character of the future Rongelap studies would be determined by the Division of Biology and Medicine.

The details of the Rongelap case were not widely known in 1956 and 1957. The decisions of those years undoubtedly were affected, and their significance deepened, however, by the accelerating emergence into public awareness of the issues of social and political importance presented by nuclear testing. There had arisen after 1954 insistent demands that atomic testing be suspended, banned, or conducted with some surer measure of possible danger. The testing issue had become increasingly sharp even though scientific opinion was confusingly divided on the broad questions of the presence or the degree of possible genetic or other hazard. Politically, the issue was complicated by the knowledge that the U.S.S.R., having detonated atomic devices in 1949 and 1951, was, in 1956, in its fourth consecutive year of weapons testing, and that Great Britain also had entered the field. The issue now definitely was a factor in the United States political climate and in the sensitive realm of international relations. The International Conference on Peaceful Uses of Atomic Energy had been held at Geneva from August 8 to 20, 1955, and on December 3, 1955, the General Assembly of the United Nations, in addition to recommending that a second conference be held within two or three years, had approved a resolution creating a fifteen-nation scientific committee to collect information from governments on the effects of radioactivity on human beings and to make a final report by July 1, 1958. In June, 1956, the National Academy of Sciences had published the first reports of six committees that had been appointed to assess and summarize what was known of the biological implications of atomic energy.* Publication occurred while Operation Redwing was in progress in the Pacific and shortly after the detonation over Bikini of the first United States airborne thermonuclear bomb. There was considerable press reference to the new "clean bomb," and Redwing itself was devoted to the testing of devices producing far less radioactive fallout, but it unquestionably was difficult for the outside observer not to believe that new tests meant that new weapons now were contributing, perceptibly or not, to some unknown or debatable potential hazard.

The National Academy report was accompanied by a digest of the committee statements and published as *A Report to the Public*.[6] The digest, like the basic reports, represented a significant

---

*NAS-NRC, *The Biological Effects of Atomic Radiation: Summary Reports,* from a Study by the National Academy of Sciences, Washington, D.C. 1956. The committees included those on the Genetic Effects of Atomic Radiation, Warren Weaver, the Rockefeller Foundation, chairman; the Pathological Effects of Atomic Radiation, Shields Warren, New England Deaconess Hospital, Boston, chairman; Meteorological Aspects; Harry Wexler, U.S. Weather Bureau, chairman; Oceanography and Fisheries, Roger Revelle, Scripps Institution of Oceanography, chairman; Agriculture and Food Supplies, A. G. Norman, University of Michigan, chairman; Disposal and Dispersal of Radioactive Wastes, Abel Wolman, the Johns Hopkins University, chairman.

effort to present in the simplest terms the information then available on which public decisions might be predicated—decisions, as the report said, involving ethical, political, economic, and military considerations. In the introduction to the digest it was said:

> Behind any discussion of radiation must necessarily loom the specter of full-scale atomic war. That a single thermonuclear weapon can cause severe radiation damage hundreds of miles beyond its area of immediate devastation is all too well known. That enough such weapons exploded in an all-out war might render the entire earth, or large parts of it, uninhabitable, is at least conceivable. . . . There has been comparatively little attempt in the study thus far to estimate the possible courses of atomic warfare or to assess the biological consequences. The present emphasis has been on peaceful development. It may be pointed out, however, that so far as radiation is concerned, the two aspects are not entirely unrelated. In the first place, when a world-wide atomic power industry becomes fully developed, its accumulated waste products might represent more radiation than would be released in an atomic war. Of course, this radiation will be imprisoned, not broadcast. But the point underscores the magnitude of the coming problem.
>
> Secondly, it becomes clear in this report that even very low levels of radiation can have serious biological effects. . . . Thus, many of the disastrous consequences of atomic war are clearly implied in this investigation of peacetime problems.[7]

The Committee on Oceanography and Fisheries, headed by Roger Revelle, of the Scripps Institution, urged strongly the expansion of studies of radioactivity in the sea.* In its summary and statement of recommendations the committee said:

> 2. Within the foreseeable future the problem of disposal of atomic wastes from nuclear fission power plants will greatly overshadow the present problems posed by the dispersal of radioactive materials from weapons tests. It may be convenient and perhaps necessary to dispose of some of these industrial wastes in the oceans. Sufficient knowledge is not now available to predict the effects of such disposal on man's use of other resources of the sea.
>
> 3. We are confident that the necessary knowledge can be obtained through an adequate and long-range program of research on the physics, chemistry, and geology of the sea and on the biology of marine organisms. Such a program would involve both field and laboratory experiments with radioactive

---

*Other members of the committee were Howard Boroughs, Dayton E. Carritt, Walter A. Chipman, Harmon Craig, Lauren R. Donaldson, Richard H. Fleming, Richard F. Foster, Edward D. Goldberg, John H. Harley, Bostwick Ketchum, Louis A. Krumholz, Charles R. Renn, M. B. Schaeffer, Allyn C. Vine, Lionel A. Walford, and Warren S. Wooster.

materials. . . . Although some research is already underway, the level of effort is too low. Far more important, much of the present research is too short-range in character, directed towards *ad hoc* solutions of immediate engineering problems, and as a result produces limited knowledge rather than the broad understanding upon which lasting solutions can be based.

4. We recommend that in future weapons tests there should be a serious effort to obtain the maximum of purely scientific information about the ocean, the atmosphere, and marine organisms. This requires, in our opinion, the following steps: (1) In the planning stage committees of disinterested scientists should be consulted and their recommendations followed, (2) funds should be made available for scientific studies unrelated to the character of the weapons themselves, and (3) the recommended scientific program should be supported and carried out independently of the military program rather than on a "not to interfere" basis.[8]

Public perception of the problem of nuclear fallout was centered to a large extent in this period on the question of strontium 90. The press of 1956 reflected the developing preoccupation with the question, particularly when discussion of it entered the presidential campaign.* The Joint Congressional Committee on Atomic Energy was preparing to hold in 1957 the first of its detailed hearings on atomic fallout.† Commissioner Libby continued to be closely identified with the Project Sunshine program, which had devised a special unit of strontium measurement, the "Sunshine unit," which was one micromicrocurie per gram of calcium, a unit which, inappropriately, had taken its name from Project Sunshine and which later would be referred to simply as the strontium unit. The Health and Safety Laboratory of the New York Operations Office was continuing to report periodically on data collected by the Commission's fallout monitoring network, which in 1956 included eighty-eight stations, twenty-six of them in the United States.[9]

The Rongelap case was by no means near the center of the

---

*In a review of the strontium 90 problem after the campaign a news magazine said, "Strontium 90 . . . is without doubt the most technical subject ever injected into a political campaign. . . . In no previous campaign had so many scientists been inspired to send so many statements to newspapers. Never had the voting public had such a difficult, if not insuperable, job of trying to understand the arguments involved." (*Newsweek*, "The 'Unpleasant Debate,' " November 26, 1956, p. 64.)

†The hearings were held from May 27 to June 3, 1957, by a Special Subcommittee on Radiation of the Joint Committee, on "The Nature of Radioactive Fallout and Its Effect on Man." A hearing on "Health and Safety Problems and Weather Effects Associated with Atomic Explosions" had been held by the Joint Committee in 1955.

anxieties evident in 1956 and 1957. Rongelap remained essentially a small and inconclusive example of the distress that might follow the release of nuclear contamination into the atmosphere. Yet it was in a time so laden with a sense of urgency that the Division of Biology and Medicine approached in December, 1956, the decision on Rongelap. Continued medical observation of the Rongelap people would involve teams from the NRDL and Brookhaven. But back of the medical aspects lay also the problem of an irradiated environment. The return of the people could only be contemplated when all risk to them had been eliminated, but at that point a new and extended study of low-level radio-activity at Rongelap—with particular attention to strontium 90 and other long-lived isotopes—might yet illuminate a record that was far from complete.

The Division's first problem had been to determine whether the long-term observations should be divided among experienced agencies—whether, for example, future aquatic studies should be separated from those of soils and land plants—or whether a total and integrated program could be devised and placed within a single laboratory. A meeting to consider the future program was held in the Division offices, on the call of Dunham, on December 17, 1956, and from this meeting, after a discussion of alternatives, there emerged general agreement that a continued long-term ecological study of Rongelap was necessary, particularly to develop understanding of the movement and disposition of strontium 90, and that the future Rongelap studies should be the responsibility of a single laboratory. The question of what laboratory, as well as the question of the scope of its operations, was reserved. These matters were to be pursued later by John N. Wolfe, chief of the Division's Environmental Sciences Branch, who recently had come to the staff from the Ohio State University, where he was a professor of botany.

On January 19 and 20, 1957, the Applied Fisheries staff produced a preliminary paper, an outline of proposed studies, to be used as a basis for discussion with Wolfe of the future Rongelap program.[10] The paper presented as alternatives two possible levels of study. One of these was no more than a continuation of biological sampling with emphasis on materials used by the natives for food. Beyond this the Laboratory attempted to describe

Rongelap's interest as the site of long-term, detailed ecological studies. The Laboratory pointed out that there would be value in studies of radionuclides in addition to strontium 90, that field observations should be concerned with the ecologic processes in the movement of radionuclides, and that the principal levels of interest were two—in the atoll as a total ecosystem and in smaller subsystems, or "microsystems," in which the uptake and transfer of radionuclides could be observed with precision. Of the inclusion of radionuclides beyond strontium 90 the draft said:

> Past experience has shown that strontium 90 is not the only potential biotic hazard resulting from nuclear weapon tests. Among the fission products cesium 137 is taken up by land plants and animals. Cerium 144 is present in the soils but is not taken up by land plants. Cerium 144 is, however, commonly found in marine organisms. Evidence is continually accumulating pointing to non-fission-product radionuclides which are present in sufficient quantities to raise questions as to their potential hazards. For example, following the 1954 test series it was reported that more than half the total activity in fish was due to non-fission products and that zinc 65 was principal among these. . . . Cobalt 60 was found in clams . . . and cobalt was found to be concentrated in the clam kidney. . . . Since the dissemination of similar mixtures of radioisotopes is more likely to be repeated than the contamination of a particular ecosystem, information of more general value might be obtained by giving priority to careful study of several radionuclides in a limited number of ecological situations rather than trying to cover numerous situations and limiting studies to strontium 90."[11]

The meeting in Washington in December, 1956, and Wolfe's discussions at the Applied Fisheries Laboratory in January, 1957, occurred while a decision on repatriation of the Rongelap people was awaited at the proving ground. As a result of his review of the preliminary proposals, Wolfe asked that the Laboratory submit a draft program of integrated basic studies of environmental and biological interrelationships. This the Laboratory did on February 5.[12] The new proposal suggested both "minimum" and "complete" programs for the first year beginning July 1, 1957, and a complete program for the year 1958-59. In each case studies would be concentrated in strontium 90, cesium 137, cerium 144, zinc 65, and cobalt 60. The minimum program was little more than an assay of total activity in selected soil and food samples, but attention would be given to preparation for later, more detailed studies beginning in 1958. The complete programs, however, would be as comprehensive as staff and support facilities would allow, including the mapping of soil types at Rongelap and Eniwetok for determining radioactivity in soil profiles and the initiation of entirely new investigations involving identification and observation of the selected radionuclides in fish, corals, mollusks (principally the *Tridacna* clam), Crustacea, echinoderms, and land plants and animals.

The character of the Rongelap program remained in suspense throughout most of 1957 while the natives were repatriated and the Laboratory went forward in July with its seventh Rongelap survey, which was, in substance, the "minimum" program proposed earlier in the year. In this period a summary of the Rongelap investigations, covering the work of all laboratories represented there from 1954, was published by Gordon M. Dunning, who in 1954 had been a representative of the Division of Biology and Medicine to Joint Task Force Seven.[13] But the year also brought a clarification of the responsibilities at Rongelap. The medical surveys were to be continued by a Brookhaven National Laboratory group headed by Robert A. Conard and including representatives of eight other medical and health agencies.* The Applied Fisheries Laboratory was to conduct the long-term environmental studies of low-level irradiation. On September 16, 1957, Wolfe asked for a new statement of research plans.

The Laboratory's view of the future program was refined in a proposal submitted on October 21, 1957.[14] This proposal anticipated continued and progressively broadened studies initiated in a preliminary survey to be conducted as soon as practicable—probably December, 1957, or January, 1958—and included the mapping of soil types and plant communities on Rongelap and Kabelle Islands, the southerly and northerly islands of primary interest, and the beginning of systematized observations of the Rongelapese in their atoll environment, particularly their diet, agricultural practices, and habits of sanitation. Of the status of Rongelap contamination, the Laboratory, summarizing its most recent observations, said:

*Affiliated agencies were the Department of Public Health, Trust Territory; Walter Reed Army Medical Center; South Nassau Communities Hospital, Rockville Centre, N.Y.; M. D. Anderson Hospital, University of Texas; National Institutes of Health; Atomic Bomb Casualty Commission, Hiroshima; Naval Medical Research Institute; and the Memorial Hospital for Cancer and Allied Diseases, New York City.

The levels of radiation at Rongelap at the present time, while not a health hazard, are sufficiently high for the ecological study. Soil samples collected at Rongelap Island and Kabelle Island during the summers of 1956 and 1957 had the following amounts of radioactivity:

Soil Samples	Rongelap Island July 1956	July 1957
Total activity d/m/g dry weight	7,747	2,654
Sr 90 activity d/m/g dry weight	230	172
Sunshine units	364	240

Soil Samples	Kabelle Island July 1956	July 1957
Total activity d/m/g dry weight	58,719	36,911
Sr 90 activity d/m/g dry weight	1,738	1,563
Sunshine units	2,511	2,276[15]

The Laboratory's October proposal, as approved by the Division, provided only guidelines for the ecological studies. But the principle of continued study, rather than intermittent sampling in response to changing interests or needs, had been established by the Division. From that point the Applied Fisheries Laboratory investigation of radiobiological processes proceeded concurrently with, and in a measure formed a background for, periodic medical surveys of the Rongelap people by the Brookhaven group.* Coordination of the two efforts was indicated, and this was accomplished early in 1958 when arrangements were made—by Held for the Applied Fisheries group and Conard for Brookhaven —to combine forces for surveys at Rongelap in March, 1958.

It was in this period, in January, 1958, that a change took place in the Laboratory itself. The superficial evidence was a change in the name in which the Applied Fisheries Laboratory became the Laboratory of Radiation Biology and thus dropped the deliberately misleading name given it fourteen years before to hide its connection with the Manhattan District program. The change was functional, however. For more than a year there had been in process an internal review of the Laboratory's role as a university research agency operating with Atomic Energy Commission sup-

*The medical examination immediately after the 1954 mishap had been followed by studies made six months later and in 1955, 1956, and 1957. The most recent examination had been conducted by the Brookhaven group in March, 1957, while the Rongelapese still were at Majuro (Conard, R. S. *et al., March 1957 Medical Survey of the Rongelap and Utirik People Three Years After Exposure to Radioactive Fallout*, BNL 501 [T-119], June 1958).

port. The experience in the Pacific, and particularly the emergence of the Rongelap problem, had shown how great were the needs for interdisciplinary approaches to complex problems and for the training of graduate students.* The enlarging views of the Pacific programs also had suggested that techniques learned at distant atolls might well be employed in the solution of biological problems nearer home. The change in name meant that, for the first time, internal specializations were set up as group programs under leaders responsible for their development. Programs at the nuclear test sites were assigned to Lowman and Palumbo. The Rongelap work was set apart under Held as a low-level radioactivity study in the field. By agreement with the Washington State Department of Game, Fern Lake, a small lake near Tacoma, Washington, was reserved for use in a new program in which selected radioisotopes were to be used in long-term observations of trace mineral metabolism in a natural water-forest environment. The Fern Lake program, under Donaldson's direction during the development period, would parallel and complement the work at distant Rongelap, and would be supported by the Division of

---

*A review of the Laboratory's program also had been in progress within the Division of Biology and Medicine. On June 26, 1957, Simeon T. Cantril, who had been an observer of the Laboratory's work from its earliest days but who then was a member of the Advisory Committee for Biology and Medicine, submitted to Dunham an evaluation of the Laboratory's contributions to that time. Cantril said that "one of the most promising aspects" of the early program, the training of scientists, had "not been realized to its fullest," but that establishment of the Laboratory "as an Institute of Radiobiology within the University" would add to its teaching potential. Of the recent program Cantril said: "The titles, and even reading, of the Applied Fisheries Laboratory reports on marine surveys in the Pacific cannot adequately convey the effort made by a small group to obtain representative material for analysis from the vast areas of the Pacific.... These studies have been important in mapping the quantitative contamination both in area and in depth, as well as the qualitative distribution of fission and non-fission radioactivity in marine versus land organisms. The recent finding (UWFL-51) of the greater abundance of long-lived non-fission radioactivity in marine organisms has important implications from the standpoint of weapons testing, marine biology, and waste disposal. Conversely, there is the demonstration of long-lived fission activity on land and in land organisms greatly overshadowing the non-fission activity. Equally important are the studies of the deposition of long-lived fission activity (including strontium 90) in the sands of the ocean floor, which would seem an important contribution to Project Sunshine...." And of the Japanese situation: "The Japanese marine biologic and oceanographic studies in the Pacific... have been extensive and of high quality. Without the studies done by the Applied Fisheries Laboratory (and others), and of a scientific thoroughness in which confidence can be had, our position referable to continued weapons testing... would be quite untenable." (Simeon T. Cantril, Evaluation of the Atomic Energy Contract with the Applied Fisheries Laboratory, June 26, 1957, report in DBM files.)

Biology and Medicine as a logical extension into "pure" radiobiology of the environmental studies that had proceeded heretofore
amid the complications of the proving ground.

III

The field trip inaugurating the extended Rongelap program
took place in February and March, 1958. The Radiation Biology
group went to Ronegelap with the Brookhaven team aboard a
Military Sea Transport Service vessel, the U.S.S. *Plumas County*,
which had been put at the disposal of the survey parties by arrangement through the Joint Task Force. Conard headed the
Brookhaven staff of sixteen persons, while the Radiation Biology
representatives, led by Held, included Bonham and Olson, of the
Laboratory staff; Professor Stanley Gessel and Dale Colé, a graduate student, of the University of Washington's College of Forestry,
who would work as soil specialists; and Gary Baker, a graduate
student in the Department of Botany. The *Plumas County* was in
Rongelap lagoon from February 26 to March 14.[16]

The year 1958 would be the last in which nuclear tests would be
held in the Marshalls by the United States. In the spring, preparations were under way for Operation Hardtack, which would be
conducted in two phases, a Pacific phase opening late in April
and extending into mid-August, and a Nevada phase, designated
Operation Hardtack—Phase II, extending from mid-September
to the end of October.

The quickening pace of preparations of the Pacific Proving
Ground meant also that the Laboratory of Radiation Biology
would be involved in new test-related surveys, primarily in connection with proposed underwater detonations. But meantime the
joint Brookhaven-Radiation Biology program proceeded at Rongelap undisturbed by the renewal of testing activities. The Brookhaven staff had developed in 1957 a whole-body gamma scintillation
spectrometer to be used in measuring, in 227 of the Rongelap
people, gamma ray activity from any internally deposited fission
products and neutron-induced activities.* The *in vivo* technique
was used to supplement quantitative radiochemical analytical

*In 1957 certain members of the Rongelap community were transported by air
to the United States for whole-body studies conducted by Argonne National Laboratory. (C. E. Miller, *Measurements on Some Residents of the Marshall Islands*,
ANL 5755, 1957.)

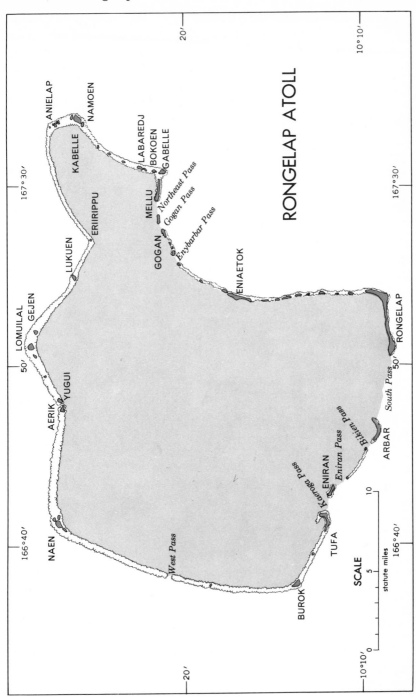

RONGELAP ATOLL

ANIELAP
NAMOEN
KABELLE
LABAREDJ
BOKOEN
GABELLE
ERIIRIPPU
MELLU
Northeast Pass
Gogan Pass
GOGAN
Enybarbar Pass
LUKUEN
ENIAETOK
GEJEN
LOMUILAL
RONGELAP
South Pass
YUGUI
AERIK
Bikien Pass
ARBAR
Eniran Pass
ENIRAN
Kierogan Pass
TUFA
NAEN
West Pass
BUROK

SCALE
statute miles
0   5   10

167° 30'
166° 40'
50'
20'
10° 10'
167° 30'
166° 40'
10°10'
20'
50'
20'

procedures, and with the repatriation of the Rongelapese it became necessary in 1958 to bring the whole-body counter to the atoll in the tank deck of the survey vessel so that the Marshallese could be brought up the landing ramp to take their turns within the device.* While the medical staff was engaged in its work with the Rongelapese, members of the Radiation Biology group pursued the collection of data along lines proposed the previous October.

Reduced to its essentials, the task of the radiobiologists in 1958 was to approach Rongelap as a new problem in which changes in ecological condition were to be observed in relation to selected radioisotopes. Information already obtained was not to be discarded, but new base lines needed to be established and, in the studies of soils, the apparatus set up for making continuous measurements. The March, 1958, survey was altogether devoted to establishing bases of information and technique from which future studies could proceed. Requirements of the International Geophysical Year made it impossible, as it proved, to enlist the assistance of a meteorologist. An ornithologist had not been available on such relatively short notice. Neither the *Plumas County* nor the small landing craft it carried, the LCVP, was appropriate for the extensive bottom-sampling program that had been proposed. But all other objectives of the initial survey were achieved at Rongelap and Kabelle Islands and extended to Eniaetok. The survey party made determinations of soil, reef, beach, and plant types by area; made collections of birds and noted their feeding and roosting areas; collected materials for the studies of the stomach contents of fish; gathered samples of plankton; collected specimens of pelagic fish; and compiled preliminary notes on Rongelapese agricultural and sanitary practices. Further, the survey group made collections of leachates from soils and ground water and assembled rat specimens for radiological assay.

*The whole-body counter was a 21-ton steel room, 5 x 5 x 6 feet with walls 4 inches thick to supply required shielding. The counter was "portable" in that it was mounted on a large trailer beside an air-conditioned wooden room designed to accommodate the electronic components of the device. During the visits to the atoll the LST would be beached at each island visited and the natives (most of whom seemed to enjoy the experience) brought aboard for whole-body counting. Available on the tank deck were shower facilities where each subject washed and changed into an uncontaminated paper suit to avoid the chance of measurement of external contamination. (Conard, *et al; Medical Survey of the Rongelap People, March, 1958, Four Years After Exposure to Fallout*, BNL 534 [T-135], May, 1959.)

By the spring of 1958 the Rongelapese were nearing the end of the first year of their adjustment to life in their new villages. Coconut cultivation was not yet re-established on the old basis. Neither breadfruit nor papaya was available, although many papaya seedlings had been started. Domestic animals and fowls were still in short supply. The native diet was, as it would continue to be for some time, supplemented by supplies of C rations provided under the auspices of the Trust Territory. As as result, the effort to study agricultural and dietary habits still was complicated by the need to account for the unusual conditions within the community. Nevertheless, the Radiation Biology group gathered samples of native food materials from land and water—coconut, pandanus, arrowroot, squash, and morinda on land, and the giant clam, coconut crab, land hermit crab, shore crab, snail, reef fish, and pelagic fish in the lagoon—and, in cooperation with the Brookhaven staff, attempted to establish in the Rongelapese an understanding of the need for continued periodic attention to themselves as individuals and to the environment in which they lived.

Almost all of the biological data were meaningless, however, until information had been obtained on atoll soils. Four years after the initial contamination, the remaining problems were related to the question of uptake of long-lived radioisotopes by plants and by animals feeding on plants. It was necessary, therefore, to seek information that never had been sought at an atoll— to discover whether radioisotopes were moving down into the soil by natural percolation; what isotopes, if any, these were; what percentage of the total burden they represented; how the processes of movement were affected by the character of the soils; and where and under what conditions the radioisotopes were available to plant life.* But before these questions could be considered, it was necessary to determine the type of soils on the atoll, the approximate distribution of these soils, the chemical and physical properties of the soils, and the relation of soils to plant distribution

---

*As has been related, soils samples had been gathered repeatedly on earlier surveys, samples ranging in size from a few grams to several hundred pounds. The smaller samples had been used for measuring total radioactivity and for studies of decay and decline. The larger samples had been sent in many instances to laboratories at U.C.L.A., Hanford, and the AEC New York Operations Office for chemical separations and had been used in experiments to measure plant uptake. At Rongelap, however, it became necessary to study the soil question *in situ* to establish any differences by type, location, and degree of contamination.

and to the distribution of radioactive materials in soils, plants, and ground water. Field work consisted of reconnaissance surveys of Rongelap, Eniaetok, and Kabelle Islands followed by the preparation of soil profiles. The profiles were established by digging some twenty pits, from four to seven feet deep, at selected locations on the three islands and making descriptive analyses of the soils and soil horizons in each. Samples for chemical and physical analysis were collected from each soil horizon, and samples for radioactive analysis were taken from the top eight to eleven inches of soil by one-inch depth groups from each soil horizon. Plant samples included leaves, fruit, roots from various depths, and borings from trunks or stems.

Plans for the 1958 survey had anticipated the use of several lysimeter stations to study the movement of water through the soil and to permit the collection of leachates for chemical analysis. Lysimeters of standard design, built in the field, were to have been used, even though these were recognized as having shortcomings stemming from the difficulty of making installations in the coralline islands sands. Before the 1958 survey party was assembled, however, Held had made contact with Cole, a graduate student in forestry, who had been designing a new type of lysimeter in which moisture was drawn from the plates by vacuum and collected above ground in glass jars sealed and otherwise prepared to prevent evaporation. Four such lysimeter installations were constructed and tested on Rongelap and Kabelle Islands during the survey, Cole accompanying the Laboratory party to supervise the operation. The new method proved altogether satisfactory.

The soil studies represented a significant development in the broader approach to the question of radiobiological process. Further, they were in themselves contributions to appreciation of the marine origins of atoll "land." The mapping of island soils was accomplished not only by field surveys but with the aid of aerial photographs provided during the 1958 test series by Task Group 7.1., but the essence of the effort was related to what would appear in radiochemical analyses of soil and water samples that held only the faintest traces of radioactive materials. This preliminary effort to attain a comprehensive understanding of the Rongelap land was essential if there were to be a later understanding of how the radionuclides of primary interest were taken up by or withheld from island vegetation. The soil studies went beyond mere inventory because they necessarily involved more detailed physical and chemical analyses than would have been attempted without the interest in biological process. It was important to sample soils at various periods throughout the year to determine seasonal variation in chemical properties. The objective was to obtain profiles of island soils, at specific points in time, from which it might be possible to determine the location, accessibility, proportion, and rate of movement of trace amounts of strontium, cesium, cerium, zinc, cobalt, or other radionuclides found to be significant within the land environment.

In subsequent expeditions, later in 1958 and in 1959, experimental procedures were instituted to study mineral balances as a means of discovering the effects of mineral deficiencies in the radiobiological situation. Initially, however, the land of Rongelap Atoll was revealed, in contour and profile, as a region holding a bewildering number of small problems, each of which was in some manner dependent on the solution of another. The naturally high alkalinity of the soils, which are composed almost completely of calcium carbonate, was a characteristic apparently modified and reduced by the presence of decayed organic matter. This organic matter was found stratified beneath the low and dunelike mounds of the islands, each of which was somehow different in age and composition. Below the surfaces of the islands would be found areas where coral had been cemented at certain depths, and in others layers of solid beach rock were encountered. The observations of strontium 90, which is taken up by plants in lieu of calcium (although not with the lack of discrimination that once was presumed), were peculiarly difficult in soils containing so large a proportion of calcium, but in addition it was necessary to understand how strontium was or was not made available to plants by the machinery of percolation. Still to be considered were such matters as the role of vegetation in atoll soil formation, the effects of ocean spray and of inundation of the island during storms, and the sea bird-soil relationships.

Throughout the survey the understanding of the Rongelapese seemed to be complete except in one particular, and that was in regard to a detail of native diet. In 1956 and again in 1957 it had been observed that while the levels of radioactivity in the biota had continued to decline, and at a rate actually more rapid than would have been expected from physical decay alone, an exception was in the crabs—the land crab, *Coenobita perlatus* and the coconut crab, *Birgus latro*—especially those from Kabelle and the northern islands, which seemed to be accumulating strontium 90 at levels which made unwise their use as native food. Coconut crabs were not numerous on Rongelap or Eniaetok islands, near the native communities, but because the crab was considered a delicacy by the Marshallese it would have been the practice of the Rongelap men to go by canoe to other islands of the atoll to hunt the crabs and to hold feasts at the sites of collection. By 1958 many Rongelapese were asking members of the medical and biology teams if they were permitted to eat crabs and clams. A conference between Held and Conard established that no instruction ever had been issued concerning clams (the clam kidney was not ordinarily eaten in any case, although Held discovered that it occasionally was used to prepare a "seasickness remedy"), but following their conference Conard and Held again asked the Rongelapese to refrain from eating the coconut crabs. The question would be brought up again in 1959.

With the general lines of inquiry established by the March, 1958, survey, it was important that planning be coordinated not only from the survey standpoint but from that of the Trust Territory administration, which was devoting particular attention to the matter of re-establishing at Rongelap a normal native economy and an attitude of self-sufficiency. Commissioner Nucker, whose representatives already had been in continuous contact with the Rongelap community, concurred in the activities proposed for 1958, and 1959, but suggested that the year 1960 be kept free of survey visits to give the Rongelapese a period of freedom from outside attention. Nucker's concern was substantial. The three years of medical care and enforced dependence at Majuro had deprived the Rongelapese of opportunities and incentives to care for themselves, and the months since their return, in which they continued to receive supplementary foods such as rice and C rations, had demonstrated that they still were far from ready to attempt to make their own way on the old basis. The visit of the *Plumas County,* which had brought to the atoll not only doctors and biologists, but the whole-body counter, staffs of technicians,

and members of the vessel's crew, had been a disturbance—
although, for the Rongelapese, apparently, a holiday—despite
efforts to make the survey brief and professional in nature. Nucker
apparently felt, quite rightly, that a balance should be struck
between the needs of the health-biology program and those
affecting Rongelap's community morale. As a result of the Washington meeting it was determined, in general terms, that 1960
should be considered reserved. The Trust Territory was to
receive all appropriate survey information, including drafts or
reports of current or future program plans, but 1960 would be a
year in which field activity was suspended at Rongelap, and the
requirements of 1961 and later would be reviewed in the light of
subsequent developments. In this was confirmation of how
generally accepted was the long view of the survey effort at
Rongelap.

On the part of the radiobiologists, the survey of March, 1958,
was followed by three additional expeditions, spaced roughly at
six-month intervals, before the beginning of the 1960 moratorium
on field work. The first of these was a late-summer trip in 1958
in which the Laboratory group went to Rongelap from Eniwetok
aboard the M.V. *Aloto,* formerly the LSM 444, which had been
acquired by the AEC on loan from the Navy, modified for proving
ground service during the Hardtack series, and placed under
operational control of Holmes & Narver. The group was at Rongelap from August 13 to 24 and then, after a week of preliminary
sample preparation and counting at the EMBL at Eniwetok,
returned to Rongelap on September 2 to collect soil leachates
captured by six of the newly designed tension lysimeters placed on
Rongelap and Kabelle Islands. In addition to Held and Gessel,
the group on this visit included two new senior scientists, Frank
Richardson, of the Department of Zoology, and Richard Walker,
of the Department of Botany, and six junior members, all graduate
students—Baker and Cole, who had worked there earlier, and
Ronald Eisler and Timothy Joyner, of the College of Fisheries;
Reid Kenady, of the College of Forestry; and James Kimmel, of
the Department of Botany of the Ohio State University.

The program now fanned out into areas suggested in the first
survey. Collections of specimens included all those made earlier,
but the presence of Richardson and Walker made possible more

M.V. *Aloto*, 1959 survey vessel, at anchor in Rongelap lagoon *(Laboratory of Radiation Biology)*

The *Aloto* taking plankton samples, Rongelap lagoon, September, 1959 *(Laboratory of Radiation Biology)*

Mathisen with coring device on the *Aloto*, 1959 *(Laboratory of Radiation Biology)*

Soil transect on Kabelle Island, Rongelap, 1959 *(Laboratory of Radiation Biology)*

detailed attention to birds and plants. The soil pits established in March were sampled and new pits dug in a transect across Rongelap Island so that a total of twenty-nine sample points were available for later reference. Three hundred pounds of Rongelap soils were shipped to the Laboratory in Seattle for use in greenhouse tests. A weather station, a U.S. Weather Bureau-type shelter housing a recording rain gauge and a wind-direction indicator, was established near the village on Rongelap Island. To permit the orderly examination of Rongelapese diet, specimens of principal locally produced food items were collected (including items consumed only by livestock), and samples of twenty-four hour rations of locally grown foods were obtained from each of fourteen Rongelap adults.[17]

The 1959 surveys extended, and in some respects modified, the observations of 1958. The spring survey, conducted from a Navy LST, the U.S.S. *Duval County,* was performed in conjunction with that of the Brookhaven laboratory, which again took to Rongelap its whole-body counter and on this occasion a staff composed of seven physicians, one dentist, two scientific specialists, and nine technicians from associated laboratories and institutions. The Radiation Biology team included Held, Richardson, Cole, Joyner, Kimmel, and Kenady. The Brookhaven and Radiation Biology personnel, moving to the Pacific late in February, worked at Majuro and at Eniwetok until the survey vessel arrived at Parry Island on February 27, and on March 2 the *Duval County* was in Rongelap lagoon, where medical and biological surveys would continue until March 14.[18]

By 1959 the attitudes within the Rongelap community were of gathering concern to the Trust Territory. For five years the Rongelapese had been the subjects of special care. Their emotionally disturbing experiences—evacuation, relocation, examination or treatment for radiation injury, repatriation, recurrent and puzzling associations with visitors who were endlessly curious about their lives, their diet, and their environment—they had met with admirable patience and understanding that somehow transcended the difficulties presented by the language barrier and the level of their culture. Their relations with the physicians who visited them always had been happy and friendly. In repeated community and council meetings throughout the years they had received with appreciation the explanations, translated haltingly by native interpreters, of the causes of their condition and of the measures that were being taken in their behalf. Certain young Marshallese practitioners assisted the medical teams by working as technicians in the field laboratories. But now, two years after their repatriation, it was evident that the Rongelapese as members of a community group were not moving as rapidly as had been expected toward readjustment to "normal" atoll life. A measure of this delay was the failure of their agricultural production to supply sufficient food for the population.* The use of supplementary supplies of C rations and rice had been protracted, necessarily, far beyond the original calculation. Trust Territory agricultural specialists were giving all possible aid to the effort to increase production of coconut, papaya, pandanus, and breadfruit, the atoll staples, but still production lagged. The mood of the Rongelapese was not now unhappy; it was, rather, one of weariness with attentions that seemed never to end, with investigations that they did not understand. They were not ready, or did not know how, to take charge of their lives again.

Neil Morriss, a Trust Territory agricultural specialist, was at Rongelap when the medical-biological survey party came there on the *Duval County* in the spring of 1959. The presence of Morriss had been arranged by Nucker, who had been informed of the survey schedule and its general objectives.[19] When the survey vessel had lowered its ramp on the Rongelap Island beach, the welcoming party consisted of Morriss and members of the Rongelap council, including a local leader, Billiman, recently elected magistrate. The greetings were cordial and arrangements were made immediately with Billiman for use of certain Rongelap buildings for medical laboratory purposes. Yet by midday members of the council had determined to raise questions about the need for renewed medical examinations and, as it developed, about continuance of the ban on consumption of coconut crabs. The second matter also led into another, the conviction that had arisen

*A measure of difference also lay in the production of copra. Although 1959 was a year of lowered production on many of the atolls, Rongelap's record appears poorer than most. In 1957, the year of repatriation, Rongelap's production was 40,882 pounds, and in 1958 the total rose to 87,768. In 1959, the total was only 6,831, lowest in the Marshalls, but it had risen to 68,517 by 1960. (Kazu Matsumuro, *Copra Production in the Marshall Islands*, Trust Territory, Majuro, March 10, 1961).

among the Rongelapese that there was an increased number of cases of fish poisoning and that these were somehow related to the events of 1954. For more than three hours of the afternoon of March 2, 1959, Conard and Held, in turn, were questioned by Rongelap spokesmen at a general meeting called by the Rongelap council. In a Brookhaven report of 1960 the occasion was recalled in the following terms:

> At the village meeting the main questions centered about the necessity for the continued medical examinations in view of statements on the part of the medical team in the past that the people were generally in good health. It was difficult to explain to them that, though they appeared in good health and to have recovered from the acute effects of radiation, very little was known about the possible late effects of radiation, and continued examinations were essential in order to detect and treat any untoward effects should they arise. The coconut crab problem was brought up again, and the reasons for prohibiting their consumption carefully explained through the interpreter. To correct a misconception that several cases of fish poisoning during the past year had been due to eating radioactive fish, it was explained that fish poisoning had been going on in these islands for years and was not connected with radioactivity. After much discussion, it seemed that the people were satisfied with answers to the questions, and preparations for the examinations proceeded. Thereafter complete cooperation and the usual friendly relations prevailed throughout the stay on the island.[20]

Held, in log notes made at the time, said that the poisonous fishes were red snappers caught in the northern portion of the lagoon.

Less than a week later, on March 8, Morriss notified the survey parties that Rongelap would be visited on the following day by a United Nations committee to the Trust Territory. The visitors, under the chairmanship of a representative from Nationalist China, included members from Burma, Belgium, and Italy and were accompanied by Maynard Neas, administrator of the Marshalls District, and members of his staff, and Marshallese interpreters. The arrival at 10:30 A.M. was followed by a three-hour meeting in the Rongelap chapel in which, after speeches of welcome and response and group singing led by Iso, the Rongelap minister, the meeting was opened to questions.* Again the discus-

---

*Held, in a letter report of the meeting written on March 11, included several notes which illustrate the atmosphere of innocence surrounding these attempts to clarify political-scientific questions and concepts. Held wrote: "A series of welcoming speeches by Clanton, the head school teacher, Billiman, and John followed the

sion covered the points that had been explained at the community meeting on March 2—the need for continued medical examinations, the cases of fish poisoning, the proscription of coconut crabs and, finally, the amount of economic assistance being given Rongelap by the Trust Territory and the Atomic Energy Commission. Every question was answered, Conard, Held, or Neas being called on to clarify special points of medical, biological, or Trust Territory plans or procedures. The subsequent report of the United Nations committee approved the actions being taken to follow the Rongelap case and to assist the people. When the spring survey ended on March 14 (and before the *Duval County* moved on to Utirik, where additional medical examinations were made), a farewell party was held by the visitors for the Rongelapese. A meal was supplied by the Navy and gifts were exchanged.

The second survey of 1959, a survey involving only members of the Radiation Biology staff, was held in September from the *Aloto*. Planning was directed toward making the visit as unobtrusive as possible. On August 7, Held forwarded to Commissioner Nucker a complete statement of survey objectives and preparations, including a list of thirteen Rongelap islands scheduled for field visits between September 2 and 25 and a description of the objectives and manner of the observations to be made at each site.[21] The September team included for the most part the senior members that had participated in earlier surveys—Held, Bonham, Gessel, Walker—and Ole Mathisen, of the University of Washington. Emphasis now was turned from the land to the lagoon, and the programs of plankton and lagoon bottom sampling were more extensive than ever before. Morriss, whose presence had been requested by Held, was assigned by Commissioner Nucker to accompany the *Aloto* from Eniwetok and to be present to conduct or facilitate any conferences with the Rongelapese. No new community conference was necessary. The now-familiar visitors were welcomed to Rongelap with warmth and friendliness, but it was now known definitely that the survey would not return in 1960.

introduction of the committee members. Iso, the minister, then said a prayer. What followed then was some of the most beautiful and moving singing I have heard in a long time. The entire group sang *a cappella* in intricate harmonies, with only the direction of the lead voice of Iso. The meeting was then thrown open for questions. John, speaking as a member of the council, asked the first question, which was, 'What is the U.N.?' "

IV

By the end of 1959 the field work at Rongelap had encompassed four separate periods of observation. No new expeditions would be scheduled until 1961, and members of the staff used the respite granted them to make further analyses of the samples and notes accumulated over a two-year period.

From the beginning, the primary interest was in biological process rather than in the biological effect of radioactivity. Observations of gamma dose levels were made routinely to establish the rate of decline and, while there was a small and probably insignificant increase in activity in August, 1958 (due, perhaps, to a general raising of the background during the Operation Hardtack tests), the levels had declined at rates consistent with the theoretical decay curves for mixed fission products. The average and maximum values at Rongelap Island in September, 1959, were 0.03 milliroentgens per hour and 0.04 milliroentgens per hour, and the highest average and maximum values were found at Naen Island, an uninhabited northerly island, where the values were 0.18 and 0.25 milliroentgens per hour.[22] In the biological system the general levels of radioactivity had continued to decline more rapidly than would be expected from physical decay alone (except in certain noteworthy instances, as in that of the coconut crab). and this, as had been demonstrated repeatedly in earlier samplings in the proving ground, was attributable to excretion, dilution, and other variable factors involved in the turnover of radioisotopic content.[23] The relatively high and stable levels of strontium 90 in the coconut crab apparently was due to the crab's selective absorption of strontium and the long-lived stability of the isotope within the organism.

Land studies, by the end of 1959, had been conducted over a period of two years in which the original soil pits and experimental lysimeter placements were extended into transects, notably on Kabelle Island, for studies of soil origin, development, fertility, and chemical content. These observations were made in connection with the analysis of the radioactively tagged minerals. An obvious condition of the atoll environment is that many plants growing in the area suffer from nutrition deficiencies, and soil and plant analyses confirmed this observation. The analyses, however,

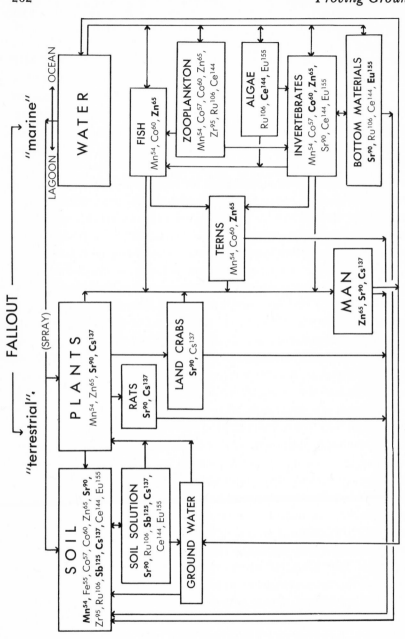

Distribution of fallout radioisotopes at Rongelap Atoll, 1959, the dominant isotopes indicated in bold-faced type. (From data by Held, 1961.)

suggested two further approaches, the first the establishment of controlled greenhouse experiments in which plant responses to altered nutritional conditions could be observed, and the second the plotting at Rongelap of a number of reserved areas in which fertilizer experiments could be conducted in the field. Tests for nitrogen at Rongelap indicated a high nitrogen content in certain plants even when these were found growing in sand along the beaches, and this observation opened up a study of the nitrogen cycle in the atoll soils.

The four field observations of 1958 and 1959 permitted intensive samplings of radioactivity on and beneath the surface of the land areas. Samplings by one-inch increments conducted along island transects at four separate points in time showed that more than 75 per cent of the gross beta radioactivity was in the top inch of Rongelap soil. A few samples were taken at one-fourth inch increments, and in some instances 50 per cent of the radioactivity was found in the top one-fourth inch. The vertical distribution of strontium 90 followed the same pattern as that of gross beta activity.[24] The horizontal variation in radioactivity was found to vary widely. In extreme cases samples taken within distances of a few meters, from the same soil types and with the same vegetative cover, were found to vary by as much as a factor of ten. In 1960, complete isotopic analyses were made of samples representing each of six major soil types at the atoll.

The lysimeter leachates, collected from four installations on Rongelap Island and two on Kabelle, were analyzed for nitrogen, phosphorous, potassium, calcium, and gamma-emitting radioisotopes. Radioisotopes detected were ruthenium 106-rhodium 106, antimony 125, cesium 137, cerium 144-polonium 144, and europium 155, but reliable quantitative estimates could be made only for cesium 137 and antimony 125, the latter collected at depths where the soil contained no measurable radioactivity above background.[25] In "recent deposit" soil, only antimony 125 (the presence of which had been discovered for the first time in 1957) was found in the leachates. Analysis for strontium 90 indicated that its movement was enhanced by the presence of potassium chloride.[26] Throughout the investigation soil chemistry presented difficulties arising from the coralline-foraminiferal character of the materials and the naturally high calcium content. Not all of these difficulties were overcome, but a procedure to determine calcium carbonate by gas evolution was used in analyses of organic matter. Broadly, the lysimeter studies revealed that there was only a slight downward movement of minerals, even in the porous soils in which leaching was a function of the natural land-water relationship.

The studies of land plants evolved from the original mapping and description of the plant communities at Rongelap, although in the processes of radiochemical analysis priority was given to food plants. Complete radiochemical analyses were made for all samples of pandanus, tacca (arrowroot), breadfruit, squash, and coconut samples. Cesium 137 was found to be the dominant isotope in these plants, accounting for 70 to 99 per cent of the total activity. Strontium 90 accounted for most of the remaining activity, although manganese 54, zinc 65, and cerium 144 were found in minute amounts in samples from the more highly radio-active northern islands.[27] All plant samples through 1959 were counted for gross beta activity and, while there were definite geographical and species differences, no seasonal variations or changes with time were apparent.

The need to determine the mobility of strontium 90 and cesium 137, elements of singular interest in relation to the original con-tamination, gave direction to the plant sampling. The results of the analyses of the 1958 samples, and observation of the initial effects of the greenhouse experiments, indicated that there were marked differences in the amounts of strontium 90, cesium 137, potassium, and calcium found in the terminal and basal leaves. Thereafter, collections in the field included both types of leaves from the same plants. Cesium 137 moved into the terminal leaves more readily than did strontium 90, yet it was less mobile than potassium. This observation led to an extension of the use of fertilization plots in the field, where tests indicated that the addi-tion of potassium as a plant nutrient reduced markedly the uptake of cesium 137. Fertilizer plots were established at Rongelap in both cultivated and uncultivated areas. With the assistance of Morriss, plots were set apart in coconut stands and certain trees marked so that repeated collections could be made from the same individuals.

A search for aberrant or atypical plants was made on most of the islands of Rongelap during the survey of September, 1959, and a number of examples of such plants were found and photographed. Yet, as had been discovered a decade before in the resurveys of Eniwetok after Operation Sandstone, it was necessary to resist the temptation to ascribe such aberrations to the effects of radioactivity alone. Multiheaded and branched coconut palm trees were found on Naen and Yugui Islands. A single double-headed palm about three feet high was discovered at Jabwan on the south end of Rongelap Island, but even the Rongelapese (who had observed other such phenomena and who were as concerned about them as they were worried about poisonous fish) said that this particular development had been caused by mechanical damage. Palms with twisted fronds were found on Rongelap, Kabelle, Gejen, Lomuilal, Yugui, Aerik, and Naen Islands, and it was noted that these occurred with greater frequency on the islands that had been more highly contaminated.[28] Dying coconut trees were in every stand of palms, again with greater frequency in the northern islands, and the same was true of palms with "pencil point," or tapering, stems. Dead or dying specimens of *Suriana, Guettarda, Scaevola, Messerschmidia,* and *Pemphis* were more prevalent in the northern islands, and a strikingly aberrant example of *Messerschmidia,* possessing only a few chlorotic terminal leaves, was found on a sand spit on Lomuilal Island. Yet despite the multiplicity of these examples, it could not be presumed, much less established, that these effects were caused by radioactivity. In general, the vegetation was in poorer condition on the northern islands, which had received about ten times as much initial contamination, than on the islands along the eastern edge and to the south of Rongelap. But it also was probable that other factors were at work. The soils of the northern islands are less well developed than elsewhere. The nitrogen content of the best northern soils averaged only 0.26 per cent compared to 0.57 to 1.71 per cent in the south. This in turn would indicate that vegetation had been sparser in the north for a considerable period of time, and there was evidence of recent overwashings of portions of the northern land, particularly at Lomuilal.[29] Finally, aberrations of island growth were known to be far from rare, even where radioactive contamination never had been a factor. Many examples are cited in the literature of tropical areas. In 1960,

(Above) *Messerschmidia* in wash area, Kabelle Island, Rongelap, a plant used in studies of root systems and growth rate *(Laboratory of Radiation Biology)*

(Left) Lysimeter plate used in soil studies, Kabelle Island, showing extent of root growth in Rongelap soil, 1959 *(Laboratory of Radiation Biology)*

(Below) *Messerschmidia,* Rongelap, showing meagre side growth, 1959 *(Laboratory of Radiation Biology)*

Morriss reported finding two multiheaded palms at Ujelang Atoll, southwest of Eniwetok, which is within the sphere of operations of the proving ground but which never had received fallout. On balance, it seemed probable that radioactivity, if it played a role in creating the observable condition of Rongelap's vegetation, was merely one of a number of factors tending to cause an increase in the numbers of aberrant plants.

The repeated surveys at Rongelap had permitted increasingly precise observations of the differences of uptake of radionuclides by organisms of land and water, differences first noted at Bikini, confirmed at Eniwetok, and extended during the ocean surveys of 1956. Long before it had been established as a general conclusion that cesium 137 and strontium 90 were the principal long-lived fission product isotopes found in the land organisms and that zinc 65, cobalt 60, manganese 54, and iron 55—nonfission products and elements which, in stable form, were in short supply in the marine environment—were those characteristically predominant in marine organisms. The distribution of radioisotopes in the biota had been found to vary from organism to organism and to be greatly different character in marine and terrestrial organisms taken from the same geographical area. Few of the induced radioisotopes were present in the plants growing in the soils, or in the tissues of the rats which feed on land plants. But in the plankton, the marine invertebrates, and in the fishes, induced radioisotopes frequently contributed up to 100 per cent of the total activity.[30] In the realm of the connections between water and land lay further questions that could be pursued in Rongelap's mildly irradiated environment. One of these connections was traced through the birds.

Richard's surveys of the birds at Rongelap provided a listing of species encountered with estimates of probable numbers and notes on feeding, nesting, breeding, and residence or migratory habits. The birds of significant interest were subject to grouping, as had been observed earlier, into categories incorporating the migratory shore birds and the resident sea birds. The migrants included species common to the atolls, such as the golden plover American and the ruddy turnstone, and those less frequently noted, the bristle-thighed curlew and the wandering tattler. The residents included the omnipresent noddy tern, the whitecapped noddy, and the white tern. It was Richardson's belief that the shore birds probably were winter residents whose southern migration tended to stop in the Marshalls in autumn and that these species probably had not contributed significantly to the development of soils and vegetation over the centuries, not only because of their intermittent presence but because they are small in size and population and live principally on the island beaches. But the numerous resident terns, excepting, perhaps, the sooty tern, which typically establishes its colonies on barren and wind-swept points, undoubtedly had helped to build the atolls and were important in the cycles of atoll life, because it is their habit to nest and breed in the inner parts of the islands where there are thick stands of *Pisonia* and *Messerschmidia* trees. The three most numerous terns, the noddy, the white-capped noddy, and the white, were noted as apparently entirely piscivorous, living on small fish caught in the lagoon or in the open sea. Their wastes and undigested food deposited in the nesting areas of plant growth seemed certain to be necessary to the development of plant life and thus to the growth of the islands themselves.

In an effort to establish an estimate of the ecological importance of the common terns, Richardson made population studies from which he might calculate the tern's contribution to island nutrients. On Kabelle Island, which has an area of some 2,400 square meters, he found that in 1959 there were 700 to 900 adult white terns, 500 to 600 noddy terns, and 200 to 300 white-capped noddy terns. Assuming that each bird would eat at least half of its own weight each day (a conservative assumption), he calculated that on Kabelle in a single year the white terns would deposit 35,000 pounds of waste, the noddy terns 51,000 pounds, and the white-capped noddy 10,000 pounds. Thus on this single medium-sized island the resident members of only three species of terns would deposit each year in the stands of vegetation approximately 48 tons of nutrients.[31] Richardson concluded that there seemed

clearly to be a relationship between the greatest concentration of breeding birds, the most extensive stands of large trees, and the best-developed soils. . . . The sequences in the development of these relationships is problematical, but one may think of them as evolving together, even though a relatively barren island would, at first, attract few birds. If certain factors, as availability of sub-surface water and protection from salt spray, led to denser vegetation in the inner parts of islands, the population of birds could then greatly accelerate the development of soils and larger and larger trees.

The food of the terns came from the lagoon and the open sea, and the island soil accordingly was being fertilized by wastes whose origins were oceanic. But the immediate significance was in the contribution of birds to the circulation of radioactivity. Repeated analyses demonstrated that within these wastes were nonfission products—primarily cerium 144 and iron 55—characteristically captured principally by marine life but now made available by the birds to island vegetation. The terns were agents for the transport of minerals from water to soil to vegetation. The tagged materials illuminated the process.

The survey of September, 1959, produced a more complete examination of lagoon ecology than had been possible earlier. Invertebrates were gathered at thirteen islands. Reef fish were observed and collected principally at Rongelap and Kabelle, but emphasis was placed on collections of goatfish and on other organisms upon which the goatfish were observed to be feeding. Plankton was collected by continuous pumping at the surface between eighty-nine stations in the lagoon. Twenty-four hour collections of plankton were made at three depths at three of the stations. Bottom cores, made with equipment designed at the University of Washington Department of Oceanography, were recovered at seventy-four stations.[32] No further field collections would be made until 1961.

Chapter Ten

1958: HARDTACK

I

THE EVENTS associated with Rongelap, particularly from the standpoint of long-term radiological interest, were secluded both by their nature and by their inevitable association with the affairs of the Pacific Proving Ground. Rongelap represented by 1958 a compartment in an increasingly diverse set of related investigations and, because it was necessary to await the unfolding of biological developments, the periodic samplings might be expected to be made at Rongelap for many years. Meantime, the year 1958 brought Operation Hardtack, which would conclude the decade of nuclear testing begun in Operation Sandstone. After Hardtack, nuclear testing would be suspended by the United States in accordance with the terms of international agreement. Testing would be suspended, but not the search for answers to the questions beyond.

Operation Hardtack was a Pacific operation to which was added a second, continental phase. The most recent continental test series, Operation Plumbbob, had been held from March 15 through October 12, 1957, at the Nevada Test Site. In these tests emphasis was placed on small weapons capable of use in defense operations and on those designed to reduce radioactivity remaining after detonation. In the Rainier shot on September 19 a low yield (1.7 kiloton) device was detonated at the end of a tunnel dug horizontally into a mesa so that the explosion occurred 790 feet underground in a chamber that would be closed and sealed by the explosion itself.[1] Tests of two devices developed at Los Alamos for the Department of Defense involved study of the effects of a relatively low aerial burst of a device suspended beneath a balloon and of a high-altitude burst of an air-to-air rocket warhead fired from an Air Force plane.[2] Such tests, as the Atomic Energy Commission continued to report, were "designed to improve and increase the United States arsenal of nuclear weapons." The U.S.S.R., which had been conducting tests each year since 1953, was experimenting in 1957 with weapons which were announced by Soviet authorities or described in this country as from "small" to "megaton range" in size. The U.S.S.R. programs of 1957 extended intermittently from January into December, and testing was resumed on February 23, 1958, while in the United States preparations went forward for the new Pacific series beginning in April.[3]

But larger currents also were in motion. The accumulating concern with the question of world-wide fallout was increasingly manifest in 1957. One of the results was a further strengthening of activities in the field of biology, and some of these investigations were incorporated into the United States testing programs. During Operation Plumbbob, the Commission's Fireball Chemistry Project, created to study ways to reduce the accessibility of radiostrontium to the biosphere, particularly to the human body, added silica sand to the fireballs of certain test shots so that debris could be analyzed for solubility and thus for probable availability to living tissue. Similar analyses were made of debris from test detonations in which large amounts of steel and aluminum had been present in the fireball. Further experiments along these lines were projected for the new Pacific series.

In March, 1957, the United States had declared that it intended "to conduct nuclear tests only in such manner as will keep the world radiation from rising to more than a small fraction of the levels that might be hazardous."[4] In May and June the Special Subcommittee on Radiation of the Joint Congressional Committee on Atomic Energy held the first of a series of public hearings on "The Nature of Radioactive Fallout and Its Effects on Man." On September 15, the Atomic Energy Commission and the Department of Defense announced that, in the absence of a disarmament agreement, a new test series would begin in April in the Pacific. This was Hardtack. "The forthcoming series," the Commission said in its subsequent semiannual report,

> will advance the development of weapons for defense against aggression whether airborne, missile-borne, or otherwise mounted. . . . An important objective of the tests will be the further development of nuclear weapons with greatly reduced radioactive fallout so that radiation hazard may be restricted to the military target.[5]

A number of significant impulses were struggling for expression in 1957 and 1958. One was in the field of international cooperation in nuclear science and industry under conditions such as were anticipated in the United States in the drafting of the Atomic Energy Act of 1954. Another was in the development of peaceful uses of atomic energy, a movement symbolized by the Plowshare Program initiated by the University of California Livermore Laboratory in July, 1957, and directed at finding nonmilitary ways to use nuclear explosive devices to create new sources of power and new harbors or canals or other facilities. A third stemmed from the growing realization that at some point mankind must come to terms with the atom and nations with each other on the question of possible nuclear warfare. The great issues were those which compounded the scientific and the political and involved large elements of the unknown.

In October, 1957, a statement on radioactive fallout was submitted to the Commission by its Advisory Committee for Biology and Medicine then headed by Giocchino Failla, director of the Radiological Research Laboratory of the College of Physicians and Surgeons of Columbia University, and including Bugher, Cantril, and Shields Warren, and Charles H. Burnett, professor of medicine at the University of North Carolina, and H. Bentley Glass, professor of biology at Johns Hopkins University. The Committee reviewed at length the uncertainties entering the calculations of the possible hazard of nuclear testing on the one hand and the requirements of national security on the other. The Committee took note of the estimate of the National Academy of Sciences Committee on the Genetic Effects of Atomic Radiation that a reasonable maximum lifetime population dose was "10 roentgens of man-made radiation to the reproductive cells,"[6] and then in its summary and recommendations said:

> As previously stated, the setting of an upper limit of 10 r in 30 years for the genetic dose to the population of the United States involved an estimated balance between possible harm and possible benefit. Since it must be assumed that some harm will result from fallout radiation, the question naturally arises as to whether this is justified by the benefit, even if it be well within recommended limits. In this country a large fraction of the annual budget is for military expenditures—which in a democracy gives a measure about the citizens' concern about the safety of their country. It seems obvious, therefore, that if we wish to maintain a first-class military organization for the safety of the country, we must at least keep abreast of new weapons developments. No such developments can be carried out successfully without tests. . . . Therefore, in terms of national security, necessary tests of nuclear weapons are justified. There are, however, other considerations that must be weighed carefully by those responsible for our national policy.
>
> Radioactive fallout from our tests spreads all over the world. Similarly, tests made by others affect us. Other countries may want to develop nuclear weapons later. In time, the situation may well become serious. Estimates of ultimate damage to the world's present and future populations, expressed in absolute terms, are large and impress many people. Judging from discussions in the public press, it is not generally realized that the estimated damage is well within tolerable limits, applicable to radiation exposure of the whole population in its normal peacetime activities. The question arises in the minds of many thoughtful persons whether the number and power of bombs exploded in the tests are being kept at the minimum consistent with scientific and military requirements. In view of the adverse repercussions caused by the testing of nuclear weapons, the Committee recommends that tests be held to a minimum consistent with scientific and military requirements and that appropriate steps be taken to correct the present status of confusion on the part of the public.[7]

The difficulty, then as always, was that no unilateral action by the United States would in itself end possible hazard. Abandonment of nuclear testing by the United States would reduce by a fraction the total of cumulative world fallout but at the risk of weakening weapons research at a time of increasing testing activity by other nations.* The alternatives, pending cessation of testing by international agreement, were (1) limiting testing to

*The United Kingdom now also was in the thermonuclear field. Three airdrops of megaton-range devices were successfully executed in Operation Grapple at the Christmas Island area in May and June, 1957.

experiments which, as the Committee had phrased it, were "consistent with scientific and military requirements"; (2) continuing emphasis on minimizing fallout; and (3) enlarging investigation of biological effects, particularly in regard to the disposition of radioactive substances of long half-life, such as strontium 90 and cesium 137.

On March 27, 1958, a month before the opening of Hardtack, Commissioner Libby delivered an address before the Swiss Academy of Medical Sciences Symposium on Radioactive Fallout at Lausanne. In the course of this talk, Libby presented calculations and extensive supporting data on the mechanism of stratospheric fallout and its probable relevance to the distribution of strontium 90, but he also emphasized that, while the precise degree of hazard was not known—and that "like many biological problems, the determination of the hazard in any exact way seems to be almost impossibly difficult"—the levels of population exposure from man-made sources were at their maximum only fractional parts of the total radioactivity to which mankind naturally is exposed. Of the breadth of the problem Libby said:

> We see, therefore, that whatever the extent of our ignorance of the biological effects of radiation, we do know that these effects are not unexperienced by the human species, even from the genetic point of view since it is clear now that persons living at high altitudes on granitic rocks always have received extra radiation many times greater than is contained in the radioactive fallout from the testing of nuclear weapons, and that even those living on certain sedimentary rocks at sea level always have received about ten to twenty times the present fallout dose.

> Of course, this does not mean that any of the effects from radioactive fallout are in any way negligible and it does not mean that certain numbers of people will not be injured by radioactive fallout radiations, even though these numbers be very small relative to the total population of the world. However, the problem is bounded, and common sense and good judgment can be brought to bear on the extent of the biological hazards even though they are not now known exactly and probably will not be well understood for many years. . . .

> From our study of radioactive fallout from testing, we have learned much of value about the circulation of the atmosphere of the world, and we have much more to learn as the study continues. . . . As we undertake the problem of locating the fallout in the oceans, we undoubtedly will learn much of interest to oceanographers about the circulation of water in the seas.[8]

New studies of radioactivity in the ocean already were scheduled for the Pacific during the coming months.

II

The mission of the Laboratory of Radiation Biology during the Hardtack series was to attempt to extend still further the accumulation of data on ocean contamination begun in the Japanese and American surveys of 1954, 1955, and 1956. The program was divided into three phases. The Laboratory was asked to develop plans:

1. To outline immediately following detonation the mass of radioactive water produced by an underwater explosion, with particular reference to the uptake of short-lived radioisotopes by marine organisms.

2. To assess radioactivity in the ocean and in marine organisms in the immediate vicinity of the test atolls during the test operations, an assessment much like that made aboard the *Walton* in 1956 but involving samplings of activity at depths below the thermocline.

3. To follow westward, as had the *Marsh* in 1956, the drift of ocean contamination after the test series had been concluded.

The three segments of the 1958 program took place at separate times and involved the use of different vessels. The survey of contamination from the underwater explosion was conducted early in the Hardtack series aboard the U.S.S. *Rehoboth* (AGS 50), a seaplane tender converted by the Navy for oceanographic work and commanded by Commander Donald J. Hackett, U.S.N. Later in the test series personnel and equipment were put aboard a destroyer, the U.S.S. *Collett* (DD 730), Commander John D. Patterson, U.S.N., for a survey of the waters of the Hardtack restricted area. Finally, in September, when the Pacific operations had been concluded, the destroyer escort U.S.S. *Silverstein* (DE 534), Commander C. S. Swift, U.S.N., carried a survey team west from the proving ground on a track similar to that of the *Marsh* in 1956.

The *Rehoboth* mission was incorporated into planning for Test Wahoo, the sixth test of the 1958 series, in which a device was to be detonated at a depth of 500 feet in the ocean southwest of Eniwetok Atoll. The date was May 16, 1958. The U.S. Navy Hydrographic Office had assigned the *Rehoboth* to the Office of Naval Research for another program related to the Wahoo event, and by arrangement through the Atomic Energy Commission the vessel also was made available to the Laboratory of Radiation Biology for its biological survey. The Radiation Biology program was itself divided into two phases, the first a predetonation survey of the adjacent ocean area to evaluate a radioactivity contributed by earlier tests of the series, and the second the postshot survey that would begin as soon as possible after detonation and proceed in whatever direction and at whatever length events dictated.

The *Rehoboth* actually carried three teams. Conducting observations in parallel with the Radiation Biology team was a group of eight Hydrographic Office staff members, headed by Alfred W. Anderson, who made oceanographic observations during both phases of the operation and who supplied water samples from four locations for measurements of radioactivity. Also aboard was a radiation monitoring team from the Radiation Technical Division of the Naval Medical Research Institute, and this group, under the direction of Lieutenant J. W. Duckworth, measured radioactivity of the water at the surface, at the intake to the ship's evaporators, and at designated depths down to 600 feet. Heading the Radiation Biology group were Lowman and Palumbo, who now were jointly in charge of the Laboratory's high-level radioactivity studies at the proving ground, and with them were Welander and Donald R. Weeks, a graduate student. In the predetonation survey the measurement of radioactivity in the surface waters was conducted by representatives of the Radiation Safety Section of the Los Alamos Scientific Laboratory under the direction of Major Gordon Jacks.

Test Wahoo was the third underwater detonation to be conducted by the United States, but the first with which biological sampling had been specifically programed. Test Baker at Bikini twelve years earlier had been a shallow-water shot inside Bikini lagoon. Operation Wigwam in 1955 had involved detonation of a device at a depth of 2,000 feet off the West Coast of the United States in a single operation in which associated activities were limited to oceanographic observations and essential monitoring. The proving ground surveys of 1955 and 1956 had traced contamination placed in the water by miscellaneous test shots, all of which had been detonated at atoll sites, either on land or in very shallow water. The *Rehoboth* program contained aspects that were, accordingly, new to test operations. In its design the differences were (1) that a biological survey was related to a designated test detonation, (2) that the contaminants would not be those associated with land or lagoon tests, and (3) that a particular interest was in the biological uptake of short-lived radioisotopes. The problem before the *Rehoboth* was to outline, follow, and sample in depth a body of water welling upward from an ocean detonation of intermediate depth.

In pre-Hardtack consultations it was decided that the *Rehoboth* would be steered along the edges of the water mass on a line at which radioactivity was at 10 milliroentgens per hour. On May 16, the day of the Wahoo event, the *Rehoboth* would stand at sea some four miles off the point at which the Wahoo bubble would burst from the surface, ready to feel her way toward the edge of the contaminated water after the base surge and airborne radioactivity had subsided. Three-man teams operating U.S. Navy survey meters (AN/PDR-27C and AN/PDR-43 [XN-2]), were assigned stations forward at the port and starboard rails of the vessel, from where they would transmit frequent telephone reports to the bridge of gamma radiation levels approximately twenty feet above the surface of the water. In this manner the ship was to be maneuvered to follow a 10 mr/hr surface field which would be plotted as the track developed.[9]

For the first time in connection with ocean surveys at the proving ground gamma spectrometry was to be performed on shipboard so that data would be available immediately on the uptake of short-lived isotopes. For this purpose the equipment aboard the *Rehoboth* included a single-channel, fifty-position, automatic advance spectrometer with a two-inch well-type sodium iodide crystal. Spectrometry was concerned primarily with uptake by plankton, although samples of water and of small fish also would be analyzed. Preparations were made for determining the radiochemical composition of samples by the use of ion-exchange techniques.

The predetonation survey of the region of the Wahoo test proceeded almost to the eve of the event. The effort to establish the background level of radioactivity was confused somewhat by fallout from other tests being conducted at Eniwetok. The Hardtack series was opened on April 28 with detonation at 86,000 feet over the ocean of a device suspended from a balloon. This event was followed on May 5 by a surface test, Cactus, and by three additional test detonations—Fir, Butternut, and Koa—on May 11 and 12.[10] A rise in radioactivity in plankton samples collected by the biologists on May 6 was attributed to fallout from the Cactus shot. On May 14 a new rise of radioactivity was noted in the area in which the *Rehoboth* was operating and subsequent general shipboard contamination raised the background in the counting room to an excessively high level.[11] In some ten days before the Wahoo test, however, the *Rehoboth* had made collections and analyses for gross beta activity of plankton from twelve stations, had obtained a series of nineteen water samples from the surface to a depth of 1,039 meters, and had made four trawl hauls of small fish and large plankton from depths of 14 to 365 meters.

On May 16, the *Rehoboth* awaited the detonation at a point 7,000 yards south and slightly west of Target Zero, a position from which the vessel would be able to withdraw quickly if necessary or drift out of the contaminated area in the event of engine failure.[12] The Wahoo device was detonated at 1:30 P.M. at a station some two miles off the southwest rim of Eniwetok atoll.

At 2:35 P.M. the Rehoboth was southeast of the target area and at the edge of the field of gamma radioactivity. When the monitors reported readings of 3 milliroentgens per hour, the ship was turned west to take up a course near what was presumed to be near the outside margin of the contaminated water mass, but during the turn the radiation levels increased rapidly to 500 milliroentgens per hour and the vessel was forced to alter her course sharply to the south to escape the field. After this penetration, the *Rehoboth* began at 2:55 P.M. a run to the southwest until readings of 10 to 30 milliroentgens were reported, then at 3:10 P.M. courses to the northwest and to the north. By 4:18 P.M., after the ship had circled back to check the westerly readings, the initial survey was completed when the *Rehoboth* was about four miles downwind, west-southwest, of the zero point.[13]

Sampling of water and marine organisms began at once and was continued for four days. In the hours immediately following Wahoo, the *Rehoboth* had established within reasonable limits the surface outline of the ocean contamination. The problem, however, was three-dimensional, and decisions about procedure rested to a considerable extent on information developed, step by step, in the analysis of samples. Collections of plankton were used as indicators of radioactivity present in the water mass. The first post-Wahoo plankton sample was obtained as the initial survey ended. This sampling, at depths of 9 to 15 meters and in an area with a gamma radiation level of 10 milliroentgens per hour, indicated that plankton radioactivity was high (32,000,000 d/m/g/, dry weight), but the level was not as high as that found in the next sample taken that evening at a position less than three miles to the southeast. The difference indicated either that there were variations in uptake by biota of the target area or that uptake still was proceeding. Samplings of water, plankton, and fish in succeeding days were conducted along lines designed to disclose the changing patterns of ocean-borne contamination, but the changes were in distance, depth, time, and quality and presented a great number of variables.

From the late afternoon of May 16, when the *Rehoboth* completed its outline of initial radioactivity, until the afternoon of May 20, the vessel worked its way westward from Eniwetok above the slowly moving water mass in which residual radioactivity was being circulated, dispersed, and diluted. The three sets of water samples obtained after Test Wahoo produced profiles of the vertical distribution of radioactivity in the ocean at six, twenty-eight, and forty-eight hours after detonation. Analyses were made of the total activity and of the particulate and colloidal-soluble fractions at depths to 300 meters to determine the degree and rate of distribution of activity within the stirred layer and the amounts of activity at and below the thermocline. During the first six hours, the survey team found, the major part of the total radioactivity was in the top 25 meters of water, the activity decreasing with depth so that through the upper edge of the thermocline, at 100 meters, the level of contamination was only one-eighth as high as that at the surface. At twenty-eight hours, the radioactivity was distributed throughout the upper half of the mixed layer, to a depth of about 50 meters, but dropped rapidly in value between that point and the upper edge of the thermocline. At forty-eight hours, the major portion of the radioactivity was concentrated at the upper edge of the thermocline. At no time, so far as could be determined, had there been an even and general distribution of activity throughout the mixed layer, where the water is stirred by the actions of winds and currents. There was, on the contrary, evidence of stratification of activity even within that region of drift and circulating movement.[14]

Below the thermocline a further difference was found. At forty-eight hours after detonation the radioactivity in the waters immediately below the thermocline, at 150 meters, was at a low value, but at still lower depths, to the 300-meter limit of the survey sampling, the amounts of radioactivity rose until the level was approximately one-half that of the thermocline. The distribution of radioactivity with depth followed a similar pattern in the analyses of the particulate and soluble fractions. At forty-eight hours the major part of the radioactivity in each fraction was concentrated at a depth of 100 meters, at the upper edge of the thermocline, while at 300 meters the radioactivity in each again was approximately half of the 100-meter value.[15]

Between May 17 and 20, twenty-one plankton collections were made by the *Rehoboth* in an area extending almost fifty miles west of Eniwetok and a further collection was made on May 26 near the extremity of the original survey area. In three successful mid-water trawls after Wahoo (in a fourth the gear was lost during the recovery operation), samples were obtained of euphausids, lantern fish, crab larvae, small squid, and miscellaneous macroplankton species. Specimens of small fish and a portion of an alga (*Turbinaria ornata*) were collected with three of the plankton hauls, and two dolphins were caught by hook and line. Analysis of activity was conducted as rapidly as possible on all specimens so that members of the teams could keep in touch with the changes in position and size of the identifiable water mass. By May 19, however, a puzzling situation had developed. The *Rehoboth* was then approximately forty miles west of the Wahoo detonation point, and the measurements of radioactivity in plankton indicated that the vessel was in an area of Wahoo radioactivity, for the radioisotopes were similar to those noted in earlier samples. The normal drift of the upper waters, however, would not be expected to exceed ten miles per day, and the waters at the lower depths probably would move more slowly. Despite the evidence of the plankton, it seemed increasingly probable that the main mass of water had been left behind. To make a lateral check, the vessel was turned south and another plankton haul was made at a distance of twenty miles. The levels of activity in the plankton were low, yet the isotopic content clearly was of Wahoo origin and radioactivity was found in samples taken above and below the thermocline. It was then considered likely that the plume of cloud from Test Wahoo had deposited across the surface of the sea a streak of airborne materials which already had been ingested by the plankton, and that the *Rehoboth* had reached the southwestern edge of a water area in which the radionuclides were both waterborne and airborne. The choice was to cruise even further west in an attempt to reach the outermost limit of the Wahoo materials or to turn back toward the area of contamination holding the principal interest. The *Rehoboth* turned back.

The data developed aboard the *Rehoboth* and later, particularly in analysis of radioisotopic content of specimens, revealed certain striking differences in radioactive composition immediately following nuclear detonation. The short-lived fission products were dominant. The gamma-emitting radioisotopes in plankton collected between May 16 and May 20 included molybdenum 99-technetium 99, with a half-life of sixty-six hours; and tellurium 132-iodine 132, with a half-life of seventy-seven hours. The larger plankton were found to have ingested larger proportions of barium 140, with a half-life of 12.8 days, while smaller plankton contained higher percentages of molybdenum 99-technetium 99, but otherwise the radioisotopic compositions were similar.

These analyses invited new considerations of the role of plankton in the distribution of radioactivity. The proportions of radioisotopes present in plankton could be expected to change with time, the changes depending on the rates of physical decay of radioisotopes present and on the speed with which concentrations of isotopes occurred within the organisms. A point of reference would be the relative amounts of gross beta radioactivity in both water and detonation. To estimate these relative amounts, the *Rehoboth* group calculated the total volumes of water filtered by the plankton nets as the tows were made and then compared the radioactivity of the water that passed through the nets with the radioactivity of the plankton captured in each. The plankton samples had been collected with a half-meter net of No. 6 mesh while the vessel was drifting at a speed of .5 to 1.8 knots per hour. The total volume of water filtered was calculated as the product of the distance the net was towed, the filtering efficiency of the net

(50 per cent), and the cross-section area. When the waterborne radioactivity that had passed through the net was compared to the radioactivity of the plankton, the values in the water were found to range from 3,000 to 11,000 times higher. It could only be concluded that in the hours immediately following the detonation the plankton had played a much less significant role in the removal of radioactivity from the water.[16]

Assessments of gross beta radioactivity of the organisms collected in the mid-water trawls reflected differences in uptake by fish, squid, and shrimp. Radioactivity in whole shrimp samples was at levels two to ten times higher than those of whole fish. Fish collected on May 17, the day after Wahoo, at a depth of 25 meters, produced a value of 259,000 disintegrations per minute per gram (of dry weight at time of collection), while shrimp from the same trawl were at 2,680,000 disintegrations per minute per gram and squid at 3,060,000. Fish collected in the last trawl late in the survey at a depth of 365 meters—250 meters below the thermocline —were found to contain gross beta activity of 756,000 disintegrations per minute and shrimp from the same trawl 1,050,000. Thus, while the level in miscellaneous small fish had tripled with time and depth, the level in shrimp had been reduced by more than half. The small fish collected after Wahoo had essentially the same radioisotopic content as the plankton samples. Samples of whole shrimp and squid had, in comparison to plankton, higher levels of tellurium 132-iodine 132. The data, as analyzed at sea and in the days immediately following the *Rehoboth* cruise, were not yet interpretable in detail. There was no doubt that the process of discrimination in the uptake of radioisotopes by marine organisms was at work in the very earliest days and hours following a nuclear detonation. In this period, too, amounts of strontium 90 were low. Only two plankton samples collected before Test Wahoo contained detectable amounts of strontium, and these were collected on May 5, the day the Cactus device was detonated at Eniwetok. After Test Wahoo, strontium 90 comprised only 0.0001 to 0.04 per cent of the total beta radioactivity. As had been demonstrated repeatedly before, the relevance of strontium in ocean contamination was not great.

The apparent tendency toward stratification of radioactivity even in the mixed layer of ocean water seemed a contradiction of earlier, theoretical assumptions that particulate materials would tend to descend to the ocean depths under the force of gravity while materials in soluble form would be distributed evenly throughout the mixed layer. Much later, after further examination of the evidence, Lowman attempted an analysis of the physical, chemical, and biological factors that seemed to be involved. He noted that homogenous dispersion of activity throughout the mixed layer unquestionably occurred in time, as Operation Troll had showed, but that in the area of the Marshall Islands such dispersion had not occurred within six to eight weeks after contamination of the water mass. Of the probable primary factors he wrote:

> When radioactive materials in the particulate forms are introduced into sea water, the particles may go into solution either because of their high solubility constant or from increased hydrostatic pressure as they sink through the water by gravity. If initially in the soluble form, they may be precipitated as particles of varying size by interaction with salts in the sea or with accompanying materials, or by adsorption to biological or inorganic particles. The particles, whether inorganic or organic, would tend to be removed from the mixed layer by gravity, although the planktonic organisms tend to offset this effect by swimming upward. Because of the effect of gravity on particles, the soluble and insoluble fractions would probably act as two independent systems as far as concentration on dispersal processes are concerned.[17]

In the operation of these "independent systems," Lowman suggested, both chemical and biological mechanisms were indicated. In the waters of the sea such naturally ocurring trace elements as zinc, cobalt, ruthenium, cesium, strontium, and iodine usually are present in solution. All of these except cesium, strontium, and iodine, when introduced into the sea in fallout, probably would be present in particulate form. But the fallout elements of cesium, strontium, and iodine, which appear in solution, were found only in trace quantities in plankton, while the radioactive fission products with the least solubility, zirconium 95 and cerium 144, were found in plankton in the greatest amounts. All evidence pointed to a discrimination by plankton against materials in soluble form, including strontium 90, and adsorption of particulates, so that the plankton, "swimming upward," were introducing a biological factor into what otherwise would have been a purely physical system of distribution. Stratification could only be explained by

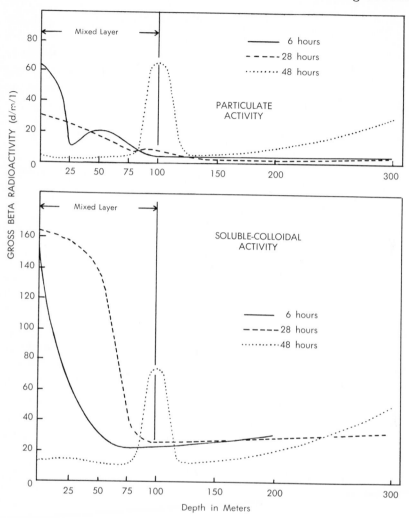

Distribution of particulate and soluble-colloidal radioactivity with depth at 6, 28, and 48 hours after an underwater detonation. (From Lowman, IAEA, Vienna, 1960.)

acknowledging the action of hydrostatic pressure on particles. Radioactive particles apparently were carried down into the ocean by gravity until they had found the levels at which they were either held in suspension or forced into solution. The thermocline, at the base of the stirred layer, represented a level at which the particles had accumulated and had produced higher amounts of radioactivity.

III

The Pacific phase of Operation Hardtack continued through June and July and into August, 1958. The Radiation Biology group from the *Rehoboth*, which returned to Eniwetok on May 20, worked for some weeks at the EMBL in continued processing of ocean samples and analysis of new collections. On June 8, the second underwater shot of the Hardtack series, Test Umbrella, was detonated on the floor of Eniwetok lagoon, and samples of water and plankton were obtained after this test for comparison with *Rehoboth* data.* In the interval, preparations went forward for the surveys to follow.

The surveys of the *Collett* and the *Silverstein* were, like those of 1956, separate segments of a comprehensive effort to observe the vertical dispersion and westward movement of contamination placed in the ocean at the test atolls. Planning and preparation reflected the experience gained in the earlier cruises. Sampling was to be performed to greater depths, and the gamma spectrometry equipment used on the *Rehoboth*, which had not been available in 1956, was used in each of the later expeditions. In view of the continuing apprehension of the Japanese, there was an even greater interest in the collection of specimens of tuna and other pelagic fish, and the *Collett*, in particular, put to sea under a specific injunction by the Division of Biology and Medicine to make every possible effort to take samples of fish. Coded reports of radioactivity found in water and plankton samples were to be transmitted daily by priority radio message through the Joint Task

*On June 6 a press association dispatch from London quoted Moscow Radio as saying that a Soviet IGY vessel, the *Vityaz*, had encountered "radioactive rain" on May 23 as the vessel made observations 1,800 miles west of the proving ground. The dispatch also quoted *Pravda* commentary to the effect that radioactivity was "a menace to the health of many people in the area" and that winds carried radioactive dust "over vast areas." The U.S.S.R.'s most recent nuclear shot had been a "medium range" detonation on March 22 in the Arctic.

Group 7.5 communications center to the Division of Biology and Medicine, the Division of Military Application, and Joint Task Force Seven. Alfred W. Klement Jr., of the Fallout Studies Branch of the Division of Biology and Medicine, had been sent to the proving ground to coordinate survey preparations and to transmit data to appropriate offices and commands. Seymour, at the Environmental Sciences Branch, had sent a memorandum to Donaldson on June 30 in which he said:

> The desired information will include the gross activity of samples of water above and below the thermocline, of plankton and of fish; the rate of decay; and any information on the isotopic composition of the samples that can be obtained while on shipboard, fully recognizing the limitations of time and equipment. As you well know, the important information about the samples is the determination of the radioisotopes, quantitatively and qualitatively rather than merely gross counts.
>
> The area to be sampled initially should be based upon the best available information as to where the spots of contamination in the ocean may be. It is suggested that the course be such as to sample as many stations within the Restricted Area as possible . . . before moving outside of the restricted area for samples. Based upon the 1956 survey, more stations in the Restricted Area and fewer in the Guam area would appear to be in order.[18]

The *Collett* survey took place between August 8 and 15, 1958 (Marshall Islands time), the sampling conducted at thirty-nine stations spaced at intervals of fifty miles on a grid in the central area of the Hardtack Restricted Area, which was approximately that of the 1956 test series but with the east and west boundaries shifted about 120 nautical miles westward.[19] Within the restricted area of 390,000 square miles the *Collett* covered some 63,500 square miles. Less than a month later, on September 3, the *Silverstein* departed Eniwetok on a cruise to Guam and return during which samples of water and plankton were taken at forty-eight stations spaced across a water area of some 400,000 square miles.

On the findings of the first survey rested a decision which, in relation to the sequence of events in the testing program, was of singular, if momentary, importance. The *Collett* cruise began almost two weeks after the final nuclear test (a barge shot in Eniwetok lagoon on July 26, 1958) in the Pacific Proving Ground. In the interim, and before the Pacific phase of Operation Hardtack was concluded, elements of Joint Task Force Seven had completed a movement to Johnston Island, 700 miles southwest of Honolulu, where two missiles carrying thermonuclear devices were to be fired into the stratosphere to obtain information on the effects of nuclear detonations at high altitudes. The first of these shots, Teak, was detonated at 9:50 P.M. on August 1 (Johnston Island time) at an altitude of 252,000 feet, the second, Orange, at 9:30 P.M. on August 12 at approximately 100,000 feet.[20] These were the first megaton devices detonated in the stratosphere by the United States. Thus, while the Pacific operations were being brought to a close at Johnston Island, the *Collett* was in the second half of her survey of the Eniwetok-Bikini area, where test facilities were in process of being returned to an inactive status. Because the *Collett* was surveying the sea immediately after the close of the atoll test series, the results of her analyses would be used by the Commission to determine when the Restricted Area could be reopened to general shipping. The *Collett* represented, at the proving ground, a final scientific activity before Eniwetok and Bikini were placed in a caretaker status that would last as long as the international discussions of the problems of nuclear testing were continued at Geneva.

The track of the *Collett* was only generally similar to that of the *Walton* two years before. The vessel, after proceeding northwest of Eniwetok, turned due east and began a series of traverses of the grid area, working eastward beyond Bikini, and then swung directly west on a southerly course to touch the final stations south of Eniwetok. The levels of activity in the plankton and water samples revealed that the fallout contaminants had been carried northwest from the test atolls before being deposited in the sea. The area of greatest activity was found approximately 170 miles northwest of Eniwetok, although this was connected to Eniwetok by a slender streak of waterborne radioactivity that extended from the atoll to the center of maximum contamination. A second and lesser center of high radioactivity lay approximately 120 miles southwest of Eniwetok, and the eastern fringes of this area touched Ujelang Atoll. The lowest levels of radioactivity were found far to the east of the survey area, between Bikini and Rongelap.

Analysis of the *Collett* samples indicated that the radioactivity in the ocean was a total product of a number of nuclear tests conducted at various points in time. Further, the process of mixing within the waters was far from complete. In the area of the highest contamination, the samples containing the highest amounts of radioactivity came from above the thermocline, but the recorded measurements varied so widely that it was obvious the radioactivity was not evenly distributed throughout the mixed layer. Maximum amounts of radioactivity were found in samples taken at Station No. 3, northwest of Eniwetok, and there the filtered water samples produced readings of 7,000 disintegrations per minute per liter at the surface, 7,700 at a depth of 25 meters, 11,000 at 50 meters, 13,000 at 100 meters (below the thermocline), and 1,700 at 300 meters, the greatest depth from which samples were taken. Yet at Station No. 4, 50 miles to the east, the measurements ranged from 16,000 at the surface to 6,200 at 50 meters, and below the thermocline the samples produced readings of only 200 disintegrations per minute at 100 meters and 570 at 300 meters. Similar variations were found in plankton samples, which had been put through a screen to permit analysis of organisms by size.*

The general situation three weeks after the close of the Eniwetok tests was one with which the survey teams now were familiar. That there were areas of relatively high contamination was not surprising, and the experience of 1956 suggested that the processes of mixing, dilution, and movement would diminish and spread the total contamination in patterns that would be more accurately determined by the *Silverstein*. The radio reports of the isotopic content of the samples were sent each day by Lowman to Klement, and the survey proceeded as scheduled toward completion of its mission except in the one respect, the collection of specimens of pelagic fish. Fishing was begun from the decks of the *Collett* when the cruise was started and was continued throughout, but the results, except for the capture of a few flying fish, were negative. Between stations the *Collett* could not proceed at trolling speed for she was working on a schedule designed to gather water and plankton samples in the shortest possible time, and only commercial gear aboard a fishing vessel, not a destroyer, would have been able to take a

---

*Plankton samples were gathered with a half-meter net of No. 6 mesh. The samples then were separated into large and small fractions by filtering through a bronze screen (99 mesh per inch) and then through a fine-meshed filter disc with a pore size of .45u. Plankton retained on the screen were designated large plankton and those passing through the screen but retained by the filter composed the small fraction.

significant number of specimens. Fish samples would be obtained later in 1958, however, and they would come from Japan. Kawabata, the young Japanese scientist who had been aboard the *Shunkotsu Maru*, and who had worked later in Seattle with Donaldson and his staff, was equally curious in 1958 about the levels and problems of ocean contamination. Weeks after Hardtack was concluded, Kawabata visited the Japanese fish markets and selected samples of tuna from fishing boats returning from the Central Pacific. These he shipped to Donaldson for analysis in the Laboratory of Radiation Biology. The act was known at the time only to the scientists and staff members immediately concerned, but this small bit of Japanese-American cooperation made possible a study of the 1958 levels of contamination in fish.[21]

The *Collett* returned to Eniwetok on August 15 and by the following day the counting and collecting equipment had been removed and stored for installation on the *Silverstein* at the end of the month. The members of the survey team, between August 15 and September 1, continued to work with the samples, making radiochemical analyses to determine more precisely their radio-isotopic content. But the data essential to a decision on the opening of the Restricted Area already had been accumulating in the daily radio reports. On August 16 a message from the Joint Task Force at Eniwetok to the Division of Military Application reported that the survey was completed, that the *Collett* had departed for the western Pacific, and that one working day would be required to install equipment on the *Silverstein* when she arrived at the proving ground about August 29. The message concluded:

> Survey information included 190 water samples to a depth of 900 feet of 195 requested, 39 plankton samples of 39 requested. Mr. Klement recommends disestablishment of EPG Danger Area based on survey findings as manifested in plankton and sea water readings.[22]

An unexpected radioelement, tungsten 185, was encountered in analysis of the *Collett* samples and found also, later, to be present in samples taken by the *Silverstein*. It was assumed then (an assumption later confirmed) that the tungsten was present as a result of its incorporation into some of the devices that had been tested as a means of tracing and identifying fallout. In the *Collett* samples, tungsten 185, which has a half-life of seventy-four days, was found at its highest levels in samples from the areas of highest general contamination. At Station No. 3 northwest of Eniwetok it comprised 83.1 per cent of the isotopic content of plankton. In the September survey, no tungsten 185 was found in plankton, but it was the principal element found in water samples, in which only traces of other radioisotopes were identified.

The *Silverstein,* leaving Eniwetok on September 3, followed a zigzag track similar to that of the *Marsh* two years before. In the interval between the August and September surveys the center of ocean radioactivity that had been noted 170 miles northwest of Eniwetok had moved west-southwest some 250 miles. Because the *Silverstein* cruise pattern permitted observations over a much wider area of ocean, four major concentrations of waterborne radioactivity were found—one 270 miles due north of Eniwetok, another 330 miles to the northwest, and two to the west-northwest at distances of 390 and 570 miles. The leading edge of the contaminated area extended in September almost to Guam. In one plankton sample taken 110 miles northeast of Guam on September 7 the gross beta radioactivity was 39,000 disintegrations per minute per gram (dry weight), and in a sample taken 80 miles southeast of the island on September 9 the level was at 28,000 disintegrations per minute. Water taken at the same stations produced readings of 6,200 and 3,000 disintegrations per minute for 5-liter amounts. Plankton taken north of Guam, toward the island of Rota, contained activity producing only 3,200 disintegrations per minute, and no activity was detectable in the water there.

As for the vertical distribution of radioactivity within the contaminated water mass, the chemical and biological processes still were unresolved. Everywhere except near Eniwetok Atoll the radioactivity was found unevenly distributed within the mixed layer. But north of Eniwetok and as far as 270 miles due west, almost all of the radioactivity was below the thermocline. In the western edge of the contamination, east of Guam, radioactivity was almost entirely in the top 50 meters of water. The general picture was of a sprawling, slowly moving water mass, irregular in outline, in which there were identifiable areas and depths of concentrated radioactivity and in which radioelements that had been placed in the sea by a number of nuclear test explosions were involved in processes of decay, dilution, biological uptake, chemical transformation, and elimination by the action of gravity. Even the most generalized conclusion was hazardous, yet it seemed evident that the processes were working toward the results noted in 1955 by the *Taney* and in 1956 by the *Marsh*. The mixing of radioelements throughout the stirred layer was far from complete, but by the time this had happened—in months, perhaps—natural decay would have reduced to trace amounts those radioactive elements which had not in the meantime been claimed by the ocean depths. The Laboratory of Radiation Biology would continue to work with its samples for at least two more years, refining its analyses in the hope that the picture would come clearer.* Meantime, the Pacific Proving Ground, garrisoned only by small detachments of Holmes & Narver and military personnel, would be quiet again.

IV

Between July 1 and August 21, 1958, a conference was held in Geneva to explore methods of detecting violations during a suspension of nuclear weapons tests. The meeting was attended by scientists from France, the United Kingdom, Canada, and the United States and from the Soviet Union, Poland, Romania, and Czechoslovakia. In a final report the delegates agreed that it would be "technically feasible to set up, with certain capabilities and limitations, a workable and effective control system for the detection of violations."[23]

The report of the United Nations Scientific Committee, appointed pursuant to the General Assembly resolution of 1955, was released to the public on August 10.[24] On August 22, the day following the close of the Geneva meeting, President Eisenhower announced that the United States was prepared to enter negotiations for a suspension of nuclear weapons testing. In his statement the President said:

> The United States, taking account of the Geneva conclusions, is prepared to proceed promptly to negotiate an agreement with other nations which have tested nuclear weapons for the suspension of nuclear weapons tests and the actual establishment of an international control system based on the experts' report.
>
> If this is accepted in principle by the other nations which have tested nuclear weapons, then in order to facilitate the detailed negotiations, the United States is prepared, unless testing is resumed by the Soviet Union,

---

*A tabulation reflecting the radioisotopic content of representative aquatic samples is presented in Appendix 1.

to withhold further testing on its part of atomic weapons for a period of one year from the beginning of negotiations.

As part of the agreement to be negotiated, and on a basis of reciprocity, the United States would be further prepared to suspend the testing of nuclear weapons on a year-by-year basis subject to a determination at the beginning of each year: (A) The agreed inspection system is installed and working effectively; and (B) satisfactory progress is being made in reaching agreement on and implementing major and substantial arms control measures such as the United States has long sought. The agreement should also deal with the problem of detonations for peaceful purposes, as distinct from weapons tests.

Our negotiators will be instructed and ready by October 31 this year to open negotiations with other similarly instructed negotiators.[25]

The United States proposal was accepted by the Soviet Union on August 29. Operation Hardtack (Phase II) began at the Nevada Proving Ground on September 12, and between that date and October 30 the United States detonated some thirty-two low-yield nuclear devices, eleven of them underground. On September 30 the Soviet Union opened a series of tests in the Arctic and by October 25 the series had produced fourteen detonations, at least seven of them in the megaton range. Two final Soviet shots of "relatively low" yield were detonated in Siberia on November 1 and 3 as the discussions were opening at Geneva.

Chapter Eleven

1959-1961: THE KNOWN, THE UNKNOWN

I

IN 1961, in March and September, teams from the Laboratory of Radiation Biology made further visits to Rongelap and Eniwetok. These visits took place three years after the cruise of the *Collett* had signaled preparations for the end of the Pacific phase of Operation Hardtack and more than seven years after Rongelap had been touched by the fallout from Test Bravo. The periods were indicative of the necessarily deliberate pace of observations geared to the unfolding of radiobiological developments.

At Rongelap the people still were the special concern of the Trust Territory administration. They lived with dimming memories of the events that occurred between 1954 and 1957, in good health, and in villages now enlarged by the addition of frame and plywood buildings erected by the Rongelap men themselves, the practice of building thatched huts having been abandoned altogether.[1] The eighteen months of respite from examinations and surveys apparently had permitted further restoration of attitudes and community activities characteristic of earlier years. Members of the Laboratory group were welcomed by the Rongelapese, but the biological surveys were conducted as usual apart from the areas of community life, principally on the northern islands and reefs, with the smallest possible intrusion into Rongelap routines.

At Eniwetok, from which Joint Task Force Seven had departed in 1958, the field work also went forward even though Eniwetok itself was in its third year of inactivity as a nuclear testing ground. By 1961 the responsibility for the atoll had been transferred from the Atomic Energy Commission to the Department of Defense in the development of westward facilities of the Pacific Missile Range. Eniwetok Island was the headquarters of administrative and security activities, but the buildings and compounds of Parry Island were unused. The Eniwetok Marine Biological Laboratory had been moved from Parry to Eniwetok Island, and it was from that altered facility that the survey teams continued their observations. About the other islands, now deserted—Japtan, Runit, Aomon-Biijiri, Eberiru, Bogallua, Mui—Eniwetok's plant and animal life, on the land and in the waters, continued to flourish.

II

The years that the Laboratory of Radiation Biology worked in the Pacific encompassed four periods which reflect with approximate accuracy four steps in the refinement of biological observations at the sites of nuclear tests.

From 1946 to 1949 the observations were confined to the atolls and were regarded merely as monitoring activities of a specialized kind. No surveys of the atoll environments were incorporated into the planning for Operation Sandstone or Operation Greenhouse, and the impulse to continue the surveys lay chiefly in the unsatisfied curiosities of members of the Applied Fisheries staff to whom the problems had begun, after 1947, to take on a peculiarly personal meaning.

By 1952, when Operation Ivy brought the first of the thermonuclear detonations, earlier concepts of the localized character of nuclear fallout were made obsolete. The questions related to the dispersal of radioactive products extended now to the ocean and to the stratosphere. So far as work in the ocean was concerned, the Laboratory, as Bugher had said, already was involved in studies pointing beyond "the small fraction of the earth that is dry." But the Laboratory was contributing in only a minor way to the total fallout studies then going forward, and what was needed was new and more imaginative emphasis on studies of the disposition of fallout in the oceanic dimension. The conference and decisions of 1951 and 1952 kept within the Commission framework the one organization that had a consistent experience with and interest in the aquatic biology problems that Ivy had enlarged.

In 1954 the issues of widespread contamination that had been presaged by Operation Ivy were thrust visibly into the field of international relations. Thus the third period began. At that moment the only substantial information in the hands of the Atomic Energy Commission on the disposition of aquatic contamination was in the reports prepared by the Applied Fisheries Laboratory in 1949 and 1952. The Bikini incident inspired a search for information that involved Japan, created the long-term investigation at Rongelap, and brought about, either directly or in connection with subsequent nuclear tests, the oceanic surveys of the *Shunkotsu Maru,* the *Taney,* the *Walton,* the *Marsh,* the *Rehoboth,* the *Collett,* and the *Silverstein.*

When the 1958 test series ended, the fourth phase followed. The cessation of nuclear testing allowed a space for consolidation of results and for the initiation of new projects without the pressure of association with nuclear operations. The Pacific experience became the background for work turned toward the use of radioisotopes in controlled environmental studies.

The experience of fifteen years had been, at the very least, panoramic. The nuclear tests had provided opportunities for observations never before necessary or possible, but the conditions of the atoll and ocean surveys had been changed repeatedly in response to transitory needs, to alterations in the Laboratory's own concepts of its mission, particularly as they were enlarged by the improvements in instrumentation, and to developments of the nuclear devices being tested. The total experience had a continuity that in the long view was interesting in its uniqueness and was, perhaps, important, but the interest was purely historical unless the experience was brought to bear on problems yet unsolved. The suspension of testing in 1958 invited such further work. Some of the matters could not have been approached while testing was in progress, and some involved questions that had not yielded to years of repeated investigation.

During the 1949 survey at Eniwetok, for example, two types of abnormal growth had been observed in *Ipomoea tuba,* the prostrate vine growing profusely over Engebi Island. In certain specimens, the stems of the plants were fasciated—flattened—and in others they were covered by tumorous growths and held only rudimentary leaves. Observation of these plants over the intervening years showed that the abnormalities had persisted in *Ipomoea tuba* while no other species was similarly affected. Other plants that seemed to have been prematurely labeled "mutants" in 1949 appeared to have recovered, and no examples of aberration were found among them in 1961. It was thought possible that, as Biddulph had surmised long before, nutrient deficiences in the soil had caused the effects noted. Yet the question of *Ipomoea tuba* remained. Seeds of normal and "diseased" *Ipomoea* were collected in 1961 for planting in fertile and nonfertile soils to determine, if possible, whether soil deficiencies were causing the persisting damage in that case. Healthy seeds also were being subjected to high and low doses of radioactivity to observe the effects of radiation on "normal" plants.[2]

The profuse regrowth of vegetation on Engebi and Bogombogo Islands, each of which had been subjected to heavy damage by nuclear operations, also had been made the subject of a special study. On these islands the grasses and vines had re-established themselves strongly, and three species of plants that had been reported extinct there in 1949 now were found in abundance.[3] At the same time, the sampling of Eniwetok's aquatic environment still was going forward. Specimens of fish, invertebrates, algae, and plankton were taken in 1961 as well as additional samples of water and of sediments at the bottom of the lagoon. This sampling was directed at determining the further distribution of radioisotopes in the environment and the ratios of isotopes in animal and vegetable tissues thirty months after the conclusion of the 1958 test series. Samples of fish collected during the 1958 series were analyzed with the 1961 samples so that results could be compared.[4]

By 1961 the Laboratory had completed tabulations of data gathered in studies of soils and biota at a number of atolls of the Central Pacific—Wotho, Rongelap, Utirik, Ujelang, and others—ranging up to hundreds of miles from the Eniwetok test site. Most of these collections had been made in 1956 and 1958, but the materials were analyzed with those of similar collections made in 1954 and 1955 at atolls near the test sites. The results showed, not surprisingly, that the levels of radioactivity decreased with distance from the proving ground and that at the remote islands the levels were not significantly above background.[5] Analysis for specific radioisotopes revealed that those present in terrestrial organisms in 1958 were cesium 137, cobalt 57, and tungsten 185, and that strontium 90, where it was found at all, comprised only the minutest fraction of the detectable nuclides. In marine organisms the principal isotopes were zinc 65, cobalt 57, and ruthenium 106-rhodium 106. The levels of activity in edible plants, the coconut, for example, were very low, even on islands nearest the test sites. The subject was not closed, for even after three years the circulatory movement of radioisotopes in the biosphere still could not be said to have run down, but the low values appeared to have reached a steady state.

Among the questions still pursued at Eniwetok were those relating to the rats of Engebi.

The intermittent samplings and observations of *Rattus exulans* had raised questions that became more intriguing with the passage of years. The survival of the rats in the face of repeated atomic bombardment had seemed in 1955 a circumstance approaching the phenomenal. Even more so was the continued health of the colonies which fed on the mildly contaminated grasses growing in the irradiated soils of Engebi's stark plain. The case was important because it seemed to bear so directly on one of the broadest of the unanswered questions of the nuclear age, the effect on warm-blooded, vertebrate animals of continued exposure to low-level irradiation. Nowhere else was there a separate and circumscribed area in which the factors of irradiation and population control created an environment holding out so many interesting prospects for study, and the Engebi case still needed to be examined with a thoroughness that never had been possible during the years of nuclear operations. The observation of the rats in the field was augmented in 1961 by radiochemical and gamma spectrometric analyses of the fission and nonfission radioisotopes present in rat tissue, in the vegetation, and in the soil. From these it was hoped to obtain some comprehension of the rates of transfer of individual radioisotopes from the soil to the animal and the levels of concentration in rat tissue. Isotopes found in the tissues included cesium 137, zinc 65, manganese 54, ruthenium 106-rhodium 106, and cobalt 60. But if the case of the rats were to be pursued, it would be necessary to conduct population studies to determine the effects of irradiation on a rat community, histological studies to determine whether radiation damage were evident in rat tissue, genetic studies to observe possible changes in chromatin material, and evaluations of cumulative doses received by the animals under natural conditions in a low-level radiation field.[6]

At Rongelap, the picture was nearer completion. Data on the soil leachates and on the nitrogen content of Rongelap soils had been assembled. Chemical and radiochemical analyses of plants proceeded to develop information on radiocesium-potassium relationships, on the uptake of radiocesium from island soils, and on the rates of growth of plants that had been marked for continued observation. Samplings of fish, birds, rats, invertebrates, and plankton were providing semiannual assessments of the faint residues of the radioactivity introduced by the 1954 fallout.* One of the Rongelap problems, however, was related to the concentration of long-lived radioisotopes by the land crab, in which radiocesium and, to a lesser extent, radiostrontium were found at nearly constant levels.

Consistent studies of the land crabs had been conducted initially at Eniwetok after Nectar tests of 1954. There the Laboratory had analyzed tissues from specimens of *Coenobita* gathered on Bogombogo Island, which lies 2.3 nautical miles southwest of the site of the Mike and Nectar detonations. These studies had showed that during the first 150 days following a nuclear detonation the rate of decline was slowed, reflecting the presence of the long-lived isotopes including cesium 137 and strontium 90. *Coenobita,* an omnivorous scavenger that feeds primarily on land plants, was concentrating these products, for the levels in the carapace, the bony exoskeleton, had remained approximately constant for the period of 537 days in which collections were made.[7] It was against the background of these Eniwetok studies that the observations were made of *Birgus latro,* the coconut or robber crab, at Rongelap.

*A graphic summary of gamma dose rates at Rongelap, as projected against theoretical decay curves, is included in Appendix 1.

It has been noted that the coconut crab, although considered a delicacy by the Rongelapese, had been found to concentrate long-lived isotopes at levels that led to its banning as an item of native diet. It was not only because the crab was a food but because it represented a step above the plants in the food chain that studies

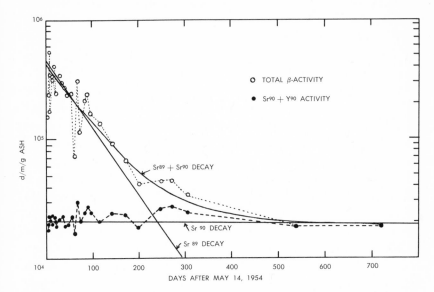

Decline of radionuclide content of the skeleton of *Coenobita perlatus,* a land crab, the specimens taken from an island about two and one-half miles from the point of detonation of the Nectar device on May 14, 1954. The radiostrontium level remains essentially constant, decreasing only with physical decay. Each point represents the average content of three specimens. (Held, UWFL 50, 1957.)

of the animal became meaningful. One of the lines of investigation concerned the possible correlation between the levels of potassium and radiocesium in the crab to determine whether proportional relationships were maintained in the crab as in the plants on which it fed.

Laboratory and a few field studies reported in the literature indicated that there was little discrimination by plants between potassium and low levels of cesium. Rainwater percolating through the soils at Rongelap had showed a proportional relationship between the movement of potassium and radiocesium, and trials with potassium fertilizer, both in the field and in the experimental greenhouses, had resulted in marked reduction by plants of radiocesium uptake. These results were consistent with the fact that plants of contaminated areas of the Marshall Islands, unlike those of continental areas, are high in radiocesium in relation to radiostrontium, a difference resulting from the deficiencies of potassium in island soils and the consequent hunger of plants for potassium and receptivity to cesium. It was not known whether this condition was reflected in the crabs.

The crab studies showed that the relationship broke down at the higher trophic levels. Samples of *Birgus* muscle from animals collected in 1958 and 1959 revealed that, while more than 90 per cent of the activity in the muscle was from cesium 137, no cesium-potassium correlation was evident.[8] Further studies of the plants at Rongelap also made more apparent the complexities inherent in the differences of species, tissues, and soil types. As the data were accumulated further in 1960 and 1961, the coconut crab was recognized with increasing certainty as a reliable indicator of the levels of long-lived radiocesium and radiostrontium in the environment.

However long it might take to understand the mechanisms at work at Rongelap, one fact had become more evident with each collection—the organisms had achieved a steady state with respect to the total of environmental contamination. The levels of radioactivity could be expected to remain much the same, declining only at the rate of physical decay of the isotopes. The studies would be continued, for the radioisotopes in Rongelap's system offered quantities of tagged elements on a scale impossible to achieve in a planned experiment.

III

In 1951, while the Korean War was in progress and the future of the Pacific radiobiological surveys was in doubt, the Applied Fisheries Laboratory had reported to the Division of Biology and Medicine that it would like to explore "the role of essential food elements such as phosphorous, calcium, iron, etc., in the food cycles of natural waters and the possibility of dilution of radioactive materials by the addition of non-active salts."[9] Ten years later, each of these ideas had reached partial fulfillment in experiments that would have been impossible to design in 1951. The fertilization experiments at Eniwetok, Rongelap, and Seattle were showing the extent to which the uptake of radioisotopes by vegetation could be modified by making available to the plants the "non-active salts" necessary to plant development. The Fern Lake program, initiated in 1957, had become the Fern Lake Trace Mineral Metabolism field station for the use of radioisotopes in studies of fresh water ecology. Further, the work initiated during the Manhattan period finally had come full circle, in a sense, after the long and devious detour through the atolls of the Pacific. The Laboratory was taking part in ocean studies at the mouth of the Columbia to determine the disposition in the Pacific of radioisotopes carried by the river from the atomic plant at Hanford, and it had begun at the University a new long-term observation of the effects on salmon of exposure in the egg stage to extremely low levels of irradiation.

The Fern Lake program represented the transfer to a controlled mainland watershed of the study techniques developed in the Pacific. Its purpose was to discover, through the use of radioactively tagged minerals, the disposition of nutritive materials in a postglacial region of low natural productivity and the amounts and kinds of materials needed to make it more productive. It was in such a program, as well as in others that rested on a familiarity with the biological disposition of radioisotopes, that there could be discerned the significant and constructive results of the years of work at the nuclear testing sites.

Fern Lake is a small (18.9-acre) lake some fifty miles from Seattle in northwest Washington. From the standpoint of resources, the lake and the hills that surround it are starved and impoverished, low in production of the fish, game, and trees that should characterize a region that has been disturbed little by man and damaged only by an occasional forest fire. Fern Lake is typical, however, of areas in which glacial action exposed layers of rocky soils and which have struggled for centuries, unsuccessfully, to build accumulations of organic matter sufficiently extensive to permit recovery. The movement of nutrients has been "downhill" and away from a potentially productive resource. The problem, as the Laboratory approached it, was to discover how this process might be reversed.[10]

Fern Lake was reserved in 1957 by the Washington State Department of Game as an area in which long-term field experiments might be conducted. From 1958 to 1961 the Laboratory and the Department, with the support of the Atomic Energy Commission, made ecological inventories of the region and constructed at the field station the controls and equipment (including weather observation and other instrumented facilities) that would be necessary for studies involving use of tagged radioisotopes. The lake was cleaned of all fish and the miscellaneous population replaced by 20,000 steelhead trout fingerlings whose migrations to the sea could be observed in Rocky Creek, the small stream traversing the lake and emptying into salt water at Rocky Bay on Puget Sound. Following pilot experiments in laboratory conditions, the first of the short-lived trace radioisotopes, phosphorous 32 and calcium 45, were introduced into the lake waters in July, 1961, and their assimilation by the biota observed in immediate sampling. Other radioisotopes, including molybdenum 99 and iodine 131, later would be employed. The observations, by 1961, were scheduled to continue for another half-dozen years while the patterns of radiobiological uptake were developed and the areas of nutritional deficiency noted.

The work at Fern Lake, even the concept of the program, reflected the fundamental orientation of the Laboratory of Radiation Biology to interests closer to home than those of the Pacific Proving Ground. It was this orientation that had produced the reluctance of the Applied Fisheries Laboratory to commit itself without reserve to monitoring studies related to weapons testing, and that had produced in the 1951-52 period what had seemed a puzzling ambivalence in its relationship to the proving ground. Fern Lake was the kind of culmination, logical and possibly productive, that justified an instinctive feeling that the puzzle of Pacific radiobiology was worth pursuing. Another such culmination was in the Laboratory's association with Project Chariot, an early and primary element of the Plowshare Project.

The Plowshare program, initiated in 1957 by the University of California Radiation Laboratory at Livermore, had instituted a search for ways to use nuclear detonation for nonmilitary and productive purposes—for the digging of harbors and canals, the production of power sources, the manufacture of radioisotopes, the recovery of deposits of oil or minerals, or for studies in seismology or geology. Within this framework, an early proposal was that nuclear devices be used to excavate a harbor on the coast of the Chukchi Sea in northwest Alaska above the Arctic Circle and at the mouth of Ogotoruk Creek, near Cape Thompson. The plan would involve the simultaneous detonation of five nuclear devices, four 20-kiloton devices sunk to a depth of 400 feet and one 200-kiloton device buried at a depth of about 800 feet. The detonations would be expected to create a channel 900 feet wide and 2,000 feet long and connecting the sea to a basin 1,800 feet in diameter resulting from the explosion of the major device.[11] It was anticipated that about 95 per cent of the resulting fission products would be entrapped underground.

The actual detonation of the devices was not approved initially by the Atomic Energy Commission. Approval had not been given, in fact, by the autumn of 1961. The program nevertheless had stimulated environmental investigations of great breadth and variety, all stemming from the need to establish the widest possible understanding of the biological and terrestrial conditions of an area in which such excavations might be accomplished. The association of the program with the prospect of nuclear explosion led (particularly in the context of the international negotiations, then continuing, on the question of weapons testing) to misunderstandings of the circumstances and probable effects of the proposed experiment. While it withheld approval of the use of nuclear devices, the Commission, in authorizing the predetonation environmental research, provided what the Committee on Environmental Studies for Project Chariot called "the first substantial opportunity for scientific appraisal of ecological systems prior to the detonation of nuclear devices. . . ."[12] The appraisal was far more complete, as the Committee pointed out, than had been possible at Bikini in 1946, the only other occasion on which predetonation ecological studies had been attempted in depth and detail.

The Laboratory of Radiation Biology found also in Project Chariot a new bioenvironmental opportunity for which the experience at Rongelap and Eniwetok had prepared it. The first approach to the matter of biological evaluations was made on March 13, 1958, when a representative of the Sandia Corporation, associated with the Livermore Laboratory, asked the Division of Biology and Medicine to determine the availability of the Laboratory of Radiation Biology for management of marine studies.* On April 8, a meeting at Livermore formulated preliminary considerations and on April 29 Donaldson submitted an outline of biological program elements the Laboratory then considered essential. Planning, preliminary reconnaissance of the Ogotoruk site, and refinement of program proposals proceeded until, in 1959, the Committee on Environmental Studies was formed by the Commission's San Francisco Operations Office to delineate the scope of the studies, to recommend organizations to carry out investigations, and to review reports and summarize findings. Wolfe was named chairman of the committee and, later, Seymour deputy chairman.†

By 1961 more than thirty Project Chariot environmental studies were reported or in progress, including those related to geology and soils, terrestrial and marine biology, oceanography, climatology, radiology, biogeography and ecology, and indigenous human populations. The work proceeded without reference to the still unresolved question of whether nuclear devices would be detonated in the region. Holmes & Narver, as the Commission site contractor, had provided on the bare coast of the Arctic sea a small campsite not at all reminiscent of those at Eniwetok and Bikini. The Laboratory of Radiation Biology was conducting surveys of all aquatic forms except marine mammals. Marine investigations had been made with the assistance of the *Brown Bear,* the research vessel of the University of Washington's Depart-

*The Sandia Laboratory, Albuquerque, N.M., which had served since 1949 as a Commission weapons development institution operated by a nonprofit corporate subsidiary of the Western Electric Company, had established a Livermore branch in 1956 to support the radiation laboratory there. Its basic role continued to be in the area of design and development of nonnuclear elements of atomic weapons.

†Other members included Max E. Britton, Geography Branch (Arctic Research), Office of Naval Research (ecological plant geography, micrometeorology); Arthur H. Lachenbruch, Theoretical Physics Branch, U.S. Geological Survey (geophysics, permafrost, geology); Kermit H. Larsen, Chief, Environmental Radiation Division, Laboratories of Radiation Biology, U.C.L.A. (soil chemistry, radiochemistry, fallout phenomenology); Robert L. Rausch, Chief, Zoonotic Disease Section, Arctic Health Research Center, U.S. Public Health Service, Alaska (mammalogy, animal ecology, parasitology); and Norman J. Wilimovsky, professor of zoology, Institute of Fisheries, University of British Columbia (ichthyology, hydrobiology, sea ice). Secretary of the committee was Ernest D. Campbell, program coordinator of the Special Projects Division of the San Francisco Operations Office.

ment of Oceanography, and the *John N. Cobb,* a U.S. Fish and Wildlife Service vessel. Institutions and agencies represented in the research included the Departments of Biology and Anthropology of the University of Alaska, the U.S. Weather Bureau, the U.S. Corps of Engineers, the Ohio Agricultural Experiment Station, the Department of Oceanography and the Laboratory of Radiation Biology of the University of Washington, the U.S. Geological Survey, the Radioecology Section of the Biology Operation of the Hanford Laboratories, the Arctic Research Center of the U.S. Public Health Service, the Bureau of Commercial Fisheries of the U.S. Fish and Wildlife Service, and the Institute of Polar Studies of the Ohio State University. Don Charles Foote, of Point Hope, Alaska, was a personal contractor for studies of human populations.

IV

The Plowshare project was an attempt to step beyond the nuclear weapon and into a phase in which nuclear explosion could be used with calculated margins of safety for useful, peaceful purposes. The power that had dug out the deep Mike crater in 1952 was large enough to excavate other large quantities of rock or soil, to link oceans, to tap resources hitherto hidden irretrievably in the earth. The power existed to do these things, but about it hung the doubt that had hung about the weapon—the question of the reasonableness of using such force unless there were a sufficient body of information concerning the radioecological prospect. It was to provide some proper base line from which the biological cost of an underground detonation could be measured that the environmental studies of Project Chariot were undertaken.

Project Chariot in its environmental phases, like the nearer studies at Fern Lake, was an exploration in biology made possible by the development of nuclear energy. The motivation of Project Chariot was in the realm of nuclear explosion, but the operating interest was at the level of inquiry for its own sake. The Chukchi Sea and the tundra behind its shores were regions of the earth almost as little known as had been the Pacific in the time of Kotzebue. Project Chariot bore the same responsibility for oceanic and terrestrial investigation as had the teams sent to Bikini before Crossroads.

What had been learned in the years of biological and environmental surveying in the Pacific between Crossroads and Chariot? What were the principles and the principal elements of the larger understanding?

It was known, for example, as it had not been known in 1943 and as it had been realized only faintly in 1946:

—that in the natural environment the extremely efficient biological uptake of nutritive elements can be measured in the uptake of the radioactive counterparts of such elements;

—that the levels of uptake of radioactive elements by the biological organism will be affected by the character of the organism—its physical complexity, its mineral needs, its metabolic processes—and by the chemical and physical form of the radioactive isotopes, the availability of stable isotopes, and the conditions of the environment;

—that radioactive elements, because they are identifiable, can be followed through food chains and biological systems virtually to the limits of their detectable lives, and that studies of elements in nature thus can be pressed much further than previously had been considered possible;

—that in aquatic environments the basic organisms, such as those comprising the masses and plankton and algae, not only are more resistant to the effects of radioactivity but are capable of blotting up quantities of radionuclides and thus placing them at the threshhold of the biological system;

—that in the natural environment the circulation of radioactive elements involves both water and land, and that between the two there will be environmental transfers, some "uphill" from water to land and some "downhill" as elements are rinsed or leached from soils or plants and carried to the rivers or oceans;

—that products of nuclear fission, significant on land, are far less so in sea water, and that, on the other hand, the nonfission products such as radioactive forms of iron, cobalt, manganese, or zinc may contribute up to 100 per cent of the radioactivity found in aquatic organisms, from the plankton and algae to the larger fishes;

—that radioisotopes introduced in large quantities into the ocean (either by initial mixture in an underwater release or by fallout after an atomic explosion) are transported both by ocean currents and by ocean organisms, but that the physical movement will be affected by the biological conditions and modified by biological rules and processes;

—that masses of radioactively tagged water may be followed and measured across thousands of miles of ocean, much farther and longer than had been supposed possible before 1954 and 1955;

—that strontium 90 and cesium 137, among the long-lived radio-isotopes of greatest public concern, are found only in low amounts in marine organisms studied under field conditions, and that the radioisotopes found in fish, for example, are predominantly the shorter-lived nonfission products elements such as iron, zinc, or manganese;

—that certain biological species, because their physiological needs are known and their places in the food chains established, may be used as reliable indicators of the nature and probable extent of the radioactive contamination of a natural environment at any point in time;

—that populations of animals and plants observed under field conditions—the sea urchins of Bikini in 1947, the grasses and shrubs restoring the natural cover of Eniwetok's shot islands, or the rats of Engebi—exhibit a capacity to maintain themselves even in environments that have been exposed to the full effects of nuclear blast and to levels of radioactivity that all laboratory experience indicated were totally lethal;

—and that every release of radioactive products in nature whether by atomic detonation, by accident, or in the disposal of industrial wastes, sets up a biological reaction peculiar to the place and condition of the release itself; that the variables are almost infinite in number; and that the individual situation can only be assessed by conducting observations with a knowledge of the biological rules governing the disposition of radioisotopes in the natural environment.

Such conclusions as these were among the parts of the total understanding. Above these were others which, although they could not be stated as conclusions, were convictions arising from the Laboratory's familiarity with the studies of fallout from nuclear tests.

The first was of the importance of water in the whole matter of the disposition of radioactive materials. The realization certainly was not the Laboratory's alone. Water is the universal solvent, the oceans the storehouses of elements essential to life on earth. The atomic era had brought with it the concept of the oceans, which cover so much of the earth's surface, as the catch basins in which the questions of large-scale radioactive contamination would be resolved. The problems of aquatic radiobiology had been the Laboratory's concern from the beginning, and water its area of interest. The Laboratory had traced radioisotopes in fresh water and in salt water. It had watched the biological interchange of radioactive elements between water and land. Every development in atomic energy—the movement toward larger weapons, the wider use of reactors for research or industrial purposes, the building of atomic submarines and other vessels—had underscored the significance of water in the accommodation of the earth to the release of atomic materials. The Laboratory worked in areas which were recognized as fundamental to the rationalization of the atomic future.

A second conviction was of the necessity for studying radiobiological problems in the field. The question of whether to continue field observations at the proving ground had been an issue in 1951. It never was an issue after that time. As nuclear testing proceeded, it became clearer that no laboratory experiment could incorporate the variables associated with the distribution of products from major nuclear detonation. Further, the findings in the field frequently denied or reversed expectations based on laboratory calculations. Laboratory results would have suggested the eradication of vegetation on the shot islands, but vegetation returned. Blast and high levels of residual radioactivity should have eliminated the colonies of rats exposed to detonation, but the colonies continued to exist. In the protective expanse of nature, the processes of healing and repopulation seemed to defy the devastation of the largest atomic devices. Whether this would continue to be so, no one could know. But the Laboratory believed that only by field observation was it possible to determine what should be attempted in laboratory study itself.

Finally, the Laboratory had developed a confidence during the years in the healing powers of the natural environment. Members of the field teams had examined the effects of nuclear blasts. They had seen islands swept clean, water churned, and the damage created by heat, pressure, and radioactivity. Yet they failed to find in the natural environment evidence of gross population or morphological change definitely ascribable to the effects of residual radioactivity alone. They realized that changes probably did occur, but neither in the ocean nor on land were examples discovered, and nowhere that they had studied the long-term effects of radioactivity as a separate phenomenon was there evidence that normal regrowth was not occurring. The aberrant *Ipomoea* of Engebi was quite as likely to have been caused by environmental changes on the island itself as by the presence of radioactivity. The multiheaded palms of Rongelap's northern islands, like those of other atolls in the Pacific, probably were the products of naturally occurring atypical growth patterns. The probabilities of remote radiation effects could not be denied, but positive evidence of such effects was not found at the test atolls or anywhere else in the Pacific.

In any such statements of the "known," the elements of the unknown were apparent. The unknowns were particularly evident in the region of oceanic radiobiology. The matter of expanded oceanographic research had become by 1958 a question of larger interest than ever before, some of this stemming from considerations of national defense but a large share also related to the importance of the ocean as a disposal area for radioactive wastes. The responsibility of the Atomic Energy Commission toward oceanographic research was implicit in its use of the ocean for disposing of wastes from reactor development programs. This responsibility went beyond the questions that had been raised by nuclear testing and that had occasioned the purely test-related surveys of 1955, 1956, and 1958 by the Health and Safety Laboratory and the Laboratory of Radiation Biology. In November, 1958, less than a month after the end of Operation Hardtack and the beginning of the international moratorium on weapons testing, the question of an expanded oceanographic research program was raised in a Commission staff paper which outlined the problems already encountered in the Pacific and suggested a coordinated Commission program strongly oriented to biological research but effecting a proper coordination of projects to be developed by the Divisions of Research, Reactor Development, and Biology and Medicine.[13] In 1959 the Committee on Oceanography of the National Academy of Sciences published certain chapters of its progressive report and one of these, "Artificial Radioactivity in the Marine Environment" (chap. v), suggested the scope of necessary oceanographic research and proposed a five-year program of studies costing, the committee estimated, $30,220,000.[14] The oceanographic problem in the era of artificial radioactivity was one of gaining understanding, literally on a world-wide scale, of all the factors of movement, temperature, chemical reaction, and physiological and biological mechanism that might affect or alter the water environment essential to life on earth.

V

The gaps in human knowledge of the effects of radioactivity were large in 1961, but the studies long before had left the area of gross evaluations and were concentrated upon the questions close to the question of life itself. It could be generally agreed that all of the radioactive products of all of the test detonations to that time had produced a total human exposure that was small compared to the exposure to natural background radiation. But it also was an assumption that any amount of nuclear radioactivity, of whatever kind and no matter how small the amount, was capable of producing some biological effect. The assumption led scientists and laymen into philosophical as well as scientific considerations that still could be expressed only in terms of relatives. No one yet actually knew whether there was a "threshhold" of exposure below which a complex, warm-blooded organism such as man might safely tolerate increases in irradiation of the environment. It was presumed that there was such a threshhold, and the presumption was recognized in the use of such terms as "maximum permissible dose" and "maximum permissible concentration." The problems were of a kind, whatever the developments of policy or program, to be of importance to all mankind.

Perhaps the most significant aspect of the handling of such problems by the United States had been the early and steady concern about them. So fundamental had been this concern that its relevance scarcely was realized. From the earliest days, from the time before the formal creation of the Manhattan District, the problem of radiation effect had been given a remarkable amount of attention. Long before the procedures had been developed for manufacture of plutonium for the atomic bomb, the persons directing the secret program had been worried (as was related in chap. i) about possible contamination of the Columbia River at Hanford. The Division of Biology and Medicine of the Atomic Energy Commission had been established in 1948, little more than a year after the Commission itself began operation, on the assumption that research in the life sciences was a natural and inevitable component of atomic energy development. Research in genetic and nongenetic biological effects of radioactivity had been an accompaniment of every phase of the program. The Division in 1961 directed medical, biological, and environmental studies at the national laboratories and implemented work on 630 "off-site" contracts with approximately 220 universities and research laboratories.[15]

It was no less significant that the United States program was capable of devoting so much attention to searches for peaceful uses of atomic energy. The nuclear tests in the Pacific and in Nevada were conducted to obtain knowledge of atomic explosive phenomena and, in the main, to advance weapons development. Yet even the test series were not limited to such purposes, and the record of the Pacific tests, from Crossroads to Hardtack, was one of investigations into many areas affected by the new phenomena, including medicine and biology. If these investigations sometimes fell short of total and comprehensive attacks on basic problems, they were, at least, acknowledgments of responsibilities beyond the purely technical and administrative and were as disciplined, imaginative, and productive as the resources and the state of knowledge would allow.

Hardship, anxiety, and suffering unquestionably were among the products of the necessity for nuclear testing. The Bikini people were removed, apparently permanently, from their ancestral home. The Rongelapese were subjected inadvertently to the direct affects of fallout and to the years of enforced absence from their atoll. The Japanese, from the fisherman aboard the *Fukuryu Maru* to the fish dealers at Japanese ports and the fearful people who refused to buy, were drawn into events that were tragic and deeply disturbing. These human costs were incalculable, yet in a period of history in which civilization was grappling suddenly with power sufficiently great to cause its destruction, it was difficult to say that the cost, however unnecessary, had been excessively heavy or occasioned by a callous disregard of human values. From the years of testing had come not just improved weapons but a maturer sense of the complexity of the nuclear problem, a beginning of wisdom. The sense, moreover, was international, evidenced quite as much in the cooperative approaches—in the exchanges of information between the Japanese and Americans, for example—as in the feelings of bitterness that frequently marked the international scene. Many and large as were the uncertainties concerning the effects of radioactivity, the years between 1946 and 1961 had in an indescribable way brought a confidence that, unless war brought complete abandonment of sanity, the earth was not yet facing some radiological point of no return. It still was possible to believe that nuclear reaction provided a power with which the wonder of life might be further revealed.

The Laboratory of Radiation Biology, created in 1943 as the Applied Fisheries Laboratory, had worked within such a belief. It had existed as an operating entity far longer than any of the laboratories or agencies with which it was associated, including the Atomic Energy Commission itself. It had been concerned about the biological effects of nuclear radiation even before the first bomb was exploded at Alamogordo. Whatever the eventual significance of its contribution, the Laboratory had fulfilled an obligation of its own, providing an unbroken thread of interest, singularly prophetic, in the large matter of radioactivity in the water environment. With that matter the future, too, would be increasingly concerned.

APPENDIX I

MATERIALS on the following pages represent selections and consolidations of significant data developed through radiobiological sampling in the area of the Pacific Proving Ground in the study of specific problems and over long periods of time.

The first exhibit, a table, is a compilation of data from samples of marine plankton, algae, clams, and fish, showing the kinds and amounts of radionuclides present in the organisms during or shortly after a nuclear test series at the Pacific Proving Ground.

The second, a graph, shows the actual gamma dose rates on Rongelap Island at various points in time after March 1, 1954, as projected against theoretical decay curves drawn from standard sources.

The third, a bar chart, shows the radioisotopic content of the organs of specific biota immediately after and 700 days following the Nectar detonation at Eniwetok in 1954.

Important in the consideration of all radiobiological data is the time factor—the factor illustrated in the Rongelap and Eniwetok exhibits and which must be recognized in examination of the accompanying table. Radioisotopic values are subject to change with time and because of such variables as (1) the physical half-life of the radionuclide present, (2) the biological half-life of the organism itself, (3) the chemical-physical form of the radionuclide (i.e., its particulate or soluble-colloidal state), (4) the concentration or dilution of materials in movement through the food web, and (5) the relative rates of movement of water masses and of the organisms within them. The values given in the table thus should be regarded only as typical of those found in aquatic specimens during and after nuclear test series in the Pacific. Other samplings at other times would have produced values of different levels.

THE RADIONUCLIDE CONTENT OF MARINE BIOLOGICAL
SAMPLES FROM THE PACIFIC PROVING GROUND AREA

Per Cent of Radioactivity of Total Sample

	Sample number	1000's of d/m/g	Mn^{54}	Fe^{55}	Fe^{59}	Co^{57}	Co^5
Plankton							
Samples: *Marsh* *	7-9	75	< 1	19	0	10	15
Area: At sea, Eniwetok to Guam.	13-15	29	< 1	19	0	8	14
Date: Sept. 1-20, 1956.	43-46	108	< 1	13	0	16	26
Radioactivity: Total as disintegrations	50-53	127	< 1	28	0	6	11
per minute per gram of ashed sample.	57-59	48	< 1	39	0	5	6
Samples: *Collett*†	2	718		0	1	8	40
Area: At sea, Eniwetok to Guam.	3	16,127		4	< 1	1	5
Collection: Aug. 8-14, 1958.	4	2,318		24	1	6	24
Radioactivity: d/m/g dry weight.	36	2,680		4	< 1	3	16
Algae							
Halimeda;‡ Eniwetok, July 22, 1956.		1,600				< 1	< 1
Caulerpa;† Eniwetok, June 25, 1958.		321**				0	0
Udotea;† Bikini, Aug. 28, 1958.		29**				0	0
Invertebrates							
Clam kidney;§ Eniwetok, Sept. 22, 1956, d/m/g wet weight.	I	1,600	2	74	< 1	10	9
Tridacna (clam) visceral mass;† Eniwetok, Sept. 27, 1958.		376**				1	5
Fish							
Liver homogenate;§ Bikini, Sept. 22, 1956, d/m/g wet weight.	II	18	6	15	0	8	4
Bonito liver;§ Bikini, Sept. 23, 1956, d/m/g wet weight.	III	50	2	56	< 1	3	1
Liver homogenate;§ Eniwetok, May–June, 1954.	IV	48	1	95	0	< 1	0
Reef fish liver;‖ Ailinginae Atoll, July 11, 1957, d/m/g wet weight.		2	1	26		22	4
Flying fish muscle;† Aug., 1958, d/m/g dry weight.		15		0	1	2	11
Flying fish liver;† Aug., 1958, d/m/g dry weight.		236		0	13	6	32
Surgeonfish liver;† Bikini, Aug. 28, 1958.		38**				10	45

* Lowman, 1958.
† Lowman, *et al*, 1959.
‡ Palumbo, 1959.
§ Lowman, *et al*, 1957.
‖ Welander, 1958.
** gamma emitters only
†† unknown anions

A Selective Compilation by Allyn H. Seymour for Congressional Hearings on *Fallout From Nuclear Weapons Tests,* May 5-8, 1959

Sr^{89}	Sr^{90}	Y^{91}	Zr^{95} Nb^{95}	$Ru^{103+106}$ $Rh^{103+106}$	Ru^{106} Rh^{106}	Cs^{137} Ba^{137m}	Ba^{140} La^{140}	$Ce^{141+144}$ $Pr^{141+144}$	Ce^{144} Pr^{144}	W^{185}	Others
0	0		25		7				5		
0	0		44		0						
0	0		12		0				13		
0	0		14		0				8		
0	0		6		0						
0	0		5	3		0	24	0	0		3
0	0		2	2		0	1	0	83		2
0	0		3	1		0	33	0	0		5
0	0		2	1		< 1	11	0	60		
		52	7		31				9		1
			72	6		0		15	7		
			32	12		0		57	0		
0	< 1	3	< 1			1	0		0		
			22	72		0	0		0		
0	0	0	0			0	0		0		< 1††
0	0	0	< 1			0	0		0		1††
0	0	0	0			0	0		0		< 1††
	0										6
			< 1	< 1							
			< 1	< 1							
			0	0		0	0		0		

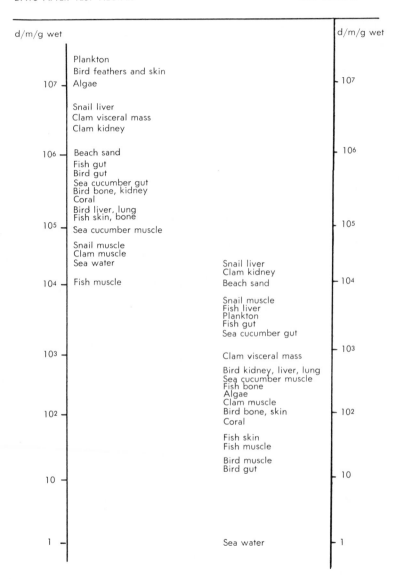

Decline of radioactivity in samples collected by the Applied Fisheries Laboratory following Test Nectar at Eniwetok in 1954, the first column showing radioactivity 1 to 3 days after the detonation and the second the levels of activity after 700 days.

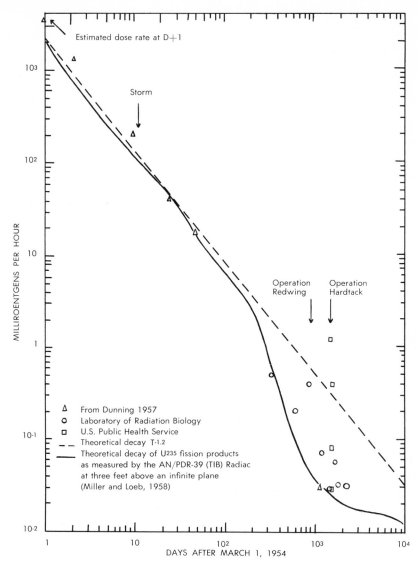

Gamma dose rates on Rongelap Island at various points in time after March 1, 1954, as projected against theoretical decay curves drawn from standard sources.

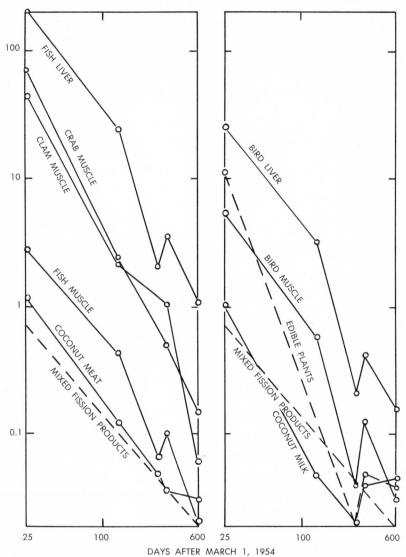

Rates of decline of radioactivity in food items from collections at Rongelap Atoll between March 26, 1954, and October 22-23, 1955.

APPENDIX II

A SELECTED listing of biota commonly sampled for radioactivity in the Marshall Islands:

FISH

Family	Genus and Species	Common Name
Isuridae	*Carcharodon carcharias*	Great white shark
Orectolobidae	*Ginglymostoma ferrugineum*	Carpet shark, nurse shark
Triakidae	*Triaenodon obesus*	White tip shark
Carcharhinidae	*Carcharhinus melanopterus*	Black tip shark
	Carcharhinus menisorrah	Gray shark
Dussumieridae	*Spratelloides delicatulus atrofasciatus*	Round herring
Synodontidae	*Saurida gracilis*	Lizard fish
	Synodus variegatus	
Congridae	*Conger noordzieki*	Conger eel
Moringuidae	*Moringua abbreviata*	Worm eel
Muraenidae	*Gymnothorax buroensis pictus flavimarginatus undulatus*	Moray eel
Belonidae	*Strongylura gigantea*	Needlefish

319

Family	Genus and Species	Common Name
Hemiramphidae	*Hyporhamphus laticeps*	Halfbeak
Exocoetidae	*Cypselurus spilonotopterus*	Flying fish
Holocentridae	*Myripristis murdjan*	Squirrelfish
	argyromus	
	Holocentrus sammara	
	laevis	
	spinifer	
	diadema	
Fistulariidae	*Fistularia petimba*	Cornet fish
Sphyraenidae	*Sphyraena barracuda*	Barracuda
	forsteri	
	helleri	
Atherinidae	*Stenatherina temminckii*	Silversides
	Pranesus pinguis	
Mugilidae	*Neomysus chaptalii*	Mullets
	Crenimugil crenilabis	
Kuhlidae	*Kuhlia taeniura*	Flagtail, saboti
Serranidae	*Epinephalus merra*	Grouper, sea bass
	hexagonatus	
	elongatus	
	fuscoguttatus	
	Anyperodon leucogrammicus	
	Variola louti	
	Cephalopholis argus	
Pseudochromidae	*Pseudogramma polyacantha*	Reef fish
Apogonidae	*Apogon erythrinus*	Cardinal fish
	snyderi	
	novemfasciatus	
Priacanthidae	*Priacanthus cruentatus*	Bigeye
Coryphaenidae	*Coryphaena hippurus*	Dolphin
Carangidae	*Decapterus muroadsi*	Scad
	Elagatis bipinnulatus	Rainbow runner
	Trachurus crumenophthalmus	Big-eyed scad
	Caranx melampygus	Jack, cavalla
	lugubris	
	sexfasciatus	
Lutianidae	*Lutianus gibbus*	Snapper
	kasmira	
	Monotaxis grandoculis	
	Aprion virescens	
	Caesio caerulaureus	Caesio
	Lethrinus variegatus	Pigfish
	miniatus	
Pempheridae	*Pempheris oualensis*	Sweeper

Family	Genus and Species	Common Name
Chaetodontidae	*Chaetodon lunula*	Butterfly fish
	trifasciatus	
	citrinellus	
	ephippium	
	auriga	
	Centropyge flavissimus	
Zanclidae	*Zanclus cornutus*	Moorish idol
Acanthuridae	*Ctenochaetus striatus*	Surgeonfish
	Acanthurus triostegus	
	olivaceus	
	nigricans	
	elongatus	
	Naso lituratus	
	unicornis	Unicorn fish
Siganidae	*Siganus rostratus*	Thorn fish
Mullidae	*Parupeneus barberinus*	Goatfish
	bifasciatus	
	Mulloidichthys samoensis	
	auriflamma	
Pomacentridae	*Dascyllus aruanus*	Damselfish
	Chromis caeruleus	
	Abudefduf saxatilis	
	sordidus	
	biocellatus	
	Pomacentrus nigricans	
	jenkensi	
Labridae	*Epibulus insidiator*	Wrasse
	Cheilinus fasciatus	
	Thalassoma hardwickei	
	quinquevittata	
	Stethojulis strigiventer	
	axillaris	
	Halichoeres trimaculatus	
Scaridae	*Scarus forsteri*	Parrot fish
	erythrodon	
	sordidus	
Cirrhitidae	*Paracirrhites forsteri*	Hawk fish
Mugiloididae	*Parapercis clathrata*	Smelt
Blenniidae	*Cirripectes sebae*	Blenny
	Istiblennius paulus	
	edentulus	
Brotulidae	*Dinematichthys iluocoeteoides*	Brotulid
Scombridae	*Grammatorcynus bilineatus*	Two-lined mackerel

Family	*Genus and Species*	*Common Name*
	Katsuwonus pelamis	Oceanic skipjack, bonito
	Thunnus albacores	Yellow-fin tuna
	Euthynnus affinis yaito	Black skipjack, bonito
	Gymnosarda nuda	Dogtooth tuna
Gobiidae	*Gobiodon citrinus*	Goby
	Valenciennea sexguttata	
Scorpaenidae	*Scorpaenodes guamensis*	Rockfish
	Pterois antennata	Turkey fish
Synanceidae	*Synanceia verrucosa*	Stonefish
Bothidae	*Bothus mancus*	Flatfish
Echeneidae	*Echeneis naucrates*	Remora
Balistidae	*Rhinecanthus rectangulus aculeatus*	Trigger fish
	Balistes undulatus	
Ostraciidae	*Ostracion punctatus*	Trunkfish
Tetraodontidae	*Arothron nigropunctatus*	Puffer
	Canthigaster solandri	
	Arothron hispidus	

INVERTEBRATES

Phylum	*Genus*	*Common Name*
Coelenterata	. . . .	Hydroid
	. . . .	Sea anemone
	Tubipora	Organ-pipe coral
	Heliopora	Blue coral
	Pocillopora	Coral
	Porites	
	Acropora	
	Fungia	Fungus coral
Echinodermata	*Linckia*	Starfish
	Holothuria	Sea cucumbers
	Stichopus	
	Actinopyga	
Arthropoda	*Palinurus*	Langusta
	Coenobita	Land hermit crab
	Calcinus	Hermit crab
	Birgus	Coconut crab
	Ocypode	Ghost crab
	Grapsus	Shore crab
	Eriphia	Red-eyed crab

Phylum	Genus	Common Name
Mollusca	*Lambis*	Spider snail
	Cyprea	Money cowry
	Drupa	Drupe snail
	Morula	Rock shell, morula
	Nerita	Sea snail shell
	Turbo	Top shell
	Isognomon	Oyster
	Chama	Rock oyster
	Tridacna	Killer clam, giant clam
	Hippopus	Giant clam, horse-hoof clam

BIRDS

Family	Genus and Species	Common Name
Laridae	*Gygis alba*	White fairy tern
	Anous stolidus	Noddy tern
	Sterna fuscata	Sooty tern
	Sterna bergii	Crested tern
	Sterna paradisaea	Arctic tern
Charadriidae	*Pluvialis dominica fulva*	Golden plover
	Arenaria interpes morinella	Turnstone

RATS

Family	Genus and Species	Common Name
Muridae	*Rattus exulans* Peale	Field rat

VASCULAR PLANTS

Some species are mentioned in the work of only one of the two principal authorities used. An asterisk (*) indicates the authority is St. John; a dagger (†) indicates the authority is Taylor.

Family	Genus and Species	Common Name
Amaranthaceae	*Achyranthes canescens*	. . . .
Sapindaceae	*Allophyllus timorensis*	. . . .
Moraceae*	*Artocarpus altilis*	Breadfruit
Nyctaginaceae	*Boerhaavia diffusa*	. . . .
	Boerhaavia tetrandra	. . . .
Leguminosae	*Canavalia microcarpa*	. . . .
Caricaceae	*Carica papaya*	Papaya

Family	Genus and Species	Common Name
Lauraceae	*Cassytha filiformis*	Dodder
Verbenaceae	*Clerodendron inerme†*	. . . .
Palmae	*Cocos nucifera**	Coconut
Boraginaceae	*Cordia subcordata*	. . . .
Amaryllidaceae	*Crinum asiaticum*	Spider lily
Euphorbiaceae*	*Euphorbia* spp.	. . . .
Cyperaceae	*Fimbristylis cymosa*	Sedge
Rubiaceae	*Guettarda speciosa*	. . . .
Convolvulaceae	*Ipomoea tuba**	Morning-glory
Boraginaceae	*Messerschmidia argentea*	. . . .
Rubiaceae	*Morinda citrifolia*	. . . .
Apocynaceae	*Ochrosia oppositifolia**	. . . .
Pandanaceae	*Pandanus tectorius*	Pandanus
Lythraceae	*Pemphis acidula*	. . . .
Nyctaginaceae	*Pisonia grandis*	. . . .
Portulacaceae	*Portulaca lutea*	Moss rose, purslane
	Portulaca quadrifida	Moss rose, purslane
Acanthaceae	*Pseuderanthemum atropurpureum*	. . . .
	Pseuderanthemum reticulatum†	. . . .
Goodeniaceae	*Scaevola frutescens*	Beach magnolia
Malvaceae	*Sida fallax*	Mallow
Simaroubaceae‡	*Soulamea amara*	. . . .
Simaroubaceae*	*Suriana maritima*	. . . .
Taccaceae	*Tacca leontopetaloides*	Arrowroot
Combretaceae	*Terminalia samoensis*	. . . .
Tiliaceae	*Triumfetta procumbens*	. . . .
Compositae*	*Wedelia biflora*	Aster
Gramineae*	*Lepturus repens*	Grass
Zosteraceae	Not identified	Eelgrass

‡ Taylor says Simarubaceae.

ALGAE

Family	Genus and Species	Common Name
Bonnemaisoniaceae	*Asparagopsis taxiformis* (Deliie) Collins and Harvey	. . . .
Caulerpaceae	*Caulerpa serrulata* (Forsskål) J. Ag.	. . . .
Caulerpaceae†	*Caulerpa* spp.	. . . .
Codiaceae	*Codium* spp.	. . . .

Family	Genus and Species	Common Name
Ulvaceae†	*Enteromorpha* spp.	. . . .
Codiaceae	*Halimeda* spp.	. . . .
Scytosiphonaceae‡	*Hydroclathrus clathratus* (Ag.) Howe	. . . .
Corallinaceae†	*Jania* sp.	. . . .
Helminthocladiaceae†	*Liagora* spp.	. . . .
Oscillatoriaceae†	*Lyngbya majuscula* Gomont	. . . .
Boodleaceae§	*Microdictyon Okamurai* Setchell	. . . .
Dasycladaceae†	*Neomeris annulata* Dickie	. . . .
Dictyotaceae†	*Padina commersonii* Bory	. . . .
Codiaceae†	*Rhipilia* sp.	. . . .
Sargassaceae‖	*Turbinaria ornata* (Turn.) J. Agardh	. . . .

‡ Taylor says Asperococcaceae
§ Taylor says Valoniaceae
‖ Taylor says Fucaceae

NOTES

The following abbreviations are used in the references:

AFL   Applied Fisheries Laboratory, University of Washington.

AFSWP   Armed Forces Special Weapons Project.

BNL   Brookhaven National Laboratory.

CNO   Office of the Chief of Naval Operations, Navy Department.

DBM   Division of Biology and Medicine, U.S. Atomic Energy Commission.

HASL   Health and Safety Laboratory, New York Operations Office, U.S. Atomic Energy Commission.

LRB   Laboratory of Radiation Biology, University of Washington.

NAS-NRC   National Academy of Sciences—National Research Council.

ONR   Office of Naval Research.

USAEC   U.S. Atomic Energy Commission.

UWFL   University of Washington Fisheries Laboratory (report series).

Chapter 1

1. Henry D. Smyth, *Atomic Energy for Military Purposes* (Princeton, N.J.: Princeton University Press, 1945), pp. 83-85.

2. *Ibid.,* pp. 112, 145.

3. *Ibid.,* p. 113.

4. Franklin T. Matthias to author, correspondence, December 1, 1961.

5. Smyth, *Atomic Energy . . . ,* p. 146. (At Hanford the date usually cited is March 22, 1943.)

6. Stafford Warren and G. H. Whipple, "Roentgen Ray Intoxication," *Journal of Experimental Medicine,* Vol. XXXV (1922); Vol. XXXVIII (1923).

7. Franklin T. Matthias, diary, April 23-24, 1943 (Hanford files), pp. 43-44.

8. Hanford Thayer, diary (Thayer files), May 20, 1943.

9. H. T. Wenzel to Hanford Thayer, transcript of telephone conversation (Thayer files), August 18, 1943.

10. National Defense Research Committee, contract information form (copy, Thayer files), n.d.

11. B. M. Duggar (ed.), *Biological Effects of Radiation* (New York: McGraw-Hill Book Co., Inc., 1936). (Chap. xiv, "The Physiological Effects of Radiation Upon Organs and Body Systems," was contributed by Stafford Warren.)

12. Stafford Warren, recollections in conversations with the author, October, 1960.

13. Smyth, *Atomic Energy . . . ,* p. 146.

14. Thayer diary.

15. L. R. Donaldson, Summary of Operations on OSRD Contracts Nos. E 134–E 135 for the Month of November (Seattle: AFL files, 1943).

16. UWFL 2. Arthur D. Welander, Studies of the Effects of Roentgen Rays on the Growth and Development of the Embryos and Larvae of the Chinook Salmon (*Oncorhynchus tschawytscha*), (Ph.D. dissertation, University of Washington, 1945).

17. Stafford Warren, correspondence (AFL files), 1944.

18. UWFL 2, p. 85.

19. UWFL 12. Richard F. Foster, Some Effects on Embryo and Young Rainbow Trout *(Salmo gairdnerii* Richardson) from Exposing the Parent Fish to X-rays (Ph.D. dissertation, University of Washington, 1948).

20. *Ibid.,* pp. 78-81.

Chapter 2

1. W. A. Shurcliff, *Bombs at Bikini* (New York: Wm. H. Wise & Co., Inc., 1947), pp. 16-17.

2. *Ibid.,* p. 20.

3. CNO, *Handbook of the Trust Territory of the Pacific Islands* (Washington, D.C.: Government Printing Office, 1948), p. 84.

4. *Ibid.*, pp. 8-9.

5. Thomas Gilbert, *A Voyage From New South Wales to Canton, in the Year 1788, with Views of the Islands Discovered* (London, 1789); *The Voyage of Governor Philip to New South Wales* (London, 1789).

6. August C. Mahr, *The Visit of the* Rurik *to San Francisco in 1816* (Stanford University Publications: History, Economics, Political Science [Palo Alto: Stanford University Press, 1932]).

7. S. E. Morison, "Historical Notes on the Gilbert and Marshall Islands," *The American Neptune*, IV, No. 2 (1944), 87-118.

8. Charles Darwin, "On Certain Areas of Elevation and Subsidence in the Pacific and Indian Oceans as Deduced From the Study of Coral Formations," *Proceedings*, Geological Society of London, II (1837), 552-54.

9. Francis Darwin (ed.), *The Life and Letters of Charles Darwin* (2 vols., New York: D. Appleton and Co., 1888).

10. Shurcliff, *Bombs at Bikini*, p. 21.

11. Kenneth O. Emery, J. I. Tracey, Jr., and H. S. Ladd, *Geology of Bikini and Nearby Atolls (Bikini and Nearby Atolls: Part I, Geology;* Geological Survey Professional Paper 260-A [Washington, D.C.: Government Printing Office, 1954]), p. 23.

12. Shurcliff, *Bombs at Bikini*, excerpt of letter of Brig. Gen. A. J. McFarland, U.S.A., Secretary, Joint Chiefs, p. 14.

13. *Ibid.*, p. 114.

14. HASL, "Announced Nuclear Detonations," compiled by Kosta Telegadas, U.S. Weather Bureau, in *Fallout Program Quarterly Summary Report* (HASL 111 [USAEC New York Operations Office, April 1, 1961]), p. 176.

15. Shurcliff, *Bombs at Bikini*, p. 24.

16. Arthur D. Welander, Recommendations Resulting From the Radiobiological Monitoring of Bikini Lagoon Subsequent to Baker Day, (letter report [copy] in AFL files, n.d.).

17. L.R. Donaldson *et al.*, Radiobiological Studies, Bikini Atoll, June 12 to August 14 (Preliminary Report, AFL files, n.d.), p. 4.

18. *Ibid.*, p. 3.

19. *Ibid.*, p. 7.

20. *Ibid.*

21. G. Carter *et al.*, Report to Chief of the Radiological Safety Section of the Radioactivity of Migratory Fish Caught at Wotho, Ailinginae, Rongelap and Rongerik Atolls, (letter report [copy] in AFL files, October 4, 1946).

Chapter 3

1. AFSWP, *Bikini Scientific Resurvey*, Vol. I, *Operations* (1947).

2. Crossroads Evaluation Board, "Observations and Conclusions,

Both Tests," in W. A. Shurcliff, *Bombs at Bikini* (New York: Wm. H. Wise & Co., Inc., 1947), Appendix 11, pp. 198-99.

3. Shurcliff, *Bombs at Bikini*, p. 172.

4. AFSWP, *Operations*, p. 3.

5. *Ibid.*, p. 9. (For report of geological studies see Kenneth O. Emery *et al., Geology of Bikini and Nearby Atolls.*)

6. *Ibid.*, p. 1.

7. *Ibid.* (Annex A), p. 75.

8. *Ibid.*, p. 6.

9. *Ibid.*, p. 29.

10. *Ibid.*, (Annex A), p. 75.

11. Navy Department, Bikini Scientific Resurvey Press Release No. 10, July 15, 1947.

12. ———, Bikini Scientific Resurvey Press Release No. 11, July 17, 1947.

13. ———, Bikini Scientific Resurvey Press Release No. 16, July 24, 1947.

14. *Ibid.*

15. AFSWP, *Operations*, p. 67.

16. AFSWP, *Bikini Scientific Resurvey*, Vol. II, *Report of the Technical Director* (1947), p. 40.

17. *Ibid.*, p. 81.

18. *Ibid.*, p. 82.

19. *Ibid.*, p. 7.

20. *Ibid.*, p. 102 (1).

21. *Ibid.*, p. 11.

22. *Ibid.*, p. 7.

23. *Ibid.* (Annex IV), p. 17.

24. *Ibid.*, p. 49.

25. *Ibid.*, p. 18.

26. *Ibid.*, p. 102 (1).

27. *Ibid.*

28. *Ibid.*, p. 102 (2).

29. *Ibid.*, p. 102 (3).

30. *Ibid.*

31. *Ibid.*

Chapter 4

1. USAEC, *Second Semiannual Report* (Washington, D.C.: Government Printing Office, July, 1947), p. 7.

2. *Ibid.*, p. 22.

3. USAEC, *Fourth Semiannual Report* (July, 1948), p. 2.

4. Adm. James S. Russell, U.S.N., recollections in conversations with the author, May, 1961.

5. CNO, "Trusteeship Agreement for the Former Japanese Mandated Islands" (Article 5), *Report on the Administration of the Trust*

Territory of the Pacific Islands, July 1, 1949 to June 30, 1950 (OPNAV P22-100-J; 1950), p. 80.

6. S. E. Morison, "Historical Notes on the Gilbert and Marshall Islands," *The American Neptune,* Vol. IV, No. 2 (1944).

7. *A Missionary Voyage to the Southern Pacific Ocean, Performed in the Year 1796, 1797, 1798 in the Ship* Duff *Commanded by Captain James Wilson,* Compiled from the Journals of the Officers and the Missionaries, and Illustrated With Maps, Charts, and Views (London, 1799).

8. P. A. Crowl and E. G. Love, *Seizure of the Gilberts and the Marshalls,* Vol. VI, *The War in the Pacific* (U.S. Army in World War II, Ser. 2 [Washington, D.C.: Office of the Chief of Military History, Department of the Army, 1955]).

9. USAEC, *Fourth Semiannual Report,* p. 2.

10. *Ibid.*

11. *Ibid.,* pp. 3-4.

12. HASL, "Announced Nuclear Detonations," compiled by Kosta Telegadas, U.S. Weather Bureau, in *Fallout Program Quarterly Summary Report* (HASL 111 [USAEC New York Operations Office, April 1, 1961]), p. 176.

13. USAEC, *Fourth Semiannual Report,* p. 4.

14. UWFL 10. Preliminary outline of a program for the second radiobiological survey of Bikini Atoll during the summer of 1948 to be sponsored by the Atomic Energy Commission and the U.S. Navy (1948).

15. UWFL 18. L. R. Donaldson *et al.,* Radiological Analysis of Biological Samples Collected at Eniwetok May 16, 1948 (1949), p. 3.

16. *Ibid.,* p. 8.

17. *Ibid.*

18. W. A. Shurcliff, *Bombs at Bikini* (New York: Wm. H. Wise & Co., Inc., 1947), p. 93.

19. J. E. Tobin, *The Bikini People, Past and Present* (Majuro, Marshall Islands, 1953), p. 7.

20. *Ibid.*

21. UWFL 16. Bikini Radiobiological Resurvey of 1948 (1949), p. 4.

22. *Ibid.,* p. 31.

23. William S. Von Arx, *Circulation Systems of Bikini and Rongelap Lagoons (Bikini and Nearby Lagoons: Part II, Oceanography [Physical];* Geological Survey Professional Paper 260-B [Washington, D.C.: Government Printing Office, 1954]), p. 271.

24. UWFL 11. L. R. Donaldson *et al.,* Concentration of Active Materials by Hydroids in the Bikini Lagoon During the Summer of 1947 (1948).

25. Von Arx, *Circulation Systems . . . ,* p. 267.

26. UWFL 16, p. 34.

27. *Ibid.,* p. 41.

28. UWFL 19. Eniwetok Radiological Resurvey July 1948 (1949).

29. USAEC, *Fifth Semiannual Report* (January, 1949), p. 87.

30. UWFL 23. Radiobiological Survey of Bikini, Eniwetok, and Likiep Atolls—July-August, 1949 (1950).

31. *Ibid.,* A. H. Seymour and Paul J. Kellogg, "Land Survey," pp. 30-36.

32. *Ibid.,* Orlin Biddulph, "Physiology of Land Plants," p. 64.

33. *Ibid.,* Arthur D. Welander, "Fish," pp. 132-34.

34. *Ibid.,* Harold St. John, "Flora of Engebi, Aomon-Biijiri, and Runit Islands," p. 39.

35. *Ibid.,* p. 43.

36. *Ibid.*

37. *Ibid.,* St. John, "Flora of Engebi . . . , pp. 52-53.

38. *Ibid.,* Biddulph, "Physiology of Land Plants," p. 92.

Chapter 5

1. USAEC, *Seventh Semiannual Report* (Washington, D.C.: Government Printing Office, January, 1950), p. 10.

2. *Ibid.,* p. 143.

3. *Holmes & Narver, Inc.* (Los Angeles: company publication, March, 1958).

4. D. Lee Narver, *Concrete From Coral* (Los Angeles: Holmes & Narver technical paper, n.d.).

5. USAEC, *Ninth Semiannual Report* (January, 1951), p. 32.

6. USAEC, *Seventh Semiannual Report,* p. 9.

7. USAEC, *Ninth Semiannual Report,* p. 6.

8. USAEC, Budget Estimate for Fiscal Year 1950, Program 600—Biology and Medicine (1949).

9. USAEC, *Sixth Semiannual Report* (July, 1949), p. 115.

10. USAEC, *Fifteenth Semiannual Report* (January, 1954), p. 72.

11. Lt. Gen. E. R. Quesada, Statement on Results of Operation Greenhouse, Department of Defense–USAEC (June 13, 1951).

12. *Ibid.*

13. *Ibid.*

14. UWFL 26. K. Bonham and R. F. Palumbo, Effects of X-rays on Snails, Crustacea, and Algae (1951).

15. L. R. Donaldson to Paul Pearson, correspondence (copy, AFL files), June 13, 1951.

16. *Ibid.*

17. AFL, Notes for conference with Dr. Paul Pearson (copy, AFL files), August 20, 1951.

18. *Ibid.*

19. UWFL 28. The Need for Continuation of Studies of Radiation Contamination of Biotic Forms at the Bikini and Eniwetok Testing Grounds (1952).

20. *Ibid.*

21. *Ibid.,* p. 7.

22. *Ibid.*, p. 9.
23. *Ibid.*, p. 15.
24. *Ibid.*

Chapter 6

1. HASL, "Announced Nuclear Detonations," compiled by Kosta Telegadas, U.S. Weather Bureau, in *Fallout Program Quarterly Summary Report* (HASL 111 [USAEC New York Operations Office, April 1, 1961]), pp. 176, 182.

2. Department of Defense—USAEC, "Joint Task Force 132 to Conduct New Series of Tests at Eniwetok Proving Grounds," news release No. 180-52, February 18, 1952.

3. USAEC, memorandum, Paul Pearson to John C. Bugher, Donaldson Proposal for Future Eniwetok Tests, March 28, 1952.

4. USAEC, memorandum, Pearson to Bugher, Donaldson's Proposal for Biological Studies at Eniwetok Tests, April 9, 1952.

5. USAEC, memorandum, Bugher to William R. Sturges, Survey of Bikini, May 2, 1952.

6. UWFL 32. Suggested Programs for the Biological Monitoring of Eniwetok Atoll Before and After the Testing Program with a Resurvey of Bikini Atoll, July 25, 1952.

7. AFL, laboratory notes, November 6, 1952.

8. L. R. Donaldson, personal log, November 7, 1952.

9. *Ibid.*, November 8, 1952.

10. AFL, laboratory notes, November, 1952.

11. *Ibid.*

12. *Ibid.*

13. *Ibid.*

14. *Ibid.*

15. *Ibid.*

16. UWFL 33. Radiobiological Studies at Eniwetok Atoll Before and Following the Mike Shot of the November 1952 Testing Program (1953), (Confidential).

17. Karl M. Wilbur to Donaldson, correspondence (AFL files), March 12, 1953.

18. AFL, notes on conference with Dr. John C. Bugher, Seattle, November 1, 1953.

19. *Ibid.*

Chapter 7

1. USAEC, "Bikini Atoll Added to Atomic Proving Ground in Pacific," news release No. 478, April 2, 1953.

2. HASL, "Announced Nuclear Detonations," compiled by Kosta Telegadas, U.S. Weather Bureau, in *Fallout Program Quarterly Summary Report* (HASL 111 [USAEC New York Operations Office, April 1, 1961]), p. 172.

3. Notes on telephone call, Duncan Curry to L. K. Donaldson (AFL files), August 14, 1953.

4. UWFL 35. Preliminary Statement of the Proposed Program for Marine Survey Unit, Section 19 (1953), p. 5-6.

5. E. S. Eunson, report of meetings with Donaldson at Los Alamos, August 25-26, 1953, TG 7.1, September 2, 1953 (AFL files).

6. *Ibid.*

7. Donaldson to Curry, letter (copy, AFL files), October 28, 1953.

8. UWFL 36. Operations Outline for Program 19, Marine Survey Unit, of Operation Castle (1954).

9. *Ibid.*

10. HASL, "Announced Nuclear Detonations," p. 177.

11. USAEC memorandum, March 16, 1954.

12. USAEC news release No. 524, March 1, 1954.

13. E. P. Cronkite, V. P. Bond, and C. L. Dunham (eds.), *Some Effects of Ionizing Radiation on Human Beings: A Report on the Marshallese and Americans Accidentally Exposed to Radiation From Fallout and a Discussion of Radiation Injury in the Human Being* (TID 5358 [Washington, D.C.: USAEC, July, 1956]), pp. 6, 27.

14. *Ibid.*, p. 15.

15. *Ibid.*, p. iv.

16. USAEC, "Statement by the Atomic Energy Commission," news release (7:00 P.M.), March 11, 1954.

17. Associated Press dispatch quoting Tsutsui in *Yomiuri* interview (Tokyo), March 16, 1954.

18. Yoshio Hiyama, "General Backgrounds of These Reports," Annex to *Research in the Effects and Influences of the Nuclear Bomb Test Explosions,* Japan Society for the Promotion of Science (2 vols.; Tokyo, 1956).

19. Associated Press dispatch (Tokyo), March 16, 1954.

20. Misashi Miyake and Seiichi Ohashi, "Pathology of the Bikini Patients," *Research in the Effects . . . ,* II, 1372.

21. Hiyama, "General Backgrounds . . . ," p. 1.

22. Yasuo Kondo, Keizo Fujita, and Hirokatu Ogura, "Economic Aspects of the Effects of Bikini H-Bomb Experiments on Japanese Fisheries," *Research in the Effects . . . ,* II, 1251-52.

23. *Ibid.*, p. 1263.

24. Toshiharu Kawabata, "Radiological Survey of the Fishes at the Landing Ports in Japan," *Research in the Effects . . . ,* II, 1085.

25. Kondo *et al.,* "Economic Aspects . . . ," II, 1278.

26. Rokuzo Kobayashi and Isamu Nagai, "Cooperation by the United States in the Radiochemical Analyses," in *Research in the Effects . . . ,* II, 1434-45.

27. USAEC, statement transmitted to Ambassador Allison (Washington, D.C., March 24, 1954).

28. Cronkite *et al., Some Effects . . . ,* Table 1.1, p. 3.

29. *Ibid.,* p. 15.

30. UWFL 42. A Radiological Study of Rongelap Atoll, Marshall Islands, During 1954-1955 (1955).

31. USAEC, Statement by Lewis L. Strauss, Chairman, Atomic Energy Commission (Washington, D.C., March 31, 1954).

32. Hiyama, "General Backgrounds . . . ," p. 2.

33. *Ibid.,* p. 3.

34. *Ibid.*

35. Shinichi Watari, "Summary of Investigation by the *Shunkotsu Maru* Into the Effects of Radioactivity in the Bikini Waters," *Research in the Effects . . . ,* II, 939.

36. L. R. Donaldson, diary, May 25-26, 1954.

37. *Ibid.,* miscellaneous entries.

38. *Ibid.,* June 11, 1954.

39. *Ibid.,* June 30, 1954.

40. *Ibid.*

41. Hiyama, "General Backgrounds . . . ," p. 12.

42. Watari, "Summary of Investigation . . . ," p. 941.

43. *Ibid.*

44. Michitaka Uda, Sadayuki Hori, and Shozo Yoshida, "Hydrographic Researches in the Equatorial Pacific Waters Adjacent to Bikini Atoll in Relation to the Radioactive Pollution of the Fishing Ground," *Research in the Effects . . . ,* II, 986.

45. John H. Harley (ed.), *Operation Troll: Joint Preliminary Report* (HASL, USAEC New York Operations Office, NYO 4656, April, 1956), p. 1.

46. Watari, "Summary of Investigation . . . ," p. 942.

47. *Ibid.*

48. Toshiharu Kawabata, "State of Radiological Contamination in Fishes," in *Research in the Effects . . . ,* II, 949-50.

49. Kondo *et al.,* "Economic Aspects . . . ," p. 1260.

50. Hiroshi Nakamura *et. al.,* "Survey by the *Daifuji-maru* Traversing the Pacific Especially on the Radioactivity of Sea Water Contaminated by H-Bomb Tests at Bikini, 1954," *Research in the Effects . . . ,* II, 997-1010.

Chapter 8

1. Gordon M. Dunning (ed.), *Radioactive Contamination of Certain Areas in the Pacific Ocean From Nuclear Tests* (Washington, D.C.: USAEC, 1957), p. v.

2. Paul B. Pearson to L. R. Donaldson (AFL correspondence), October 10, 1954.

3. Yoshio Hiyama, "General Backgrounds of These Reports," Annex to *Research in the Effects and Influences of the Nuclear Bomb Test Explosions,* Japan Society for the Promotion of Science (2 vols.; Tokyo, 1956), p. 13.

4. *Ibid.*, pp. 13-14.

5. John H. Harley (ed.), *Operation Troll: Joint Preliminary Report* (HASL, USAEC New York Operations Office, NYO 4656, April, 1956), p. iv.

6. *Ibid.*

7. *Ibid.*, pp. 2-3.

8. Hiyama, "General Backgrounds...," p. 12.

9. Harley, *Operation Troll*, p. 4.

10. *Ibid.*, p. 12.

11. *Ibid.*, p. 8.

12. *Ibid.*, p. 13.

13. *Ibid.*, p. 11.

14. *Ibid.*, p. 13.

15. Frank G. Lowman, notes (AFL files), 1955.

16. *Ibid.*

17. *Ibid.*

18. *Ibid.*

19. *Ibid.*

20. Lowman, abstract of oral report, USAEC, May 19, 1955 (AFL files).

21. AFL files.

22. USAEC, "The Effects of High-Yield Nuclear Explosions— Statement by Lewis L. Strauss, Chairman, and a Report by the United States Atomic Energy Commission" (Washington, D.C., February, 1955).

23. UWFL 42. A Radiological Study of Rongelap Atoll, Marshall Islands, During 1954-1955 (1955).

24. *Ibid.*, Abstract.

25. *Ibid.*, p. 24.

26. *Ibid.*, p. 31.

27. UWFL 43. Radiobiological Resurvey of Rongelap and Ailinginae Atolls, Marshall Islands, October-November, 1955 (1955), p. 44.

28. *Ibid.*, pp. 4-6, 66-69.

29. W. R. Boss to Donaldson (AFL correspondence), November 7, 1955.

30. UWFL 43. Radiobiological Resurvey..., p. 60.

31. *Ibid.*, p. 56.

32. UWFL 41. Annual Report for the Fiscal Year 1954-1955, With Suggested Program for the Next Fiscal Year (Seattle, March 15, 1955), p. 23.

33. UWFL 45. Program of the Applied Fisheries Laboratory, University of Washington, for the 1956 Test Series at Bikini and Eniwetok Atolls, Marshall Islands (Seattle, 1956).

34. *Ibid.*, pp. 9-10.

35. C. L. Dunham to Donaldson (AFL correspondence), March 28, 1956.

36. UWFL 46. L. R. Donaldson *et al.*, Survey of Radioactivity in the Sea Near Bikini and Eniwetok Atolls, June 11-21, 1956 (1956), pp. 7-8.

37. *Ibid.*, p. 16.

38. *Ibid.*, p. 15.

39. *Ibid.*, p. 17.

40. UWFL 47. A. H. Seymour *et al.*, Survey of Radioactivity in the Sea and in Pelagic Marine Life West of the Marshall Islands, September 1-20, 1956 (1957), p. 49.

41. *Ibid.*

42. Toshiharu Kawabata, "State of Radiological Contamination in Fishes," *Research in the Effects . . .* , II, 949.

43. UWFL 47. Survey of Radioactivity . . . , p. 45.

44. UWFL 54. Frank G. Lowman, Radionuclides in Plankton Near the Marshall Islands, 1956 (1958).

Chapter 9

1. Holmes & Narver, Inc., *Report of Repatriation of the Rongelap People for the U.S. Atomic Energy Commission, Albuquerque Operations Office, Albuquerque, N.M.* (Holmes & Narver, Inc., n.d.)

2. *Ibid.*

3. *Ibid.*

4. *Ibid.*

5. Robert A. Conard *et al.*, *Medical Survey of Rongelap People Five and Six Years After Exposure to Fallout* (BNL 609; USAEC, 1960), p. 4.

6. NAS-NRC, *The Biological Effects of Atomic Radiation: A Report to the Public* (Washington, D. C., 1956).

7. *Ibid.*, p. 2.

8. NAS-NRC, *The Biological Effects of Atomic Radiation: Summary Reports* (Washington, D.C., 1956), pp. 81-82.

9. Merril Eisenbud and John H. Harley, "Radioactive Fallout Through September, 1955," *Science,* CXXIV (August 10, 1956), 251.

10. AFL, Suggested Study Areas for Rongelap Atoll for Discussion with Dr. John Wolfe, United States Atomic Energy Commission, Division of Biology and Medicine (University of Washington, 1957).

11. *Ibid.*, p. 14.

12. AFL, The Rongelap Radiological, Food, and Ecology Studies, February 5, 1957. Unpublished report to USAEC.

13. Gordon M. Dunning (ed.), *Radioactive Contamination of Certain Areas in the Pacific Ocean From Nuclear Tests* (Washington, D.C.: USAEC, 1957).

14. AFL, Revised Proposal for Rongelap Radiological, Ecological, and Native Food Study Program, October 21, 1957. Unpublished report to USAEC.

15. *Ibid.*, p. 2.

16. AFL, field log, 1957.

17. E. E. Held to A. H. Seymour, letter report (LRB files), September 23, 1958.

18. LRB field log, 1959.

19. Held to D. H. Nucker (LRB correspondence), 1959.

20. Conard *et al., Medical Survey of Rongelap People . . .*, p. 6.

21. Held to Nucker (LRB correspondence), 1959.

22. LRB, Summary of Activities at Rongelap Atoll, 1958-1959 (informal report, n.d.).

23. *Ibid.*

24. D. W. Cole, S. P. Gessel, and E. E. Held, "Tension Lysimeter Studies of Ion and Moisture Movement in Glacial Till and Coral Atoll Soils," *Proceedings, Soil Science Society of America,* XXV, No. 4 (July-August, 1961), 321-25.

25. *Ibid.*

26. Held, personal communication.

27. Held, personal communication; Held, "Qualitative Distribution of Radionuclides at Rongelap Atoll," *Proceedings of the First National Symposium on Radioecology,* Vincent Schultz and A. W. Klement, Jr. (eds.) (DBM, USAEC, 1962).

28. Held, personal communication.

29. Reid M. Kenady, Jr., The Soils of Rongelap Atoll, Marshall Islands (unpublished Master's thesis, University of Washington, 1962).

30. UWFL 51. Frank G. Lowman *et al.,* The Occurrence and Distribution of Radioactive Non-Fission Products in Plants and Animals of the Pacific Proving Ground (1957).

31. Frank Richardson, Preliminary Report on the Birds of Rongelap and Eniwetok, Especially in Relation to Soil and Plant Development (unpublished MS, University of Washington), 1960.

32. W. A. Anikouchine, Bottom Sediments of Rongelap Lagoon, Marshall Islands (unpublished Master's thesis, University of Washington, 1962).

Chapter 10

1. Gerald W. Johnson and Charles E. Violet, *Phenomenology of Contained Nuclear Explosions* (University of California, Lawrence Radiation Laboratory, December, 1958).

2. USAEC, *Twenty-third Semiannual Report* (Washington, D.C., July-December, 1957), p. 275.

3. HASL, "Announced Nuclear Detonations," compiled by Kosta Telegadas, U.S. Weather Bureau, in *Fallout Program Quarterly Summary Report* (HASL 111 [USAEC New York Operations Office, April 1, 1961]), p. 183.

4. Bermuda communique, March 24, 1957.

5. USAEC, *Twenty-third Semiannual Report,* p. 277.

6. NAS-NRC, "Report of the Committee on Genetic Effects of

Atomic Radiation," *The Biological Effects of Atomic Radiation: Summary Reports* (Washington, D.C., 1956), pp. 29-30.

7. USAEC, "Statement on Radioactive Fallout by the Advisory Committee on Biology and Medicine," *Twenty-third Semiannual Report* (Appendix 13).

8. Willard F. Libby, "Remarks Prepared for Delivery Before the Swiss Academy of Medical Sciences Symposium on Radioactive Fallout, Lausanne, Switzerland, March 27, 1958," USAEC, *Twenty-fourth Semiannual Report* (Appendix 12), January-June, 1958.

9. LRB field log.

10. HASL, "Announced Nuclear Detonations," p. 179.

11. LRB field log.

12. *Ibid.*

13. *Ibid.*

14. Frank G. Lowman, "Marine Biological Investigations at the Eniwetok Test Site," in *Disposal of Radioactive Wastes* (Vienna: International Atomic Energy Agency, 1960), p. 113.

15. *Ibid.*, p. 110.

16. LRB field log.

17. Lowman, "Marine Biological Investigations . . . ," p. 116.

18. A. H. Seymour to L. R. Donaldson, Post-Hardtack Oceanographic Survey, memorandum (LRB correspondence), June 30, 1958.

19. USAEC, "Health and Safety Precautions for the Eniwetok Proving Ground Tests," *Twenty-fourth Semiannual Report* (Appendix 10), p. 349.

20. HASL, "Announced Nuclear Detonations," p. 179.

21. UWFL 75. L. R. Donaldson *et al.*, Radiation Levels in Samples of Tuna Fish Collected in the Western Pacific Ocean During 1958.

22. Joint Task Force message (copy, LRB files), August 16, 1958.

23. USAEC, *Twenty-fifth Semiannual Report*, July-December, 1958, p. 179.

24. United Nations, *Report of the United Nations Scientific Committee on the Effects of Atomic Radiation*, General Assembly Official Records, Thirteenth Session, Supplement No. 17 (New York, 1958).

25. USAEC, *Twenty-fifth Semiannual Report*, p. 180.

Chapter 11

1. E. E. Held, personal observations, September, 1961.

2. Ralph F. Palumbo, "Eniwetok Studies," *Annual Report of the Laboratory of Radiation Biology, 1960-1961* (University of Washington, July 15, 1961), p. 10.

3. *Ibid.*, p. 11.

4. *Ibid.*, p. 8.

5. *Ibid.*, p. 9.

6. *Ibid.*, p. 7.

7. UWFL 50. E. E. Held, Land Crabs and Radioactive Fallout at Eniwetok Atoll (1960).

8. UWFL 64. D. Chakravarti and E. E. Held, Potassium and Cesium-137 in *Birgus latro* (Coconut Crab) Muscle Collected at Rongelap Atoll (1960).

9. L. R. Donaldson to Paul B. Pearson (AFL correspondence), June 13, 1951.

10. Lauren R. Donaldson *et al.,* "The Fern Lake Trace Mineral Metabolism Program," (1959), p. 5.

11. USAEC-DBM, *Bioenvironmental Features of the Ogotoruk Creek Area, Cape Thompson, Alaska: A First Summary by the Committee on Environmental Studies for Project Chariot* (TID-12439; December, 1960), p. 1.

12. *Ibid.,* p. 1.

13. USAEC, Oceanography Research Program: Report to the General Manager by the Director of Biology and Medicine (AEC 180/9), November 28, 1958.

14. NAS-NRC, *Oceanography: 1960 to 1970: Report of the Committee on Oceanography* (Washington, D.C., 1959), p. 31.

15. USAEC-DBM, *Biological, Medical, and Environmental Research Program* (TID-13228; April, 1961), p. 46.

BIBLIOGRAPHY

THE REPORTS OF THE LABORATORY (UWFL SERIES)

UWFL 1 Donaldson, L. R. Equipment and Procedures Used in the Study of the Effects of Irradiation of Fish with X-rays. 1945.

UWFL 2 Welander, A. D. Studies of the Effects of Roentgen Rays on the Growth and Development of the Embryos and Larvae of the Chinook Salmon (*Oncorhynchus tschawytscha*). 1945.

UWFL 3a Bonham, K., *et al.* The Effect of X-ray on Mortality, Weight, Length, and Counts of Erythrocytes and Hematopoietic Cells in Fingerling Chinook Salmon, *Oncorhynchus tschawytscha* Walbaum. Published in *Growth*, XII (1948), No. 2, 107-21.

UWFL 4 Bonham, K. Histological Effect of X-rays on Adult Male Silver Salmon (*Oncorhynchus kisutch* Walbaum). 1946.

UWFL 5 Bonham, K., *et al.* Lethal Effect of X-rays on Marine Microplankton Organisms. Published in *Science*, CVI (1947), 246.

UWFL 6 Bonham, K. and A. H. Seymour. Sections I and II of Series of Experiments Involving the Effect of X-rays on Fishes: Chinook Salmon (*Oncorhynchus tschawytscha*) "Preliminary Report Concerning X-ray Effects Upon Chinook Salmon (*Oncorhynchus tschawytscha* Walbaum) Observed Through More Than One Generation." 1947.

UWFL 7   Radiobiological Resurvey of Bikini Atoll During the Summer of 1947. 1947.

UWFL 8   Welander, A. D., *et al.* The Effects of Roentgen Rays on the Embryos and Larvae of the Chinook Salmon. Published in *Growth,* XII (1948), No. 3, 203-42.

UWFL 10   Preliminary outline of a program for the second radiobiological resurvey of Bikini Atoll during the summer of 1948 to be sponsored by the Atomic Energy Commission and the U.S. Navy. 1948.

UWFL 11   Donaldson, L. R., *et al.* Concentration of Active Materials by Hydroids in the Bikini Lagoon During the Summer of 1947. 1948.

UWFL 12   Foster, R. F., *et al.* Some Effects on Embryo and Young Rainbow Trout *(Salmo gairdnerii* Richardson) from Exposing the Parent Fish to X-rays. 1948. Published as "The Effect on Embryos and Young of Rainbow Trout from Exposing the Parent Fish to X-rays" in *Growth* XIII (1949), 119-42.

UWFL 13   Bonham, K. Progress Report of the Samish Chinook Salmon Project (Sections I, II) Through the Summer of 1948. 1948.

UWFL 14   Bonham, K. Lethal Effects of X-rays on Marine Amphipods. 1948.

UWFL 16   Bikini Radiobiological Resurvey of 1948. 1949.

UWFL 17   Welander, A. D., *et al.* The Effects of Roentgen Rays on Adult Rainbow Trout. 1949.

UWFL 18   Donaldson, L. R., *et al.* Radiological Analysis of Biological Samples Collected at Eniwetok May 16, 1948. 1949.

UWFL 19   Eniwetok Radiological Resurvey July 1948. 1949.

UWFL 20   Proposed Program of Study of Radiation Biology at Bikini and Eniwetok During the Summer of 1949. 1949.

UWFL 21   Bonham, K. Effects of X-rays upon the Fresh-Water Snail, *Radix japonica.* 1949.

UWFL 23   Radiobiological Survey of Bikini, Eniwetok, and Likiep Atolls—July-August, 1949. (Reproduced by Technical Information Service, Oak Ridge; published as *AECD 3446* by Office of Technical Services, U.S. Dept. of Commerce, 1950.)

UWFL 23   Biddulph, S. F., and O. Biddulph. A Description of
(App.)   Tumors on *Ipomoea tuba* from the A-Bomb Test Sites on Eniwetok Atoll, Appendix to Radiobiological Survey of Bikini, Eniwetok, and Likiep Atolls—July-August, 1949. (Reproduced by Technical Information Service, Oak Ridge; published as *AECD 3446* [App.] by Office of Technical Service, Dept. of Commerce, 1950.)

UWFL 26   Bonham, K., and R. F. Palumbo. "Effects of X-rays on

Snails, Crustacea, and Algae," *Growth*, XV (1951), 155-88.

UWFL 28   The Need for Continuation of Studies of Radiation Contamination of Biotic Forms at the Bikini and Eniwetok Testing Grounds. 1952.

UWFL 31   Biddulph, O., and R. Cory. The Relationship between Ca[45], Total Calcium and Fission Product Radioactivity in Plants of *Portulaca oleracea* Growing in the Vicinity of the Atom Bomb Test Sites on Eniwetok Atoll. (Washington State College) (Reproduced by Technical Information Service, Oak Ridge; published by Office of Technical Service, Dept. of Commerce, 1952.)

UWFL 32   Suggested Programs for the Biological Monitoring of Eniwetok Atoll Before and After the Testing Program with a Resurvey of Bikini Atoll. 1952.

UWFL 33   Radiobiological Studies at Eniwetok Atoll Before and Following the Mike Shot of the November 1952 Testing Program. 1953. (Confidential.) (WT 616.)

UWFL 35   Preliminary Statement of the Proposed Program for Marine Survey Unit, Section 19. 1953.

UWFL 36   Operations Outline for Program 19, Marine Survey Unit, of Operation Castle. 1954.

UWFL 38   Welander, A. D. Some Effects of X-irradiation of Different Embryonic Stages of the Trout *(Salmo gairdnerii)*. Published in *Growth*, XVIII (1954), 227-55.

UWFL 39   Bonham, K. Sensitivity to X-rays of the Early Cleavage Stages of the Snail *Helisoma subcrenatum*. Published in *Growth*, XIX (1955), 9-18.

UWFL 40   Donaldson, L. R., *et al.* Radiation Levels in Biological Samples Collected at Ponape, Caroline Islands, December 16-17, 1954. 1955.

UWFL 42   A Radiological Study of Rongelap Atoll, Marshall Islands During 1954-1955. (Reproduced by Technical Information Service, Oak Ridge; published by Office of Technical Services, U.S. Dept. of Commerce, 1955.)

UWFL 43   Radiobiological Resurvey of Rongelap and Ailinginae Atolls, Marshall Islands, October-November, 1955. (Reproduced by Technical Information Service, Oak Ridge; published by Office of Technical Services, U. S. Dept. of Commerce, 1955.)

UWFL 44   Palumbo, R. F. Uptake of Iodine-131 by the Red Alga *Asparagopsis taxiformis*. (Reproduced by Technical Information Service, Oak Ridge; published by Office of Technical Services, U.S. Dept. of Commerce, microfilm, 1955.)

UWFL 46   Donaldson, L. R., *et al.* Survey of Radioactivity in the Sea Near Bikini and Eniwetok Atolls, June 11-21, 1956.

(Reproduced by Technical Information Service, Oak Ridge; published by Office of Technical Services, U.S. Dept. of Commerce, 1956.)

UWFL 47   Seymour, A. H., *et al.* Survey of Radioactivity in the Sea and in Pelagic Marine Life West of the Marshall Islands, September 1-20, 1956. (Reproduced by Technical Information Service, Oak Ridge; published by Office of Technical Services, U.S. Dept. of Commerce, 1957.)

UWFL 49   Welander, A. D. Radioactivity in the Reef Fishes of Belle Island, Eniwetok Atoll, April 1954 to November 1955. (Reproduced by Technical Information Service, Oak Ridge; published by Office of Technical Services, U.S. Dept. of Commerce, 1957.)

UWFL 50   Held, E. E. Land Crabs and Radioactive Fallout at Eniwetok Atoll. (Reproduced by Technical Information Service, Oak Ridge; published by Office of Technical Services, U.S. Dept. of Commerce, 1957.) Also published as "Land Crabs and Fission Products at Eniwetok Atoll," *Pacific Science,* XIV (1960), No. 1, 18-27.

UWFL 51   Lowman, F. G., *et al.* The Occurrence and Distribution of Radioactive Non-Fission Products in Plants and Animals of the Pacific Proving Ground. (Reproduced by Technical Information Service, Oak Ridge; published by Office of Technical Services, U.S. Dept. of Commerce, 1957.)

UWFL 52   Kawabata, T., and E. E. Held. A Method for the Determination of Strontium-90 in Biological Materials. MS. 1958.

UWFL 53   Bonham, K. Radioactivity of Invertebrates and Other Organisms at Eniwetok Atoll During 1954-1955. (Reproduced by Technical Information Service, Oak Ridge; published by Office of Technical Services, U.S. Dept. of Commerce, 1958.)

UWFL 54   Lowman, F. G. Radionuclides in Plankton Near the Marshall Islands, 1956. (Reproduced by Technical Information Service, Oak Ridge; published by Office of Technical Services, U.S. Dept. of Commerce, 1958.)

UWFL 55   Welander, A. D. Radiobiological Studies of the Fish Collected at Rongelap and Ailinginae Atolls, July 1957. (Reproduced by Technical Information Service, Oak Ridge; published by Office of Technical Services, U.S. Dept. of Commerce, 1958.)

UWFL 56   Palumbo, R. F. and F. G. Lowman. The Occurrence of Antimony-125, Europium-155, Iron-55, and Other Radionuclides in Rongelap Atoll Soil. (Reproduced by Technical Information Service, Oak Ridge; published by Office of Technical Services, 1958.)

UWFL 57   Lowman, F. G., *et al.* The Biological and Geographical Distribution of W^{185} in the Vicinity of the Eniwetok Test Site, April-September, 1958. 1959. (Secret.)

UWFL 58   Palumbo, R. F., *et al.* Distribution of Radioactivity in Sea Water and Marine Organisms Following an Underwater Nuclear Detonation at the Eniwetok Test Site in 1958. 1959. (Secret.)

UWFL 59   Chakravarti, D., and R. Eisler. Strontium-90 and Gross Beta Activity in the Fat and Non-Fat Fractions of Coconut Crab *(Birgus latro)* Liver Collected at Rongelap Atoll During March 1958. Published in *Pacific Science,* XV (1961), No. 1.

UWFL 60   Chakravarti, D., and T. Joyner. Potassium as an Index of Naturally Occurring Radioactivity in Tuna Muscle. Published in *Transactions of the American Fisheries Society,* LXXXIX (1960), No. 3.

UWFL 61   Palumbo, R. F. Gross Beta Radioactivity of the Algae at Eniwetok Atoll, 1954-1956. (Reproduced by Technical Information Service, Oak Ridge; published by Office of Technical Services, U.S. Dept. of Commerce, 1959.)

UWFL 63   Bonham, K. Further Contributions on Gross Beta Radioactivity of Biological and Related Samples at the Eniwetok Proving Ground, 1952-1958. (Reproduced by Technical Information Service, Oak Ridge; published by Office of Technical Services, U.S. Dept. of Commerce, 1959.)

UWFL 64   Chakravarti, D., and E. E. Held. Potassium and Cesium-137 in *Birgus latro* (Coconut Crab) Muscle Collected at Rongelap Atoll. Published in *Journal of the Marine Biological Association of India,* II (1960), No. 1, 75-81.

UWFL 65   Lowman, F. G. Marine Biological Investigations at the Eniwetok Test Site. *(Disposal of Radioactive Wastes,* International Atomic Energy Agency, Vienna, 1960.)

UWFL 66   Palumbo, R. F. Radioactivity and Recovery of Land Plants at Eniwetok Atoll, 1954-1957. Published in *Radiation Botany,* I (1962), No. 2, 182-89.

UWFL 67   Kenady, R. M., *et al.* Major Soil Types of Rongelap Atoll.

UWFL 68   Joyner, T., and D. Chakravarti. Analysis of Some Trace Elements in Fish Tissues. 1960.

UWFL 69   Held, E. E., and D. J. South. Calcium, Potassium and Radionuclides in Pandanus from Rongelap Atoll.

UWFL 70   Held, E. E., *et al.* Radionuclides in Fish Collected at Rongelap Atoll.

UWFL 71   Lowman, F. G. Radioisotopes in Sea Water and Bottom
           Sediments from the Target Area of an Underwater
           Nuclear Detonation.

UWFL 72   Lowman, F G., *et al.* Survey of Radioactivity in the Sea
           and in Pelagic Marine Life Near the Marshall and
           Mariana Islands, August 8-14 and September 3-13, 1958.
           (The *Collett-Silverstein* Survey.)

UWFL 73   Cole, D. W., *et al.* Use of the Tension Lysimeter in Coral
           Atoll and Glacial Till Soils. Paper presented at the Na-
           tional Meeting of the Soils Society of America, November,
           1959.

UWFL 74   Seymour, A. H. Radionuclides in Marine Organisms
           from Guam, Palau and the Gulf of Siam. First Sym-
           posium on Radioecology, Colorado State University,
           September, 1961.

UWFL 75   Donaldson, L. R., *et al.* Radiation Levels in Samples of
           Tuna Fish Collected in the Western Pacific Ocean during
           1958.

UWFL 76   Lowman, F. G. Radioisotopes in *Tridacna* Clams from
           Eniwetok, 1956-1961.

UWFL 77   Chakravarti, D., and E. E. Held. A Study of the Chemi-
           cal and Radiochemical Composition of Food Rations of
           the Rongelapese Collected during September, 1959.

UWFL 78   Bonham, K. Abundance of Sea Cucumbers *Holothuria
           atra* and *H. leucospilota* on the Shores of Islets of Ronge-
           lap Atoll, Marshall Islands, September, 1959. To be
           published in *Pacific Science.*

PRINCIPAL ADDITIONAL SOURCES

Anikouchine, W. A. Bottom Sediments of Rongelap Lagoon, Marshall
    Islands. Unpublished Master's thesis, Department of Oceanography,
    University of Washington, 1962.
AFL, LRB, daily field logs, 1954-1958.
AFL. Suggested Study Areas for Rongelap Atoll for Discussion with
    Dr. John Wolfe, United States Atomic Energy Commission, Division
    of Biology and Medicine. January 19 and 20, 1957.
AFL. Revised Proposal for Rongelap Radiological, Ecological, and
    Native Food Study Program. May, 1957.
AFSWP. *Bikini Scientific Resurvey,* Vol. I, *Operations* (Restricted),
    December, 1947.
AFSWP. *Bikini Scientific Resurvey,* Vol. II, *Report of the Technical
    Director* (Confidential). December, 1947.
Arnold, James R. and E. A. Martell. "The Circulation of Radioactive
    Isotopes," *The Scientific American,* CCI (September, 1959), No. 3,
    84-93.

CNO. *Handbook on the Trust Territory of the Pacific Islands.* Washington, D.C.: Government Printing Office, 1948.

CNO. *Report on the Administration of the Trust Territory of the Pacific Islands,* July 1, 1949 to June 30, 1950. Transmitted to the United Nations (OPNAV P22-100-J), June, 1950. Washington, D.C.: Government Printing Office, 1950.

Cole, D. W., S. P. Gessel, and E. E. Held. "Tension Lysimeter Studies of Ion and Moisture Movement In Glacial Till and Coral Atoll Soils," *Proceedings, Soil Science Society of America,* XXV, No. 4 (July-August, 1961), 321-25.

Conard, Robert A., *et al. Medical Survey of Rongelap People Five and Six Years After Exposure to Fallout* (With Addendum on Vegetation). BNL Associated Universities, Inc., BNL 609 (T-179), September, 1960.

Cronkite, E. P., V. P. Bond, and C. L. Dunham. (eds.). *Some Effects of Ionizing Radiation on Human Beings: A Report on the Marshallese and Americans Accidentally Exposed to Radiation From Fallout and a Discussion of Radiation Injury in the Human Being.* (TID 5358) Washington, D.C.: USAEC, July, 1956.

Crowl, Philip A. and E. G. Love. *Seizure of the Gilberts and the Marshalls,* Vol. VI, *The War in the Pacific.* (U.S. Army in World War II, Ser. 2.) Washington, D.C.: Office of the Chief of Military History, Department of the Army, 1955.

De Vore, Robert. "The Man Who Made Manhattan," *Collier's,* October 13, 1945, p. 12.

Donaldson, Lauren R. "Radiobiological Studies at the Eniwetok Test Site and Adjacent Areas of the Western Pacific," *Transactions of the Second Seminar on Biological Problems of Water Pollution,* U.S. Public Health Service. Robert A. Taft Sanitary Engineering Center, Cincinnati, April 20-24, 1959.

Donaldson, Lauren R. and Richard F. Foster. "Effects of Radiation on Aquatic Organisms." Chap. x, *The Effects of Atomic Radiation on Oceanography and Fisheries* (NAS-NRC Publication No. 551). Washington, D.C., 1957.

Donaldson, Lauren R., Paul R. Olson, and John R. Donaldson. "The Fern Lake Trace Mineral Metabolism Program," *Transactions of the American Fisheries Society,* Vol. LXXXVIII, 1959.

Dunham, Charles L. "Responsibilities of the Division of Biology and Medicine in the U.S. Atomic Energy Program," *Proceedings of the Second Inter-American Symposium on the Peaceful Application of Nuclear Energy.* Buenos Aires, June 1-5, 1959.

Dunning, Gordon M. (ed.). *Radioactive Contamination of Certain Areas in the Pacific Ocean From Nuclear Tests.* Washington, D.C.: USAEC, August, 1957.

Emery, Kenneth O., J. I. Tracey, Jr., and H. S. Ladd. *Geology of Bikini and Nearby Atolls. (Bikini and Nearby Atolls: Part I, Geology;*

Geological Survey Professional Paper 260-A.) Washington, D.C.: Government Printing Office, 1954.

Harley, John H. (ed.). *Operation Troll: Joint Preliminary Report.* HASL, USAEC New York Operations Office, NYO 4656, April, 1956.

HASL. *Fallout Program Quarterly Summary Report (December 1, 1960, through March 1, 1961).* (HASL 111) USAEC New York Operations Office, April 1, 1961.

Held, E. E. "Qualitative Distribution of Radionuclides at Rongelap Atoll," *Proceedings of the First National Symposium on Radio-ecology,* Vincent Schultz and A. W. Klement, Jr. (eds.), Washington, D.C.: DBM, USAEC, 1962.

Hines, Neal O. "Bikini Report," *The Scientific Monthly,* LXXII (February, 1951), No. 2.

Hiyama, Yoshio. "General Backgrounds of These Reports," Annex to *Research in the Effects and Influences of the Nuclear Bomb Test Explosions.* Tokyo: Japan Society for the Promotion of Science, 1956.

Holmes & Narver, Inc. *Report of Repatriation of the Rongelap People for the U.S. Atomic Energy Commission, Albuquerque Operations Office, Albuquerque, N.M.* (Official use only.) Holmes & Narver, n.d.

Holmes & Narver, Inc., AEC Facilities Division. *Working at Eniwetok.* Los Angeles, 1960.

Japan Society for the Promotion of Science. *Research in the Effects and Influences of the Nuclear Bomb Test Explosions.* Compiled by the Committee for Compilation of Report on Research in the Effects of Radioactivity. 2 vols. Tokyo, 1956.

Johnson, Gerald W. and Charles E. Violet. *Phenomenology of Contained Nuclear Explosions.* (UCRL-5124 Rev. I.) University of California, Lawrence Radiation Laboratory, December, 1958.

Kenady, Reid M., Jr. The Soils of Rongelap Atoll, Marshall Islands. Unpublished Master's thesis, College of Forestry, University of Washington, Seattle, 1962.

Lowman, Frank G. "Marine Biological Investigations at the Eniwetok Test Site," in *Disposal of Radioactive Wastes.* Vienna: International Atomic Energy Agency, 1960.

Mahr, August C. *The Visit of the* Rurik *to San Francisco in 1816.* (Stanford University Publications: History, Economics, Political Science.) Palo Alto: Stanford University Press, 1932.

Matsumuro, Kazu. Copra Production in the Marshalls. Majuro, Marshall Islands: Trust Territory of the Pacific Islands, March 10, 1961. Mimeographed.

Matthias, Franklin T. Excerpts from personal diary. Hanford, Wash., 1943–45.

Miller, C. F., and P. Loeb. Ionization Rate and Photon Pulse Rate of Fission Products From Slow Neotron Fission of U^{235}. USNRDL-TR-247, U.S. Naval Radiological Defense Laboratory, San Francisco, 1958.

Morison, S. E. "Historical Notes on the Gilbert and Marshall Islands," *The American Neptune,* Vol. IV, No. 2 (1944).

NAS–NRC. *The Biological Effects of Atomic Radiation: A Report to the Public.* From a Study by the National Academy of Sciences. Washington, D.C., 1956.

NAS–NRC. *The Biological Effects of Atomic Radiation: Summary Reports.* From a Study by the National Academy of Sciences. Washington, D.C., 1956.

NAS–NRC. *The Biological Effects of Atomic Radiation: Summary Reports.* From a Study by the National Academy of Sciences. Washington, D.C., 1960.

Oliver, Douglas L. *The Pacific Islands.* Cambridge, Mass.: Harvard University Press, 1951.

Osborn, Fairfield. *The Pacific World.* New York: W. W. Norton & Company, Inc., 1944.

Richardson, Frank. Preliminary Report on the Birds of Rongelap and Eniwetok, Especially in Relation to Soil and Plant Development. Unpublished MS., University of Washington.

St. John, Harold. "Flora of Eniwetok Atoll," *Pacific Science,* XIV (October, 1960), 313-36.

Schultz, Leonard P. and collaborators. *Fishes of the Marshall and Marianas Islands.* (U.S. National Museum Bulletin No. 202. 2 vols.) Washington, D.C.: Smithsonian Institution. Vol. I, 1953; Vol. II, 1960.

Seymour, Allyn H. *Fallout in the Ocean,* a Statement Prepared for the Special Subcommittee on Radiation, Joint Committee on Atomic Energy, Congress of the United States, for Public Hearings on Fallout from Nuclear Weapons Tests, May 5-8, 1959.

————. "The Distribution of Radioisotopes Among Marine Organisms in the West Central Pacific," *Marine Biological Applications of Radioisotope Techniques* (Symposium). Pubblicazioni delle stazione zoologica di Napoli, Vol. XXXI, supplement, 1959.

Shurcliff, W. A. *Bombs at Bikini.* New York: Wm. H. Wise & Co., Inc., 1947.

Smyth, Henry D. *Atomic Energy for Military Purposes.* Princeton, N.J.: Princeton University Press, 1945.

Strauss, Lewis L. *The Effects of High-Yield Nuclear Explosions—Statement by Lewis L. Strauss, Chairman, and a Report by the United States Atomic Energy Commission.* Washington, D.C., February, 1955.

Sverdrup, H. V., M. W. Johnson, and R. H. Fleming. *The Oceans.* New York: Prentice-Hall, Inc., 1946.

Taylor, William R., *Plants of Bikini and Other Northern Marshall Islands.* Ann Arbor: University of Michigan Press, 1950.

Thayer, Hanford. Personal diary, 1943-45.

Tobin, Jack (J.E.). *Kili Journal: August 28 to September 18, 1954.*

Report of the District Anthropologist, Marshall Islands District. Majuro, Marshall Islands, September 21, 1954. Mimeographed.

———. *The Bikini People, Past and Present.* Majuro, Marshall Islands, October, 1953. Mimeographed.

United Nations. *Report of the United Nations Scientific Committee on the Effects of Atomic Radiation.* General Assembly Official Records. (Thirteenth Session, Supplement No. 17 [A/3838].) New York, 1958.

USAEC. *Semiannual Reports, Second through Twenty-fifth.* Washington, D.C.: Government Printing Office, July, 1947, through December, 1958.

USAEC–DBM. *Marine Sciences Research.* (TID-4040.) January, 1960.

———. *Bioenvironmental Features of the Ogotoruk Creek Area, Cape Thompson, Alaska: A First Summary by the Committee on Environmental Studies for Project Chariot.* (TID–12439.) December, 1960.

———. *Biological, Medical, and Environmental Research Program.* (TID–13228.) April, 1961.

U.S. Congress. *Radiation Research in the Life Sciences, Current Projects in the United States and Throughout the World.* Prepared for the Committee on Government Operations, U.S. Senate, November 28, 1960. Washington, D.C.: Government Printing Office, 1960.

———. *Applications of Radioisotopes and Radiation in the Life Sciences.* Hearings Before the Subcommittee on Research, Development, and Radiation, Joint Committee on Atomic Energy, Eighty-seventh Congress, March 27-30, 1961. Washington, D.C.: Government Printing Office, 1961.

———. *Background Material for the Review of the International Atomic Policies and Programs of the United States.* Report to the Joint Committee on Atomic Energy by Robert McKinney, Vol. II. Washington, D.C.: Government Printing Office, 1960.

———. *Fallout From Nuclear Weapons Tests.* Hearings Before the Special Subcommittee on Radiation, Joint Committee on Atomic Energy, Eighty-sixth Congress, May 5-8, 1959. Washington, D.C.: Government Printing Office, 1959.

———. *The Nature of Radioactive Fallout and Its Effect on Man.* Hearings Before the Special Subcommittee on Radiation, Joint Committee on Atomic Energy, Eighty-fifth Congress, May 27–June 7, 1957. Washington, D.C.: Government Printing Office, 1957.

Von Arx, William S. *Circulation Systems of Bikini and Rongelap Lagoons.* (*Bikini and Nearby Atolls: Part II, Oceanography* [Physical]; Geological Survey Professional Paper 260-B.) Washington, D.C.: Government Printing Office, 1954.

Warren, Shields. "Ionizing Radiation and Medicine," *The Scientific American,* CCI (September, 1959), No. 3.

Warren, Stafford and G. H. Whipple. "Roentgen Ray Intoxication," *Journal of Experimental Medicine.* Vol. XXXV (1922): I. Unit dose over thorax negative; epithelium of small intestine sensitive to X-rays (187-202); II. A study of the sequence of clinical, anatomical, and histological changes following a unit dose of X-rays (203-11); III. Speed of autolysis of various body tissues after lethal X-ray exposures; the remarkable disturbance of the epithelium of the small intestine (213-24). Vol. XXXVII (1923): I. Bacterial invasion of the blood stream as influenced by X-ray destruction of the mucosal epithelium of the small intestine (713-23); II. The cumulative effect or summation of X-ray exposures given at varying intervals (725-30); III. The path of a beam of hard rays in the living organism (731-39); IV. Intestinal lesions and acute intoxication produced by radiation in a variety of animals (741-52).

Yanaihara, Tadao. Pacific Islands Under Japanese Mandate. London and New York: Oxford University Press, 1940.

INDEX

Subjects and Places

Aaraanbiru Island, Eniwetok, 163

Aberdeen Proving Ground (Army), 85

Aberrations, biological: absence of, Bikini, 1947, 76; at Eniwetok, 1949, 109; at Rongelap, 1959, 264-67; healing processes of nature, 308-9

Able, Test, Operation Crossroads, 36-37, 62

Ailinginae Atoll: early visits, 30; fish collection after Crossroads, 49; and 1954 fallout, 165; natives evacuated, returned, 168, 197; surveyed, 1955, problem of terns, 219

Airukiiji (Arji) Island, Bikini, 47

Aitsu Island, Eniwetok, 87, 109, 163

Alaska, University of, 305

Algae: Crossroads samples of, 44; on Engebi reefs, 1948, 101; and Operation Ivy, 147-48; uptake of iodine, 222

Aloto, M.V., and Rongelap survey, 255, 260

Alpha radioactivity: presumed presence in biota, Crossroads (Welander), 44-45; Joint Crossroads Committee's interest in, 56; attention to, 1947, 65

Aomoen Island, Bikini, 47, 62, 74

Aomon Island, Eniwetok: former site of Eniwetok community, 87; plants studied by St. John, 109-10; sampling stations, 1952, 137; levels of radioactivity high after Test Mike, 141

Applied Fisheries Laboratory: establishment, initial staff, 10; housing, installation of X-radiation equipment, 14; early reports to OSRD, 15; accomplishments in Columbia River period, 18-19; contracts transferred to U.S. Atomic Energy Commission, 19; at Operation Crossroads, 36; represented in Bikini Scientific Resurvey, 52; proposal for continued Bikini survey, 88; surveys at Bikini, Eniwetok (1948) approved by AEC, 90, 94-101; Bikini-Eniwetok Resurvey, 1949, 102-10; prepares survey of Eniwetok in 1950, 122; budget, staff for 1950, 124; contact with Nevada programs, 126; begins experiment with rainbow trout, 1951, 127; period of consolidation, 1951, 127; program analysis by Donaldson, 127-28; need of further Pacific studies, 128-29; urges use of field test plots, 129; response to Pearson questions, 129; continuous field observations, 129; cites differences between land and water studies, 131; brought back into field work at Eniwetok, 135; plans, personnel, for 1952 sampling, 137; sampling before Test Mike, 137-38; sampling after Mike test, 141, 145; view of Pacific programs, 1953, 152; conference with Bugher, November 1, 1953, 155-56; plan for 1954 surveys, 161; in Task Group 7.1, 1954, 161; prepares final plan for 1954 surveys, 162-63; makes Rongelap survey, 1954, 180-82; begins "succession studies" at Eniwetok, 1954, 182; 1949 reports cited by Kawabata, 194; visit to Rongelap, 1954, 197; continues surveys at Eniwetok, 1955, 206; observations of rats, 1955, 206-13; summary of Eniwetok operations, 1954-1955, 214; surveys of Rongelap, 1955, 216; summary of collections, 1954-1955, 217; surveys Rongelap, 1955, 219; sends Rongelap reports to Dunham, Boss, 1955, 220; report to Division of Biology and Medicine, 1955, 220-21; and for Operation Redwing, 221-23; suggests ocean survey in 1956, 223; *Walton* survey, 1956, 223-29; *Marsh* survey, 1956, 229-33; surveys of Rongelap by 1956, 234; Rongelap study proposal, 1957, 243-44; assigned Rongelap environmental studies, 245; summarizes Rongelap contamination, 246; program reviewed by Cantril, 247n; reorganized, renamed, 246-47

Aquatic Biological Laboratory, Hanford, 17

Arctic Research Center, U.S. Public Health Service, 305

Argonne National Laboratory: Radiobiology Experiment Station established, 103; research in biology and medicine, 124

Armed Forces Special Weapons Project: establishment, 52; publishes Bikini Resurvey reports, 74; at Operation Sandstone, 85; represented on medical team, Kwajalein, 1954, 168

Arriikan (Aran) Island, 62

Atolls: characteristics, physical, 28. *See also* Ailinginae; Bikini (Eschscholtz); Eniwetok; Jaluit; Kwajalein; Lae; Likiep; Majuro; Mili; Rongelap; Rongerik; Ujae; Ujelang; Utirik; Wotho

Atomic bomb: transfer of contracts to Manhattan District, 3; effects of Bikini detonation, Evaluation Board's analysis of, 51

Atomic Bomb Effect Research Commission (Japan), 183-84

Atomic energy, interest in peaceful uses of, 196, 240, 272

Atomic Energy Act, 1946, 19, 79, 134

Atomic Energy Act, 1954, 197-272

Atomic Energy Commission, U.S.: created by Atomic Energy Act of 1946, 19; establishment, objectives, 78; initial organization, 79; approves surveys at Bikini, Eniwetok, 1948, 90; use of advisory committees, 101-2; decides to improve Eniwetok facilities, 112; establishment of test division, 113; develops weapons manufacture, 121-22; assists civil defense training, 121; need

for trained personnel, 123; support of biological studies, 123-24; and university contract programs, 124; and plans for 1952 test series, 134-35; and inclusion of Bikini in proving ground, 1953, 158; and beginning of 1954 tests, 168; organizes medical team at Kwajalein, 1954, 168; announcement of 1954 fallout, 169; and radiation hazard, 1954, 177-78; reports levels of 1954 fallout, 216-17; authorizes Rongelap repatriation, 236; and ocean research, 309

Atomic Energy Project, U.C.L.A., 126, 133

Atoms-for-Peace program, 196-97

Baker, Test, Crossroads: operation, 38-40; radioactivity in water, 40-41; pretest calculations of effect, 41; studies of (Welander), 44-45; effects of explosion on lagoon bottom, 70, 74

Biijiri Island, Eniwetok, 87

Bikini Atoll: meets test site specifications, 22; selection for 1946 tests, 24; Navy arrangements for use, 25; discovery, 29; and early scientific inquiry in Pacific, 29; named Eschscholtz by Kotzebue, 30; and World War II, 31; physical character, 33-34; continued scientific interest in, 1947, 50, 51; turbidity of lagoonal waters, 1947, 67-68; lagoon bottom coring, 1947, 69; condition of lagoon bottom, 1947, and reef corals, 70-71, 72; presumption of short-term use for Operation Crossroads, 93; 1950 survey canceled, 122; decision to test on, 157, 158, 160; surveys scheduled in 1954, 162; Test Bravo, 165; restricted zones, 1952, 1954, 166

Bikini community: population, 24; offered alternate site, 25; transported to Rongerik, 1946, 25; Council approves use of Bikini for tests, 25; question of return after Crossroads, 48; question of return as related to survey of radiobiological effects, 75; question of return to atoll, 92-93; prepares to move to Ujelang Atoll, 94; move to Kwajalein Atoll, Kili Island, 94; return to Bikini suggested, 129

Bikini Council, 93

Bikini Island: dimensions, 34; wave height, Baker, test, 40; reef corals dying, 1946, 47; site of preliminary landing, 1947, 59; as collecting station, 62; corals dying on reef, 1947, report of, 71, 74

"Bikini Incident," Hiyama note, 172

Bikini Investigation Commission. *See Shunkotsu Maru* Survey

Bikini Scientific Resurvey: early origin of idea, 50; Hederman named task group commander, 52; concluding phase of Crossroads, 52; support and

organization, 53-54; interest in residual radioactivity, 54, 56; purposes as stated by Leahy, 56; public information concerning, 56-57; scientific atmosphere, 59-60; press releases, 60-61, 61-62; Medical-Legal Board, 61; visit of Juda, 64; absence of observable effects of nuclear tests, 67; studies of lagoon floor, 69-71; impressions of atoll condition, 1947, 71-72; end of operations, 72; conclusions in summary reports, 74-76
Bikini Waters Investigation Team, 185-86
Biology, studies of: at Bikini Atoll, (1946) 32, (1947), 53-54; supported by AEC, 123-24; strengthened in 1957, 271; at Eniwetok, 1961, 295-300
Biology and Medicine, Division of: Advisory Committee for, 101; membership, 101, 101n; establishment, 102; programs, 1948, 103; statement on responsibilities, 123; reliance on universities, 123-24; budget allocations, 1950-1952, 124; doubts need of continued Pacific surveys, 128; Bugher named director, 135; view of Pacific programs in 1953, 152; sends LeRoy, Dunham to Kwajalein, 1954, 169; suggests wider surveys, 1954 (Pearson), 198; presses for field data, 1955, 217; interest in strontium 90 at Rongelap, 1955, 220; and ocean survey, 1956, 223; Seymour joins Environmental Sciences Branch, 233; question of Rongelap studies, 243; Advisory Committee on fallout, 1957, 273-74; program elements, 1961, 311
Biology Operation, Hanford, 305
Biota, Pacific types, 43. *See also* Algae; Birds; Clams; Coconut; Crabs; Fish; Hydroids; Invertebrates; Plankton; Plants; Rainbow trout; Rats
Birds: sampling, (1952) 150-51, (Rongelap, 1955) 218-19; assist circulation of radioactivity, 268; Richardson's studies of, 268-69
Bogallua Island, Eniwetok, 137-144
Bogombogo Island, Eniwetok, 137, 143-44, 296
Bokoaetokutoku (Boku) Island, Bikini, 62
Bokororyuru (Boro) Island, Bikini, 62
Bowditch, U.S.S. (AGS-4), 33
Bravo, Test, Operation Castle, 165, 166-68
Brookhaven National Laboratory: research in biology and medicine, 124; and Rongelap medical studies, 245, 250, 250n, 257; meeting with Rongelapese, 1959, 259
Buster-Jangle, Operation, 126

California, University of: atomic laboratories at, 1942-1943, 4; in nuclear research in World War II, 124; animal studies, Operation Greenhouse, 126
California, University of at Los Angeles, 96
California Institute of Technology, 126
California Radiation Laboratory at Livermore, 135, 160, 302
Castle, Operation: 1954 test series opened at Bikini, 165; end, 183; Japanese studies of results, 192-95
Cesium 137: significance in soil studies, 253, 263; mobility studied, Rongelap, 1959, 264; studies in crab, 296
Chariot, Project: LRB association with, 302; environmental investigations, 303-5
Chicago (University of) Group: as "Metallurgical Laboratory," 4; meeting on Columbia River problem at, 1943, 8; in nuclear research, 124
Chilton, U.S.S. (APA 38), 53, 54
Chinook salmon, 15
Circulation of radioactivity, biological, evidence at Bikini, 1948, 97-98
Civil defense, 121, 125
Clams: differences in uptake of radioactivity after Crossroads, 47; at Rongelap, 254
Clinton Engineer Works, 4, 14
Clinton Laboratories, Oak Ridge, 54
Coconut: radioactivity in Bikini trees, 1949, 98; studies by Biddulph, 1949, 107; palms dying, Rongelap, 265
Coconut crab *(Birgus latro)*: and strontium 90 at Rongelap, 254; studies of radiocesium balance, 296
Collections, biological: methods at Crossroads, 46-47; gear, methods, and stations, 62, 64; of Radiobiology group, 1947, 64-65; at Kwajalein and Rongerik, 1947, 65-66
Collett, U.S.S.: 1958 ocean survey vessel, 275; schedule, scope, results, of survey, 286-88
Colorado School of Mines, 53
Columbia River: explored for plutonium plant site, 5; description, 6; need for studies of aquatic radiobiology, 7; possible contamination discussed at Chicago meeting, 8; concern about toxic effects of effluents, 12, 14; Donaldson urges laboratory there, 17; new studies by LRB, 301
Columbia University: atomic laboratories at, 1942-1943, 4; in nuclear research in World War II, 124
Commercial Fisheries, U.S., Bureau of, 305
Concentration of radioactivity, Bikini, 1948, 97-98
Conferences, Japanese-American. *See* Japanese-American conferences
Congressional Committee on Atomic

Energy, Joint: establishment, 79; early meetings with AEC, 80; at Operation Sandstone, 86; and fallout hearings, 1957, 242, 242n; hearings of Special Subcommittee on Radiation, 1957, 271-72

Contamination, radioactive, consistent study of by U.S., 310

Continental test site: considered in 1947, 80; considered by Test Division in 1949, 115; considered in 1950, 123

Coordination of Researches for Measures Against Atomic Bomb Injuries, Council for (Japan), 184

Coral: collections at Bikini, 1946, 47; condition at Bikini, 1947, 71; Bikini Resurvey report of, 74-75; deposits of radioactivity on, 1948, 97-98; rock used for concrete, 118-20; studies at Eniwetok, 1952, 148; particles in Bravo cloud, 165; observations of, Rongelap, 253

Coring, lagoon bottom: at Bikini, 1947, 69; at Rongelap, 1959, 269

Corps of Engineers, 3, 7, 19, 305

Coucal, U.S.S. (ASR 8), 53, 57-58

Crabs: strontium 90 in, 222; in native diet, 253-54; *Birgus latro* observed at Rongelap, 1961, 299-300. *See also* Coconut crabs; Land crabs

Crossroads, Operation: proposal, organization of, 20-21, 22; scientific impact, 32; total personnel, 32; new date established, 33; studies of test animals, 35n; "Division of Radiobiology" established, 41; end of operations, 47; Evaluation Board's preliminary statement, 50-51; Joint Committee established, 51; feasibility of Bikini Resurvey studied, 51, 52

Danger area. *See* Restricted Zone

David Taylor Model Basin (Navy), 85

Decline in radioactivity, rate of at Rongelap, 1959, 261

Defense, Department of: and decision on testing, 1951, 112-13; and preparations for 1952 series, 134-35; organizes medical team at Kwajalein, 1954, 168

Distribution of radioisotopes noted at Rongelap, 1955, 217-18

du Pont, E. I., de Nemours & Co., 4, 17

Duval County, U.S.S. (Rongelap survey vessel, 1959), 257, 258

Eberiru Island, Eniwetok: contamination of algae, 1952, 147; tests planned there, 1954, 160, 162

Effects of Radioactivity, Special Committee on (Japan): assumes coordinating role, Japan, 1954, 184; receives report of Japanese-American discussions, 200n

Ejit Island, Majuro: becomes home of Rongelapese, 1954, 197; Rongelapese depart for former home, 236-38

Elugelab Island, Eniwetok, 139, 140

Engebi Island, Eniwetok: Operation Sandstone test site, 87; inspection of reefs, 1948, 100-101; plants studied by St. John, 109-10; source of coral rock for concrete, 118-20; sampling station, 1952, 137; covered by surge from Mike test, 140; effects of Test Mike, 1952, 143; sampling of rats, 1952, 150-51; history of nuclear operations there, 207; observations of rats, 1955, 209-13; studies continued, 1961, 297-98

Eniaetok Island, Rongelap, 250, 252, 254

Eniirikku Island, Bikini, 34

Eninman Island, Bikini, 34, 59, 160

Enirik Island and Pass, Bikini, 34, 59, 62

Eniwetok, Battle of, 84-85

Eniwetok Atoll: as support area for Operation Crossroads, 22; selected as test site, 78; location, 81, 83; as U.S. base after World War II, 81, 85; history, 83; strategic position in World War II, 84; Battle of Eniwetok, 84-85; physical characteristics, 86-87; condition of facilities, 1948-1949, 111; uncertainty concerning continued use, 112; test site surveyed by Holmes & Narver, 1948, 113; requirements for test use, 114; construction of facilities, 115-18, 120; Operation Greenhouse planned there, 1951, 122; advantages for field study, 131; site of Operation Ivy, 1952, 135; sampling stations, 1952, 137-38; contamination of waters by Test Mike, 146; joined by Bikini in proving ground, 157-58; plans for 1954 surveys, 161-62; site of Test Wahoo, 1958, 276; Laboratory of Radiation Biology visits, 1961, 294; administration and facilities, 294; condition, 1961, 294; question of *Ipomoea tuba* (aberrant), 296

Eniwetok: community, 81; Island, 114

Eniwetok Marine Biological Laboratory (EMBL): establishment, 1953, 154; plans "on drawing board," 162; Rongelap samples counted, 1958, 255; use in Operation Hardtack, 285

Environmental Sciences Branch, Division of Biology and Medicine, 233, 243

Environmental Studies, Committee on (Project Chariot), 303, 304, 304n

Environmental studies, Laboratory of Radiation Biology, summary statement, 306-7

Enyu Island, Bikini, 34, 100

Fallout: 1954, levels reported by AEC, 216-17; hearings by Joint Congressional Committee, 1955, 1957, 242, 242n; monitoring network, 242; wider concern, 1957, 272; Advisory Committee (Biology and Medicine) statement on, 272-73

Fern Lake (Washington): becomes mineral metabolism field station, 247; description, and objectives, 301-2; product of 1951 proposal, 302

Fertilization studies, Rongelap, 260, 301

Fish: Pacific types, 43; collections at Crossroads, 45-46, 47; Rukoji samples, 1949, 107; sampling, Operation Ivy, 149-50; *Shunkotsu Maru* findings, 192-93; sampling at Rongelap, 1954-1955, 217; collections by U.S.S. *Rehoboth*, 1958, 282; efforts to sample from U.S.S. *Collett*, 285, 288; samples supplied by Kawabata, 289

Fish and Wildlife Service, U.S.: and Columbia program, 1946, 18; study of Bikini area before Operation Crossroads, 24, 33n; represented, Bikini Scientific Resurvey, 53; survey vessel *John N. Cobb* used in Project Chariot, 305

Fisheries, U.S. Bureau of Commercial. (*See* Bureau of Commercial Fisheries, U.S.)

Fisheries, Washington State Department of, 8

Fisheries group, Bikini Scientific Resurvey, 53, 66

Fishermen, Japanese. *See Fukuryu Maru*

Fission products: disposition after Test Baker, 75-76; studies of mixed products urged, 131

Food and Drug Administration, U.S., 214n

Foods, native, 217, 254, 258

Fukuryu Maru: in path of 1954 fallout, 165; makes way to Japan, 169; crew members experience effects of exposure, 169-70; arrival at Yaizu City, 169, 171; press reports reach United States, 170

Fukuryu Maru case: inquiries by Japanese government, 171; Allison proposes joint inquiry of, 171-72; radio operator ill, 172; reaction in Japan, 172-73; control ports established, Japan, 173-75; Japanese press asks compensation for fishermen, 175; statement by U.S. Department of State, 1954, 176; first Japanese-American conference, 176-77; ocean monitoring arranged by Eisenbud, 178; Japan's scientific mobilization, 183-86; Japanese plans for ocean survey, 185-87;

monitoring at 13 ports, 194; death of radio operator, 194

Game, Washington State Department of, 18, 36, 247

General Advisory Committee, AEC, establishment, function, and initial membership of, 79

Geneva Conference, 291

Geological Survey, U.S., 33n, 305

Geology group, Bikini Scientific Resurvey, 53, 69

Geology surveys, Bikini Atoll, 1946, 32

Geophysics Branch, Office of Naval Research, 53

Germany (Pacific possessions). *See* Pacific Islands

Grand Coulee, 5, 8

Great Britain. *See* United Kingdom

Greenhouse, Operation: to include thermonuclear research activities, 121, 125; projected for 1951, 122; biomedical studies, 125

Greenhouse experiments. *See* Fertilization studies

Guam, 202, 230, 232, 290

Hanford Engineer Works, 6, 17

Hanford Laboratories, 305

Hardtack, Operation (1958 nuclear test series): Pacific phase concurrent with Rongelap studies, 248; continental phase added, 270; last series in Eniwetok-Bikini area, 270; statement of objectives, 272; missions of Laboratory of Radiation Biology, 275; beginning, 277-78; Johnston Island tests, 286-87; Phase II, Nevada, 292

Haven, U.S.S., 36, 44

Hawaii, University of, 96

Health and Safety Laboratory, USAEC, 176, 199, 242

Health and Welfare Ministry (Japan), 173-75, 184

Holmes & Narver, Inc.: awarded Eniwetok contract, 113; conducts Eniwetok survey, 1948, 113; engineering experience, 113-14; survey report a base for J Division planning, 115; coordination of communications, 118; use of coral rock in concrete, 118-20; designs aluminum housing units, 120; Operation Greenhouse manning, 125-26; preliminary reconnaissance at Bikini, 1952, 157-58; and Rongelap repatriation, 235, 238; at Project Chariot site, 304

Hydrographic Office, U.S. Navy, 166, 276

Hydrography surveys at Bikini atoll, 1946, 32

Hydroids, marine, observations at Bikini, 1947, 1948, 97

Igurin Island, Eniwetok, 87, 136

Induced radioisotopes, predominance in marine biota, 1959, 267

Interior, U.S. Department of: and Donaldson, 8; represented at Bikini Scientific Resurvey, 53; interest in Bikini case, 136; proving ground agreement with AEC cited, 158

International cooperation, effect of Atomic Energy Act of 1954, 196-97

Institutions of higher education. *See* entries under names of institutions

Invertebrates: observations, (1947) 66, 70, 71, 73, 76, (1948-49) 96-97, 100, 101; and Operation Ivy, 148; and Rongelap, 267

Ipomoea tuba, 106, 296

Islands, Bikini. *See* Airukiiji; Aomoen; Arriikan (Aran); Bikini; Bokoaetokutoku (Boku); Bokororyuru (Boro); Eniirikku; Eninman; Enyu; Namu; Romurikku; Rukoji

Islands, Eniwetok. *See* Aaraanbiru; Aitsu; Aomon; Biijiri; Bogallua; Bogombogo; Eberiru; Elugelab; Engebi; Eniwetok; Igurin; Japtan; Mui; Parry; Rigili; Rojoa; Runit

Islands, Majuro. *See* Ejit

Islands, Rongelap. *See* Eniaetok; Kabelle; Labaredj; Naen; Rongelap community

Ivy, Operation, 1952 test series in Pacific: plans, 135; development of joint task force concept, 139; preparations for tests, 139-40; Test Mike, 140; sampling of water, plankton, algae, invertebrates, corals, 146-49; whole-fish counts of radioactivity, 149-50; examination of birds and rats, 151; stimulates plan for Eniwetok Marine Biological Laboratory, 152-54

Jaluit Atoll, 30

Japanese - American conferences: of March 24, 1954, 176-77; of June 30, 1954, 188-89; of November 15–19, 1954, 198-200; Operation Troll, April 14, 1955, 202

Japtan Island, Eniwetok, 87, 137

J Division. *See* Test Division

Joint Chiefs of Staff, 22, 35, 52

Joint Congressional Committee on Atomic Energy. *See* Congressional Committee on Atomic Energy

Joint Staff Planners (Crossroads), 21

Joint Task Forces. *See* Task Forces, Joint

Jughead, Test, 160

Kabelle Island, Rongelap: survey of March, 1954, 181; survey of October, 1955, 219-20; survey of February-March, 1958, 250; soil transects on,

261; lysimeter installations, 263; studies of birds on, 268

Kili Island, 93, 94

King, Test, 1952, 135

Kwajalein Atoll: as support area for Bikini tests, 22; physical characteristics, 25-27; collections there, 1947, 66; 1954 fallout victims, 168

Labaredj Island, Rongelap: site of survey, March, 1954, 181; collections, resurvey (1955), 219-20

Laboratory of Radiation Biology: succeeds Applied Fisheries Laboratory, 246; new approach to Rongelap problem, 250; Rongelap surveys, (1958) 251-52, (1959) 257-60; missions, Operation Hardtack, 275; U.S.S. *Rehoboth* survey, 276-77, 278-85; surveys before Hardtack, 277-78; *Collett* survey, 286-90; *Silverstein* survey, 290-91; periods of Pacific observations, 294-95; studies on Engebi and Bogombogo Islands, 1961, 296; and Project Chariot, 303-4; summary statement of findings, 306-9

Lae Atoll, 25

Land crab (*Coenobita perlatus*), 254, 298-99

Land surveys: at Bikini, 1949, 106; at Eniwetok, 1952, 143; at Rongelap, 1954-55, 181, 219; at Rongelap, 1958-59, 251-53, 261-63

LCI(L) 1054, Bikini-Eniwetok Resurvey vessel, 1948, 94

Likiep Atoll: dimensions, 27; visited by Resurvey, 1949, 110-11; samplings in 1955, 221

Lithothamnion (algal) ridge, 28

Livermore Laboratory. *See* California Radiation Laboratory at Livermore

Lomuilal Island, Rongelap, 265

Los Alamos Scientific Laboratory: reports need of field tests, 80; permanent test division established, 113; freed of weapons manufacture, 1950, 121-22; studies test animals, Operation Greenhouse, 126; anticipates radiobiological surveys in 1954, 155; in Task Group 7.1, 1954, 160; meeting on 1954 marine surveys, 161-62

LSI(L) 1091, resurvey vessel, 1949, 103

Lysimeter stations: Rongelap, 252, 261, 263

Majuro Atoll, 197

Manhattan Engineer District: transfer of authority to (from OSRD) 3; Groves named head, 3; Warren (Stafford) heads Medical Section, 7; interest of Medical Section in Applied Fisheries program, 10-11; transfers contracts to Corps of Engineers, 19

Mariana Islands, 191, 230

Marine Survey Program, Applied Fisheries Laboratory (Program 19, Project 19.1), 1954, 161
Marsh, U.S.S. (DE 699), 229-33
Marshall Islands: control by Navy Military Government, 22; inhabitants of, 24; description, 25, 27; naming, 27
Medical Board of Review, AEC, 102
Medical-Legal Board, Bikini Scientific Resurvey, 61
Medical Section, Manhattan District, 7
Michigan, University of, 33n
Mike, Test: plans, conditions, 135, 139-40; pretest sampling, 137-39; detonation, appearance of crater, 140; counting of samples by AFL, 145; radiobiological problems, findings, after, 145-51; Bugher cites significance of, 156
Mili Atoll, 27
Military Air Transport Service, 118
Military Application, Division of, AEC, 80
Military Government, U.S. Navy. *See* Navy Military Government
Military Liaison Committee, AEC, 79, 80
Military Sea Transport Service, 118
Minnesota, University of, 54, 96
Monitoring, fallout. *See* Fallout
Moratorium, on tests, 291
Mount McKinley, U.S.S., 45, 86
Mui Island, Eniwetok, 87, 163

Naen Island, Rongelap, 261, 265
Namu Island, Bikini, 62, 225
National Academy of Sciences, 240-42
National Defense Research Committee (NDRC), 4, 9
National Museum, U.S., 53, 54
Naval Medical Research Institute: represented in medical team, Kwajalein, 1954, 168; surveys Rongelap, April 13, 1954, 197; provides monitors, U.S.S. *Rehoboth*, 1958, 276
Naval Medical Research Section, Joint Task Force One, 35n
Naval Ordnance Laboratory, 85
Naval Radiological Defense Laboratory, U.S.: represented on medical team, Kwajalein, 1954, 168; surveys Rongelap, April 13, 1954, 197; in Rongelap survey, 1955, 216; surveys of Rongelap by 1956, 234
Naval Research, Office of, 52, 201, 275
Naval Research Laboratory, 85
Navy, U.S.: interest in resurvey of Bikini, 51; asked to conduct Bikini Scientific Resurvey, 1947, 52; and Bikini Resurvey field work, 64; and Bikini as equivalent of military target, 74; prepares to support 1950 survey, 122
Navy Military Government, 22, 24
Nectar, Test, Operation Castle, detonation at Eniwetok, 1954, 183

Nevada Proving Ground: establishment, first tests, 123, 124-25; radiobiological studies by U.C.L.A. Atomic Energy Project, 126; monitoring program by U.C.L.A., 1952, 133; third series (Tumbler-Snapper), 1952, 133; 1953 series (Upshot-Knothole), 158-59; Operation Teapot, 1955, 213; Operation Plumbbob, 1957, 270-71; Phase II, Operation Hardtack, 292
New York Operations Office, AEC: shares facilities at EMBL, 154; designs ocean probe, 201, 204; analyzes Rongelap soil samples, 216; provides probe for 1956 ocean survey, 223-24
Nicholas, U.S.S. (DDE 449), 180, 182n
Nonfission products, 233, 267
Notre Dame, University of, 54
Nuclear testing: implications of need, 1947, 78; issue emerges, 1956-1957, 239-41; reduction of fallout, 1957, 271; moratorium, 292; suspension invites further biological studies, 295

Oakhill, U.S.S. (LSD 7), 1952 Eniwetok survey vessel, 136
Oak Ridge National Laboratory, 124, 126
Oceanographic research: responsibility of AEC toward, 309; needs of reported by NAS, 309-10
Oceanography and Fisheries, Committee on, 240
Oceanography, Committee on, 309-10
Ocean studies, significance, Libby cites, 1958, 274
Ocean surveys (Japan): *Shunkotsu Maru*, 183, 186, 191-95; *Keiten Maru*, 1954-1955, 195; *Daifuji Maru*, 1954-1955, 195; 1956 cruise by *Shunkotsu Maru*, 222, 222n
Ocean surveys (U.S.): Operation Troll, 201-2; *Walton*, 225-26; *Marsh*, 229-33; *Rehoboth*, 1958, 276-85; *Collett*, 1958, 287-89; *Silverstein*, 1958, 285, 290-91
Office of Scientific Research and Development (OSRD), 3, 9-10
Ohio Agricultural Experiment Station, 305
Ohio State University, 53, 243, 305
Orange, Test, 1958, 287

Pacific Islands, 24, 30-31
Pacific Ocean, 25, 27, 28, 31
Pacific Proving Ground. *See* Proving Ground
Parry Island, Eniwetok: position, 87; suggested as scientific center of proving ground, 114; initial site plats, 117; center of proving ground community, 120-21; site of Eniwetok Marine Biological Laboratory, 154

Pasco, Washington, 6
Peaceful uses (atomic energy), 196, 240, 272
Plankton: observations of movement, Crossroads, 45; tows and analysis of samples in 1947, 68; initiation of studies, 1947, 68; lagoonal populations at Bikini and Rongerik, 68; interest in, 1948, 98; analyses of, Operation Ivy, 146-47; observations by Kawabata, 193-94; interest in radiation uptake by, 1955, 201; collections, (Operation Troll) 204, *(Marsh)* 232, (U.S.S. *Rehoboth*) 281-82; analysis by size, 288
Plants (land): 1949 studies, (Biddulph) 107, (St. John) 109-10; Rongelap studies, 264, 265-66; *Ipomoea tuba*, Eniwetok, 296
Plowshare Project, 272, 302-3
Plumas County, U.S.S., Rongelap survey vessel, 1958, 248, 250
Plumbbob, Operation, Nevada series, 1957, 270-71
Plutonium: production, manufacturing problems, 4, 5; first delivery, 1944, 14; discovery of in New Mexico, 131
Polar Studies, Institute of, Ohio State University, 305
Press: Japanese coverage of *Fukuryu Maru* case, 169, 175, 200n; reports of *Fukuryu Maru* case, 170, 175n; and strontium 90, 242, 242n
Probe (scintillation): designed for Operation Troll, 204; used *(Walton* survey), 223-24, *(Marsh* survey), 230
Proving Ground: establishment, 78; site selection, 80-81; as radiobioligical study site, 131; addition of Bikini, 1953, 158; disestablishment, 1958, 289
Public Health Service, U.S., 305

Radiation Biology, Laboratory of. *See* Laboratory of Radiation Biology
Radiation effects, National Academy of Sciences statement on, 241
Radiation Safety Section: Joint Task Force One, 35; Joint Task Force Seven, 1954, 160
Radioactivity, general. *See* Alpha radioactivity; Cesium 137; Circulation, biological; Decline; Fallout; Fission products; Induced radioisotopes; Nonfission products; Plutonium; Radiation effects; Strontium 90; Thermocline; Uptake, biological; X radiation
Radioactivity in nature, summary statement, 306-7
Radiobiology, Division of, Crossroads, 41, 44, 48
Radiobiology, marine: Bugher urges additional emphasis on, 155
Radiobiology Group, Bikini Scientific

Resurvey: membership, 54; collecting stations, 62; collections, total, 65; preliminary report, 72-73
Radiochemistry, Radiophysics group, Bikini Scientific Resurvey, 54, 69
Radiological Safety (RadSafe) Section (Group): at Crossroads, 35, 36, 41; at Sandstone, 87-88, 88n; at Ivy, 140, 143; on Test Bravo fallout, 1954, 165
Rainbow trout, 16, 17, 127
Ranger, Operation, first Nevada series, 124-25
Rainier, Test, Nevada, 1957, 271
Rats *(Rattus exulans):* Lowman begins studies of, 106; sampling in 1952, 150-51; history of colonies on Engebi, 207; character, size, Engebi population, 209-10; calculated doses, Engebi, 210-11; isolation on Engebi, 211-12; summary of Engebi study, 212-13; Engebi colonies, condition of, 1961, 297-98.
Redlands, University of, 96
Redwing, Operation, 1956, 221
Rehoboth, U.S.S., 1958 ocean survey vessel: mission, 275; survey plans, 276-77; water mass, apparent loss of main body, 281; analysis of results, 282-85
Repatriation, Rongelapese, 236-38
Research on Measures Against Atomic Bomb Injuries, Council for (Japan), 200n
Restricted zone, 166, 182
Resurvey, Bikini-Eniwetok, 1948: schedule and staff, 94-95; sampling and sampling methods, 96-97; biological retention of radioactivity, Bikini lagoon, 97; biological uptake of radioactivity, 100; inspection of Engebi reefs, 100-101
Resurvey, Bikini-Eniwetok, 1949, 103-11
Richland, Washington, 6
Rigili Island, Eniwetok: position, 87; collections, 1948, 100; sampling station, 1952, 137; effects of Test Mike, 141, 145
Rochester, University of, 123, 126
Rojoa Island, Eniwetok: radioactivity levels, 1952, 143; site of rat collections, 1952, 144; camp facilities reactivated, 1953, 160
Romurikku Island, Bikini, 34
Rongelap Atoll: discovery, early visits, 27, 30; fish collection after Crossroads, 49; in path of 1954 fallout, 165; natives evacuated to Kwajalein, 1954, 168; not habitable in December, 1954, 198; estimate of radioactivity on lagoon bottom, 220-21; rehabitation doubtful, 1956, 234; surveys by 1957, 234; levels of radioactivity, 1959, 261; aberrations discovered, 1959, 264-65; Laboratory of Radiation Biology visits, 1961, 293
Rongelap case: evacuation, care of ex-

posed persons, 179; survey by U.S.S. *Nicholas,* 180-82; reoccupation not possible, 197; question of rehabilitation, 1955, 215-17

Rongelap community: condition of abandoned village, 1957, 234; repatriation planned, 235-36; Council consulted on plans for new community, 235; construction of village, 1957, 236; natives returned from Majuro, 236-37; continued medical observations needed, 238-39; comparison population in, 239; diet problems, 253-54, 258; surveys suspended, 1960, 254, 260; attitudes cause concern, 257-58; agricultural production low, 1959, 258, 258n; visit of UN committee, 259; condition in 1961, 293

Rongelap studies: Brookhaven National Laboratory assigned long-term medical, 245; AFL given environmental studies, 245-46; inauguration, 1958, 248; new approach, problems (1958), 250, 251-52; land crabs, 1961, 298-300

Rongerik Atoll: temporary home of Bikini people, 25; fish collection after Crossroads, 49; Juda brought to Bikini from, 64; collections there, 1947, 66; Bikini people inadequately fed there, 93-94; in path of 1954 fallout, 165; military personnel evacuated, 1954, 168

Rukoji (Ruji) Island, Bikini, 62

Runit Island, Eniwetok: Operation Sandstone Test Site, 87; effects of 1948 detonation, 89; site of biological collection, 1948, 89; plants studied by St. John, 110; as scientific station, 117; site of Test King, 1952, 135; sampling station, 1952, 137; effects of Test Mike, 141

Samish River, Washington: point of salmon release, 1944, 11; salmon return beginning, 1945, 17; studies of salmon returns in 1951, 127

Sandia Corporation, 303-4, 304n

Sandstone, Operation, 1948: organization and command, 85; character of tests as planned, preparations, 86; biological uptake of radioactivity observed, 89-90

San Francisco Operations Office, AEC, 305

Science Council of Japan, 184

Scripps Institution of Oceanography: in pre-Crossroads studies, Bikini, 33n; represented, Bikini Scientific Resurvey, 53; represented at Operation Troll meeting, 201

Ships, Pacific operations. *See* U.S.S. *Bowditch;* U.S.S. *Haven;* U.S.S. *Mount McKinley;* U.S.S. *Oakhill;* U.S.S. *Sumner*

Ships, survey. *See* M.V. *Aloto;* U.S.S. *Bowditch;* U.S.S. *Chilton;* U.S.S. *Collett;* U.S.S. *Coucal;* U.S.S. *Duval County;* U.S.S. *Haven;* LCI(L) 1054; LSI(L) 1091; U.S.S. *Marsh;* U.S.S. *Nicholas;* U.S.S. *Oakhill;* U.S.S. *Plumas County;* U.S.S. *Rehoboth; Shunkotsu Maru;* U.S.S. *Silverstein;* U.S.S. *Sumner;* U.S.S. *Roger B. Taney;* U.S.S. *Walton*

Shunkotsu Maru Survey (Japan): survey begun, 1954, 183; preparations and scope, 185-86; vessel sails without Americans, 187; consultations at U.S. Embassy, Tokyo, 188; area covered, course, 191; samples, 191-92; summary of findings, 192-94; Bikini Waters Investigation team dissolved, 192; vessel used for 1956 cruise, 222, 222n

Silverstein, U.S.S., 1958 ocean survey vessel: operation plan, 275; scope of 1958 survey and observations, 290-91

Smithsonian Institution, 33n

Soils: samplings at Rongelap, October, 1955, 219; Rongelap studies, 1958, 251-53, 257; observations, Rongelap, 1959, 261-62

Stanford Research Institute, 53

Stanford University, 53

Strontium 90: present at Bikini and Eniwetok, 131; question discussed by Bugher, 156, 156n; in Engebi rat specimens, 212; concern in U.S., 214; interest by Dunning, 1955 (mentioned by Boss), 220; absent in *Marsh* samples, 233; public focus on, 1956, 242, 242n; question in Rongelap case, 244; at Rongelap, 253, 254, 263; low values in marine organisms after Test Wahoo, 282; evidence of discrimination against by marine organisms, 1958, 283; levels low at Rongelap, 1961, 297; stability in land crabs, Rongelap, 289-99

Sumner, U.S.S. (DD 692), 32

Sunshine Project, 156n, 242

Taney, U.S.S. *Roger B.,* 201

Task Forces, Joint: Task Force One, 22, 31-32, 51; Task Force Seven (1948), 85, 86; Task Force Three, 125-26; Task Force One Hundred Thirty-two, 134-35, 139; Task Force Seven (1953), 160, 161, 235, 286-87

Teak, Test, high-altitude detonation, 1958, 287

Teapot, Operation, Nevada series, 1955, 213

Tennessee, University of, 54

Test Division, 113, 115, 122, 125

Test Operations, Nevada. *See* Buster-

Jangle; Hardtack (Phase II); Plumb-
bob; Ranger; Teapot; Tumbler-
Snapper; Upshot-Knothole
Test Operations, Pacific. *See* Castle;
Crossroads; Greenhouse; Hardtack
(Phase I); Ivy; Redwing; Sandstone;
Wigwam
Tests, Nevada. *See* Rainier
Tests, Pacific. *See* Able (Crossroads);
Baker (Crossroads); Bravo; King;
Mike; Nectar; Orange; Teak; Um-
brella; Wahoo; Wigwam; Yoke
Thermocline, 280, 281
Thermonuclear device: preliminary dis-
cussions of, 101; announcement of
intention to develop, 121; nears devel-
opment, 1952, 133; policy considera-
tions, 134; occasions enlargement of
proving ground, 1953, 160
Tokyo, University of, 171
Tokyo First Hospital, National, 172
Troll, Operation: initial conference
planning, personnel, 201; cruise pattern, 201-2; meeting with Japanese,
202; summary of operations, 202-6
Trust Territory of the Pacific Islands:
U.S. responsibilities, authority, establishment, 81, 81n; sends consultants
to Kwajalein, 1954, 169; plans Rongelap repatriation, 234-35; encourages
self-sufficiency of Rongelap community, 254; augments Rongelap diet,
254, 258
Tumbler-Snapper tests, Nevada series,
1952, 133
Tuna scare (U.S.), 214n

U.C.L.A. *See* California, University of,
at Los Angeles
Ujae Atoll, 25, 93
Ujelang Atoll, 81
Umbrella, Test, 1958, 285
United Kingdom, 155n, 240, 273n
United Nations: notified of closing of
Bikini, 1953, 158; Eisenhower's address, 1953, 196; General Assembly
creates committee on radiation effects,
240; Committee on Trust Territories
visits Rongelap, 259; Scientific Committee report issued, 1958, 291
United Nations Atomic Energy Commission, 32
Upshot-Knothole series, Nevada test
series, 1953, 158-59
Uptake, biological (of radioactivity), 90,
98-100
U.S.S.R.: possession of atom bomb
(1949), 101n; nuclear detonations,
(October, 1951) 132, (1953) 155n, (1956)
240, (1957) 271; accepts U.S. test-sus-
pension proposal, 292
Utirik Atoll, 166, 168, 197

Wahoo, Test, 1958: underwater detonation, 276; objectives, radiobiological
survey, 276-77; predetonation surveys,
277-78; movement of water mass, 278-
81
Waikiki Aquarium, University of Hawaii, 96
Walton, U.S.S. (DE 361): 1956 survey by,
225-26; results, 226-28
Washington, University of: as source
of aquatic biologists, 7; in nuclear research in World War II; represented
in Project Chariot, 305
Washington University, St. Louis, 124
Water: opacity of Bikini waters, 1947,
67-68; analyses of, Operation Ivy, 146;
sampling in Eniwetok Lagoon, 1952,
146; *Shunkotsu Maru* samples, findings, 191-92; sampling by *Marsh*,
230-32; significance of, 307-8
Weather Bureau, U.S., 305
Wigwam, Test, West Coast underwater
detonation, 1955, 213-14
Woods Hole Oceanographic Institution,
33n, 200
Wotho Atoll, 93

X radiation: initial application to salmon by AFL, 11; limited knowledge
of effects, 1943, 11-12; levels of exposure of salmon by AFL, 15

Yaizu City, 169
Yoke, Test, Operation Sandstone, 87
Yomiuri (Tokyo newspaper), 169

Persons

Agassiz, Alexander, 30, 31
Allison, John, U.S. Ambassador to Japan,
171-72, 176, 177-78
Amano, Keishi, 185n, 189
Anderson, Alfred W., 276
Anker, Rudolph, 201

Bacher, Robert F., 79
Baker, Gary, 248
Barnes, Charles, Major, U.S.A.F., 180
Bayer, F.M., 54
Beadle, G. W., 102n
Bishop, Francis, 14
Biddulph, Orlin, 105, 107, 110
Blandy, W. H. P., Vice Admiral, U.S.N.,
22, 32-33, 35
Blinks, L. R., 53
Bonham, Kelshaw: joins Applied Fish-
eries Laboratory staff, 10; with Bikini-
Eniwetok Resurvey, 1949, 105; in
1952 Eniwetok survey, 137; in Ronge-
lap surveys, (1955) 216, (1958) 248,
(1959) 260
Boroughs, Howard, 241n

Boss, W. R.: named representative to Japan's scientific community, 1954, 187; informal visit to Japanese research agencies, 1954, 188; at Japanese-American conference, June 30, 1954, 189; at Japanese-American conference, Nov. 15–19, 1954, 199; in Operation Troll planning, 201; letter to Donaldson on Rongelap data, 1955, 220

Brereton, Lewis H., Maj. Gen., U.S.A., 79

Britton, Max E., 304n

Brock, Vernon E., 33n, 53, 57, 68

Bronk, Detlev W., 102n

Brooks, P. M., 53

Bugher, John C.: director, Division of Biology and Medicine, 135; encourages establishment of Eniwetok Marine Biological Laboratory, 154; visits Applied Fisheries Laboratory, 155; refers to Project Sunshine, 1953, 156; observes studies of Rongelap cases, 1954, 169; member, Advisory Committee for Biology and Medicine, 272

Bullock, Theodore, 96

Burnett, Charles H., 272

Bush, Vannevar, 3, 4

Butts, Joseph S., 154

Campbell, Ernest D., 304n

Cantril, Simeon T.: as Applied Fisheries adviser, 11; reviews Applied Fisheries program, 1957, 247n; member, Advisory Committee for Biology and Medicine, 272

Carpenter, Albert J., Comdr., U.S.C.G., 201

Carritt, Dayton E., 241n

Chamisso, Louis Charles (Adelbert) de, 29-30

Chartier, Wilfred G., Comdr., U.S.N., 229

Chipman, Walter A., 241n

Clarkson, Percy W., Maj. Gen. U.S.A, 135

Claus, Walter D., 198, 199

Cohn, Stanton, 197

Cole, A. C., 54, 66

Cole, Dale, 248, 257

Compton, Arthur H., 4, 5, 8

Conant, James B., 479

Conard, Robert A.: and Rongelap medical studies, 245, 246; at Rongelap, 1958, 248

Coryell, C. D., 8

Craig, Harmon, 241n

Curry, Duncan Jr., Capt., U.S.N. (Ret.), 160, 161

Darwin, Charles, 30, 31

Davis, Jared, 198

Denebrink, Francis E., Rear Adm., U.S.N., 86

Donaldson, John R., 96, 230

Donaldson, Lauren R.: considered for Columbia River studies, 8; invited to OSRD conference, 8; selects OSRD research title, 10; at Operation Crossroads, 36; joints Bikini Scientific Resurvey, 52; consultant to AEC on Hanford work, 53; as head of Radiobiology group, Bikini Scientific Resurvey, 54; cochairman of seminar series on *Chilton*, 57; member, Advisory Board, Bikini Scientific Resurvey, 57; member of landing party, Bikini, 1947, 59; makes Runit Island collection, Operation Sandstone, 89; heads Bikini-Eniwetok Resurvey, 1948, 94; heads Bikini-Eniwetok Resurvey, 1949, 105; confers on 1950 survey, 122; visits Nevada Proving Ground, 126; proposes new inquiry, letter to Pearson, 1951, 127-28; in 1952 Eniwetok survey, 137; drafts preliminary plan for 1954 surveys, 161; at Eniwetok, 1954, 180; named representative to Japanese scientific community, 1954, 187; visits Japanese research agencies, 1954, 188; at Japanese-American conference, June 30, 1954, 189; visits Rongelap, July, 1954, 197; in *Walton* survey, 1956, 225; in Rongelap survey, 1956, 234; member, NAS-NRC, Committee on Oceanography and Fisheries, 241n; directs Fern Lake program, 247; outlines biological program, Project Chariot, 304

Du Bridge, Lee A., 79

Dunning, Gordon, 220, 245

Dunham, Charles L.: as chief, Medical Branch, represents Division of Biology and Medicine at Kwajalein, 1954, 169; letter of authority for 1956 ocean survey, 223-24; calls meeting on Rongelap studies, 1956, 243

Eisenbud, Merril: confers in Japan on *Fukuryu Maru* case, 176-77; represents U.S. at first joint scientific conference, Tokyo, 176; arranges for monitoring outside restricted area, 1954, 178; at Japanese-American conference, Nov. 15–19, 1954, 199; suggests U.S. ocean survey, 200; at Operation Troll meeting, 200-201

Eisenhower, President, 182, 196, 291-92

Eisler, Ronald, 255

Emerson, Arthur T. Jr., Comdr., U.S.N., 225

Emery, K. O., 33n

Engleman, C. L., Comdr., U.S.N., 52, 57, 59, 72

Failla, Giocchino, 272

Farr, R. S., 197

Ferenbaugh, Claude B., Brig. Gen., U.S.A., 86
Fermi, Enrico, 79
Fleming, Richard H., 241n
Foote, Don Charles, 305
Foster, Richard F.: joins AFL staff, 10; at Hanford Laboratory, 17; in Bikini Scientific Resurvey, 54; member, NAS-NRC Committee on Oceanography and Fisheries, 241n
Friedell, H. L., 8
Froman, Darol K., 80-81, 85
Fujinaga, Motosaku, 185, 189

Gessel, Stanley, 248, 260
Gilfillan, E. S., Jr., Comdr., U.S.N.R., 52, 59, 60, 68
Gilkey, Robert W., 201
Glass, H. Bentley, 272
Goldberg, Edward D., 241n
Goodpasture, Ernest W., 102n
Goreau, T. F., 53
Gortner, W. A., 53
Graves, Alvin C.: deputy scientific director, Eniwetok Proving Ground, 86; named director of J (Test) Division, 113; heads scientific task group, Operation Greenhouse, 125; deputy scientific director, Operation Ivy, 135
Gregg, Alan, 102
Groves, Leslie R., Brig. Gen., U.S.A.: heads Manhattan District, 3; in atomic policy group, 4; institutes search for plutonium plant site, 5; concern with possible contamination of Columbia River, 7; member, Military Liaison Committee, 1947, 79

Hackett, Donald J., Comdr., U.S.N., 275
Harley, John H.: at Japanese-American conference, Nov. 15–19, 1954, 199; heads Operation Troll, 201; member, NAS-NRC Committee on Oceanography and Fisheries, 241n
Hastings, Baird, 102n
Hederman, T. A., Capt., U.S.N., 52
Held, Edward E.: with Bikini-Eniwetok Resurvey, 1948, 96; joins Applied Fisheries Laboratory staff, 128, 128n; in Nevada with U.C.L.A. group, 1952, 133; in 1952 Eniwetok survey, 137; at EMBL, 1954, 180; visits Rongelap, December, 1954, 198; in Rongelap surveys, 1955, 216; at Rongelap, November, 1955, 219; with *Marsh* survey, 1956, 230; coordinates Rongelap studies with Conard, 246; heads Rongelap studies, 247; at Rongelap, (1958) 248, (1959) 257, 260
Hendricks, Sterling B., 199
Hiatt, R. W., 53, 66
Hiyama, Yoshio: describes Japanese reaction to *Fukuryu Maru* case, 172; assists planning for Japanese ocean survey, 1954, 185; as guide to Boss, Donaldson, 1954, 188; at Japanese-American conference, Nov. 15–19, 1954, 199; cites American cooperation (statement), 199
Hollenberg, George, 96
Holmes, James T., 113
Hull, John W., Lt. Gen., U.S.A., 85

Isaacs, John D., 201

Jacks, Gordon, Major, U.S.A.F., 276
Johnson, J. Harlan, 53
Joyner, Timothy, 255, 257
Juda, Bikini magistrate, 25, 64, 93

Kawabata, Toshiharu: studies of *Shunkotsu Maru* fish, observations on findings, 193-94; samples fish from Tokyo markets, 289; with Applied Fisheries staff, Seattle, 289
Kaya, Seiji, 184
Kellogg, Paul, 105
Kenady, Reid, 255, 257
Kepner, William E., Maj. Gen., U.S.A.F., 86
Ketchum, Bostwick, 241n
Kimmel, James, 255, 257
Kimura, Kenjiro, 199
Klement, Alfred W. Jr., 286, 288, 289
Kobayashi, Rokuzo, 183
Koch, John J., 96
Kotzebue, Otto von, 29, 30
Krumholz, Louis A., 241n
Kuboyama, Aikichi, 172, 194

Lachenbruch, Arthur H., 304n
Ladd, H. S., 53, 57, 69
Larsen, Kermit H., 304n
Lausch, Robert L., 304n
Lawrence, Ernest O., 135
LeVine, Harris D., 204
LeRoy, George V., 122, 126, 169
Leahy, W. D., Fleet Adm., U.S.N., 52, 56
LeMay, Curtis E., Maj. Gen., U.S.A.F., 21
Libby, Willard F., 214, 242, 274
Lilienthal, David E., 79
Lill, G. G., 53
Loeb, Robert F., 102
Lowman, Frank G.: with Bikini-Eniwetok Resurvey, 1948, 96; with Bikini-Eniwetok Resurvey, 1949, 105; visits Nevada Proving Ground, 126; in Nevada with U.C.L.A. group, 1952, 133; in 1952 Eniwetok survey, 137; visits Rongelap, July, 1954, 197; studies of Engebi rats, 206-13; in Rongelap surveys, 1955, 216; with *Walton* survey, 1956, 225; with *Marsh* survey, 1956, 230; with Palumbo, directs test site studies, 247; with U.S.S. *Rehoboth*

survey, 1958, 276; observes discrimination against strontium 90 by plankton, 283

Marquiss, L. B., 59
Marr, J. C., 53, 66, 68
Marshall, George C., Gen., Chief of Staff, 4
Mason, Leonard, 93-94
Mathisen, Ole, 260
Matthias, Franklin T., 5, 6, 6n
Meigs, R. C., 54
Miyake, Yasuo: member, planning group, *Shunkotsu Maru* survey, 185n; at Japanese-American scientific conference, Nov. 15–19, 1954, 199; discusses *Shunkotsu Maru* cruise with Eisenbud, 200
Morrison, J. P. E., 54, 57, 67
Morriss, Neil, 255, 260
Morse, Robert S., 201
Morton, John, 176
Munk, W. H., 33n
Myers, G. S., 53, 66, 68

Nakaizumi, Masanori, 199
Narver, D. Lee, 113
Neas, Maynard, 259
Nichols, K. D., 5
Nishikawa, Kakuichi, 170
Norman, A. G., 240n
Nucker, Delmas H., Commissioner, Trust Territory of the Pacific Islands: reviews Rongelap village plans, 235; suggests no surveys in 1960, 254; receives 1959 Rongelap survey plans, 260

Ofstie, Ralph A., Rear Adm., U.S.N., 80
Ogden, David A. D., Brig. Gen., U.S.A., 86
Ogle, William E., 160, 161
Okazaki, Katsuo, 171
Olson, Paul: at Eniwetok, 1954, 180; visits Rongelap, December, 1954, 198; with *Walton* survey, 225; in Rongelap survey, (1956) 234, (1958) 248
Oppenheimer, J. Robert, 79, 134
Osborn, Richard H., 96

Palumbo, Ralph: with Bikini-Eniwetok Resurvey, (1949) 105, (1952) 137; at EMBL, 1954, 180; with Lowman, directs test site studies, 247; with *Rehoboth* survey, 1958, 276
Parsons, W. S., Adm. (Commodore) U.S.N., 35, 51, 80, 86
Patterson, John D., Comdr., U.S.N., 275
Pautzke, Clarence F., 36, 54
Pearson, Paul B.: and Donaldson on 1950 surveys, 122; projects visit to AFL, 128; visits Laboratory with questions, 129; recommends Applied Fisheries survey at Eniwetok, 1952, 135;

notes to Bugher, March, April, 1952, 135-36; sends radiation data to Donaldson, 1954, 198; at Japanese-American conference, Nov. 15–19, 1954, 199
Pike, Sumner T., 79

Quesada, E. R., Lt. Gen., U.S.A.F., 125, 126

Rabi, I. I., 79
Ramey, Roger M., Maj. Gen., U.S.A.F., 86
Renn, Charles R., 241n
Revelle, Roger: as member of Joint Crossroads subcommittee, 52; first project officer, Bikini Scientific Resurvey, 52; joins Bikini Scientific Resurvey in field, 54; seminar lecturer, *Chilton*, 1947, 57; confers on plankton problem, 1947, 68; chairman, Committee on Oceanography and Fisheries, National Academy of Sciences, 241
Richardson, Frank, 255, 257, 267-69
Roberson, J. H., 54, 57
Rodenbaugh, F. H., Sr., 53, 54, 57, 59, 61
Roosevelt, President, 4
Russell, James S., Capt., U.S.N.; deputy director, Division of Military Application, 80; selects Eniwetok site, with Froman, 81; test director, Operation Sandstone, 85; aids biological sampling, Sandstone, 89
Russell, Richard D., 57, 69

Salisbury, Morse, 199
Schaeffer, M. B., 241n
Schubert, Jack, 54
Schultz, Leonard: in pre-Crossroads studies, Bikini, 33n; in Bikini Scientific Resurvey, 53, 57; studies of fish populations, 66; and plankton problem, 1947, 68
Seaborg, Glenn T., 79
Seatz, L. F., 54
Sedgwick, Cabot, 189
Servis, John D., 161
Sewell, Duane, 160
Seymour, Allyn H.: in Bikini Scientific Resurvey, 54; with Bikini-Eniwetok Resurvey, 1948, 94; with Bikini-Eniwetok Resurvey, 1949, 105; in 1952 Eniwetok survey, 137; member, Operation Troll team, 201; in Rongelap surveys, 1955, 216; at Rongelap, November, 1955, 219; with *Walton* survey, 1956, 225; heads *Marsh* survey, 1956, 230; assigned to Environmental Sciences Branch, Division of Biology and Medicine, 233; memo on ocean sampling, 1958, 286; deputy chairman, Committee on Environmental Studies, Project Chariot, 304
Shipman, Thomas L., 161, 180
Shuler, Edward H., 69

Smith, G. M., 53
Smith, James W., 201
Smith, O. R., 53
Solberg, Thorvald A., Rear Admiral, U.S.N., 52, 80
Somervell, Brehon, Maj. Gen., U.S.A., 4
Stakman, E. C., 102n
Stimson, Henry L., Secretary of War, 4
St. John, Harold: with Bikini-Eniwetok Resurvey, 1949, 105; studies at Eniwetok, 1949, 109-10
Stone, Robert S., 8, 11
Strauss, Lewis L.: member, AEC, 1947, 79; announces 1954 tests, 168; statement to Eisenhower on proving ground visit, 1954, 182
Sturges, William R. Jr., 136
Swift, C. S., Comdr., U.S.N., 275

Taft, Robert, 218-19
Thayer, Hanford, 8, 9, 14
Tinker, Spencer W., 96, 105
Tobin, J. E., 93
Tomiyama, Tetsuo, 188, 188n
Tracey, J. I., Jr., 53, 57, 69
Travis, J. E., 8
Truman, President: approves Crossroads test plans, 22; orders delay of Crossroads tests, 33; approves atomic test program, 80; approves Eniwetok as test site, 81; and completion of Operation Sandstone, 87; and end of U.S. atomic monopoly, 1949, 101; and development of thermonuclear weapon, 121
Tsurumi, K., 189
Tsutsui, Hisakichi, 170-71

Vine, Allyn C., 200-201, 241n
von Arx, W. S., 33n
von Neumann, John, 35

Walford, Lionel A., 241n
Walker, Richard, 255, 260
Warren, Shields: Executive Officer, Naval Medical Research Section, Operation Crossroads, 35n; first head, Division of Biology and Medicine, 102; suggests Likiep Atoll for control collections, 1949, 103; succeeded by Bugher as director of Division of Biology and Medicine, 135; chairman, NAS-NRC Committee on Pathological Effects of Radiation, 240n; member, Advisory Committee for Biology and Medicine, 272
Warren, Stafford L.: Chief, Medical Section, Manhattan District, 7; consulted by Groves on Columbia River, 7; at 1943 Chicago meeting on Columbia River, 8; invited Donaldson to OSRD conference, 8; visits Applied Fisheries Laboratory, 14, 15; interest in blood-forming centers of fish, 15; to Donaldson, 1944, 15-16; Radiological Safety Adviser, Crossroads, 36; interest in Test Baker effects, 41; director, U.C.L.A. Atomic Energy Project, 126
Waymack, William W., 79
Wearn, Joseph T., 102n
Weaver, Warren, 240n
Welander, Arthur D.: joins Applied Fisheries Laboratory staff, 10; dissertation, 1945, 15; at Operation Crossroads, 36; report of Baker Test studies, 44-45; in Bikini Scientific Resurvey, 54; seminar lecturer, *Chilton*, 1947, 57; with Bikini-Eniwetok Resurvey, 1948, 96; with Bikini-Eniwetok Resurvey, 1949, 105; with 1952 Eniwetok survey, 137; visits Rongelap, July, 1954, 197; with *Walton* survey, 1956, 225; with Rongelap survey, 1956, 234
Wells, J. W., 53, 57
Wenzel, H. T., 9
Wexler, Harry, 240n
Whitaker, D. M., 53, 57, 66, 71
White, Asher A., 96
White, Thomas N., 180
Wigner, Eugene, 8
Wilbur, Karl M., 154
Wilimovsky, Norman J., 304n
Williams, R. R., 54
Wolfe, John N.: reviews Rongelap program proposals, 243; asks new Rongelap study plan, 244; chairman, Committee on Environmental Studies, Project Chariot, 304
Wolman, Abel, 240n
Wooster, Warren S., 201, 240n

Yabe, Hiroshi, 185
Yamasaki, Fumio, 199

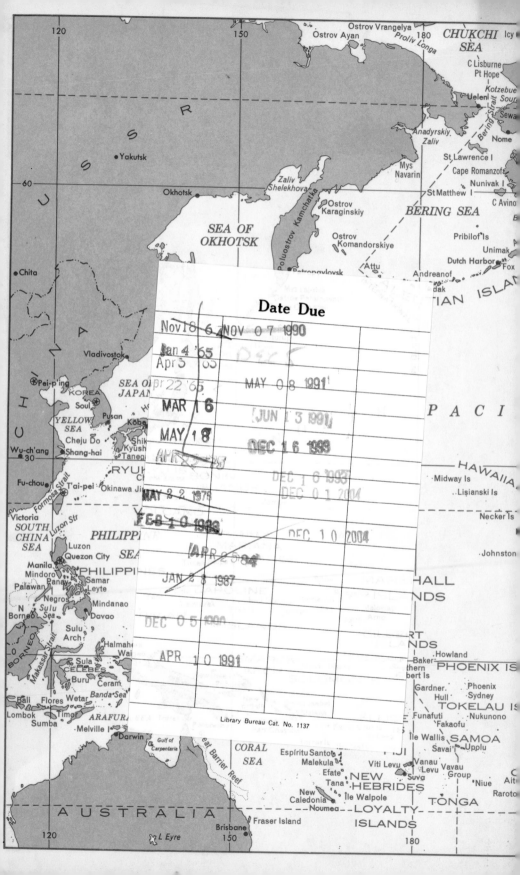